THE LANGUAGE OF MATHEMATICS

THE LANGUAGE OF
MATHEMATICS

FRANK LAND

DOUBLEDAY & COMPANY, INC.
GARDEN CITY, NEW YORK
1963

Preface to American Edition

IN PREPARING this book for American readers, the editors have made only those few alterations which will make the text more readable and meaningful, but the essential character of the discussions, explanations and even the exercises remains essentially British. Many illustrative examples and problems involve English monetary units, but the references will not pose any serious problems after the reader has completed the section on Money Units on pages 25, 26 and 27. Dollar equivalents have been included in a number of places to give the text additional meaning. These equivalents are based upon a conversion rate of $2.80 to one pound ($\pounds$).

The English conventions regarding decimal points and the use of a dot to represent multiplication are exactly the reverse of the American convention. The raised dot in this text indicates a decimal point whereas a dot in the position of a period when placed between adjacent symbols indicates multiplication. The latter use occurs only rarely as, for example, on page 103 in the formula $d = 52 + 14 \cdot N$, and on page 90 in the equation $4(2 + 3 + 7) = 4 \cdot 2 + 4 \cdot 3 + 4 \cdot 7$, where the dots indicate multiplication.

The reader will find a few references to "vulgar fraction". This phrase is equivalent to "common fraction" or simply "fraction". Once the decimal point and multiplication conventions noted above are understood, we feel that American readers will welcome the occasional departure from American usage and, above all, enjoy Mr. Land's beautiful style which makes his thorough explanations immediately meaningful—a quality not often found in mathematics books.

Contents

1

Numbers

QUITE YOUNG children seem to enjoy counting. Once they have learned the names of the numbers to twelve, then the numbers thirteen, fourteen, fifteen, as far as nineteen, trip happily off the tongue with a light trochaic rhythm, ending with "twenty", spoken with the finality of an "amen". After a delay of some months, the system for numbers from twenty to a hundred is rehearsed privately until one night, long after bedtime, a little voice calls out "Daddy", and in reply to the inevitable "I thought you were asleep", a pleased and contented child announces "I've counted all the way up to a hundred". The interest in counting shown by these young children seems to lie in the numbers themselves, in repetition and in the patterns of the numbers, rather than in actually counting things. It is a preliminary enjoyment of pure rather than of applied mathematics.

A sequence of words, remembered in order, enables simple counting to be performed, but it is of little use for any other purpose. By grouping "ten", "two tens (twenty)", "three tens (thirty)", "four tens (forty)", etc., we have extended our number system so that counting can be continued almost indefinitely without the need to introduce many additional words. It was the introduction of means of recording numbers, however, which extended the uses of counting and led on to developments in arithmetic and algebra.

Numbering Systems

The pattern in which the whole set of numbers is organized in sub-sets characterizes the number system. Because counting on the fingers was convenient during the primitive stages of arithmetical development, fives and tens have dominated the grouping into sub-sets, and the whole pattern of arithmetic has been conditioned by the physiological fact of the shape of the human hand rather than by intrinsic properties of numbers. This chapter describes very briefly a few number systems, and refers to a few number patterns that are not brought out very clearly in a counting system based on tens.

The number names in most languages are built up in relation to the grouping pattern and their evolution is associated with the recording of numbers. Our own language contains vestiges of a system based on twenty with such archaisms as "three-score years and ten", and the French language still retains, somewhat anomalously, *quatre-vingts*, but these are exceptional.

If we look at the peoples who use a system of twenty we find them in Australia, New Guinea, in parts of India, in the African Bantu, Togo and Niger people, and with the Aztecs and Mayas in Central and South America. It would be tempting to think that these people used a system of twenty because, living in warm climates, they did not need to cover their feet and had not lost the art of wiggling their toes, but this would not be true of the Eskimos who also use a vigesimal (based on twenty) system of counting. Apart from the Eskimos, people who normally see their hands and their uncovered feet might well think of all twenty digits as representing their whole person and make use of twenty as their base.

After number names have been invented, progress depends upon the efficiency of the recording system. For the simple recording of events or the number of things, a simple tally of notches cut in wood or marks made on paper suffices for the small numbers. These may begin with either vertical I, II, III, or horizontal ‒ , = , ≡ strokes, but after three or four have been written to form a group, it becomes a little difficult to see at a glance whether a group is, say, six or seven strokes. In most of the primitive number systems a new symbol is introduced, sometimes for four, sometimes for five.

In the West we usually write across a page and use vertical strokes like I, II, . . . for counting, but in the East, several languages, including Chinese, which is the most important today, are written down the page in columns, and the simpler numbers seem to consist of horizontal strokes.

Of the systems of recording numbers, the Roman is probably the simplest to understand because it is so little distorted from the original finger counting which it portrays in a formal way. I, II, III, IIII are simply representations of fingers, and the five, written formally as V, is simply a picture of a hand held up as in Fig. 1.1 (a).

Fig. 1.1 (a)   Fig. 1.1 (b)

Then six is one handful and one, or VI, and so on until ten is two handfuls or two Vs placed together, X forming an X. After that there is simple repetition, XXXII being three tens and two, or thirty-two. This simple representation of finger counting was slightly modified by substituting IV for 4 and IX for 9, but these were introduced long after the Roman numerals were established. It looks very much as though a handful of tens, as in Fig. 1.1 (b), could be formalized to look like an L, or fifty, and two fifties combined, like the Vs, to give ꝲ, which suggests a C for a hundred, and it is convenient to think of these symbols in this way. The experts, however, particularly Mommsen writing in 1850, have more complicated explanations for L for fifty although they agree on the derivation of the V and the X. Ancient inscriptions write Ⅽ|Ɔ for a thousand, a form not unlike an M in some ways and one which could readily be converted to an M, particularly when the initial letter of *Mille*, a thousand, is M. Half this symbol, or |Ɔ, probably gave rise to the D for half a thousand. In Roman numerals several tens or hundreds are indicated simply by repetition, as for example in MDCCCLXXVIII or 1878. The Roman numeral for three hundred and twenty-three would be CCCXXIII and for three hundred and two would be CCCII. We could write these numbers as 3*h* 2*t* 3*u* and 3*h* 2*u* respectively where it is understood that *h* stands for hundreds, *t* for tens and *u* for units. This is just what the Chinese do (Fig. 1.2).

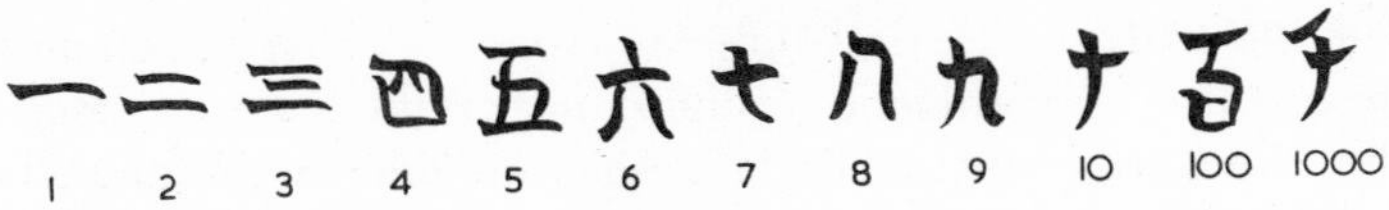

一二三四五六七八九十百千
 1   2   3   4   5   6   7   8   9 10 100 1000

Fig. 1.2

The Chinese write downwards in vertical columns, and the numbers 1878, 324 and 302 are written as in Fig. 1.3.

Fig. 1.3

1878   324   302

15

50

The sign 零 corresponds to the "and" when we say three hundred and two.

The Greeks had an unsatisfactory system of using the letters of their alphabet to stand for numbers until they were used up, and then repeating the alphabet with dashes for numbers in the thousands; but this very intelligent race made little contribution to arithmetic and their letter system seems to have been a handicap rather than a help.

The most important contribution to the writing down of numbers was made by the Hindus of Northern India. As early as the third century B.C. it is known that they had nine signs for the first nine numbers, but the essential contribution which distinguished their symbols from the even more ancient Chinese system, which also had nine signs, was the use of a sign for zero. We have not been able to determine exactly when this was introduced but one authority on the subject (D. E. Smith, *History of Mathematics*) states that "Hindu literature gives some evidence that the zero may have been known before our era, but we have no actual inscription containing this symbol before the ninth century". Once a form of zero has been introduced it is possible to use our present system in which the position of a digit in a number determines whether it refers to units, tens, hundreds, thousands, etc. Our present numbers are derived from these old Hindu numbers and came into use in Europe during the fourteenth and fifteenth centuries. There are occasional instances of their use from as early as the year 976 in Spain, and Arabs, with their contacts with both East and West, seem to have known about these numerals two hundred years before this. In the course of a thousand years, and particularly in the centuries before printing, the forms of the number symbols altered quite considerably. 1 is recognizably the vertical stroke, derived from the Roman I, and both 2 and 3 seem to be cursive forms of the eastern forms = and ≡, which when written become **z** and **Ƹ**. At one time and another the other symbols have had a variety of forms which can be found, by anyone who is interested, in D. E. Smith's *History of Mathematics* or Rouse Ball's *A Short Account of the History of Mathematics*, but it is noticeable how little they have changed since Caxton, in 1480, set up his type for the printing of the *Mirrour of the World* in which his numerals were

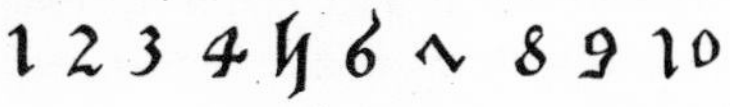

1 2 3 4 5 6 ⋏ 8 9 10

Fig. 1.4

Methods of Calculating

From the point of view of arithmetic the most important historical fact is that until the introduction into Europe of the Hindu-Arabic numerals with the zero and the idea of place value, the numerals were treated as recording symbols and not working symbols. Pencil and paper arithmetic is very difficult with Roman numerals, almost impossible with the Greek letter numerals, and, although the Chinese numerals would seem to offer similar facilities to our own, the Chinese continue to use, as they have done for over four thousand years, a bead frame, or abacus, for their calculating. Until the fifteenth century, bead frames, pebbles, counting boxes, chequer boards with "counters" and such-like paraphernalia were used to perform what to us seem quite simple calculations. The word "calculate" is derived from the Latin word *calculus*, a pebble. Writing of the Jesuit missionary, Ricci, in China in 1591, Vincent Cronin says:

> "Ricci had discovered that the young graduate was intent on learning only one thing: how to change cinnabar into silver. However, as their lessons progressed, he was able to interest his pupil in other more marvellous if less rewarding subjects. He began to teach Ch'u mathematics, a subject which, like medicine, the Chinese had no incentive to learn and which had remained at a rudimentary stage. In particular, Chinese arithmetic, conditioned by the abacus, was clumsy and slow. If a mistake were made, since previous calculations were effaced, the whole reckoning had to be started again. Ricci, who had been surprised to find that China had always used a decimal system, showed that by means of written numbers, for which ideograms already existed, more complicated problems could be solved."
>
> (*The Wise Man from the West*, Rupert Hart-Davis, 1955.)

In passing, we might remember that the Chancellor of the Exchequer derives his title from the chequer board and counters on which his medieval predecessors performed their computations.

The difficulties of using other notations for quite simple arithmetical operations may be illustrated by the simple calculation of seventy-eight multiplied by twenty-six, using Roman numerals. We must multiply by one symbol at a time, remembering that multiplying by I simply gives the original number, multiplying by V involves replacing I by V, V times V is XXV, V times X is L, V times L is CCL. The calculation would be:

$$
\begin{array}{r}
\text{LXXVIII} \\
\text{times} \quad \text{XXVI} \\
\hline
\text{LXXVIII} \\
\text{CCLLLXXVVVV} \\
\text{DCCLXXX} \\
\text{DCCLXXX} \\
\hline
\text{MMXXVIII}
\end{array}
$$

where in adding the rows together we replace two Vs by one X, five Xs by L, two Ls by C, five Cs by D, and two Ds by M.

The reader can best appreciate the work which is involved by first writing seventy-six and thirty-seven in Roman numerals and then multiplying them together. If the answer is then checked by ordinary multiplication, the labour required by the two methods may be contrasted.

If multiplication is somewhat laborious, division becomes almost impossible. There is, according to Rouse Ball, a record of a man who, in A.D. 944, when he wanted to divide 6152 by 15, wrote out all the multiples of 15 until he reached 6000 and counted that he had then written out 400 of them. He then subtracted 6000 from 6152, checked through his list of multiples of 15, found there were 10 in 150 and so obtained 410 remainder 2. If you picture what this involved, when all the multiples of 15 had to be written out in Roman numerals, you will appreciate that the labour was tremendous, and you will understand why abaci and counters were used.

NAPIER'S RODS

John Napier, a Scotsman born in 1550, made considerable contributions to the art of calculating. His most important claim to fame is the invention of logarithms (published in his *Mirifici Logarithmorum Canonis Descriptio* in 1614). He died in 1617 and his last work included a description of what are known as Napier's Rods or Napier's Bones. They consist of nine rods, each nine times as long as it is wide, the face of the rod being divided into nine squares. The first rod is numbered in ones, 1, 2, 3, 4, 5, 6, 7, 8, 9; the second rod in twos, 2, 4, 6, 8, 10, 12, 14, 16, 18; the third rod in threes, 3, 6, 9, 12, 15, 18, 21, 24, 27 and so on. Where a number contains two digits they are printed diagonally in the square like this ⌀, ⌀, etc. The whole set of rods then looked like Fig. 1.5 (*a*).

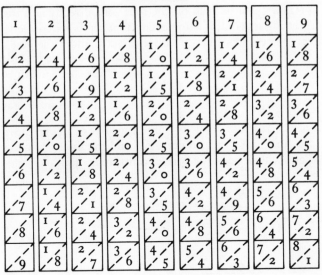

Fig. 1.5 (*a*)

Fig. 1.5 (*b*)

To multiply, say 1959 by 365, the rods corresponding to 1, 9, 5 and 9 are removed from the box and placed beside one another like Fig. 1.5 (*b*).

If from this array of rods we pick out the third row,

the numbers have the appearance of being arranged in diagonals, with the 3 "under" the 2, with the 7 under the 1, with the 5 under the 2. The addition of these pairs of numbers

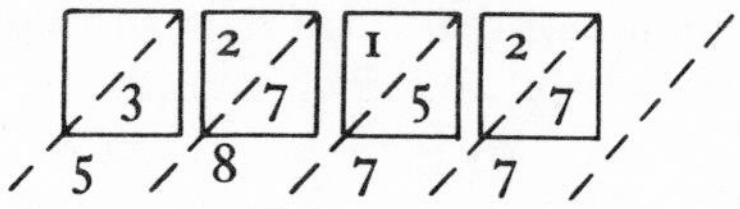

gives the product 1959 × 3 = 5877.

If the sixth row is now picked out, adding diagonally gives

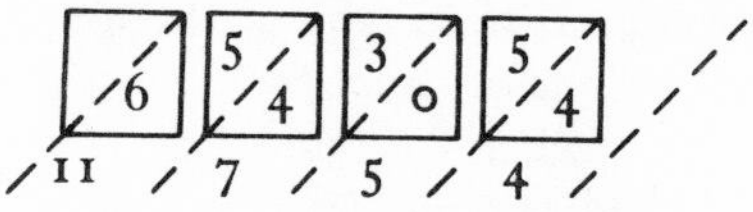

and the fifth row gives

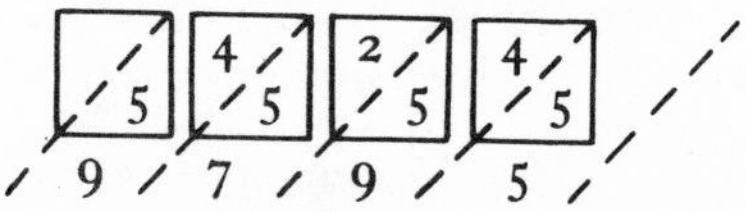

These products of 1959 and 3, 6 and 5 can be read off the four rods directly and the products simply written down. In setting this out, it is important that digits are correctly placed in the appropriate columns. Write down the multiplier directly under the given number, thus:

$$\begin{array}{cccc} 1 & 9 & 5 & 9 \\ & 3 & 6 & 5 \end{array}$$

Then write the right-hand digit of the row obtained for three times 1959 under the 3 and then, in the next line, place the final 4 of 11754 under the 6 and the final 5 of 9795 directly below the 5 of 365. The digits will all be in the correct units, tens, hundreds, etc. columns.

$$\begin{array}{ccccc} & 1 & 9 & 5 & 9 \\ & & 3 & 6 & 5 \\ \hline 5 & 8 & 7 & 7 & \\ 1 & 1 & 7 & 5 & 4 \\ & & 9 & 7 & 9 & 5 \\ \hline 7 & 1 & 5 & 0 & 3 & 5 \end{array}$$

In so far as multiplication enters into a long division calculation, the rods could be used also to help in division.

In the multiplication illustrated above, two columns of nines were used. Several columns can be made available if the rods are made of square section and different sets of numbers are printed on the four sides (Fig. 1.6).

Fig. 1.6

Counting and Recording Numbers

Any of the number systems fill the need for *recording* the results of counting, but the particular merit of the Hindu-Arabic numerals is their value as *working* tools. The written number is a permanent record but, in counting and adding, something more flexible than this is required. One primitive way of getting round this difficulty is illustrated by the observation during the early years of this century, in South Africa, of two Africans counting. One counted the units, up to ten, on his fingers, and the other counted the number of tens, also using his fingers, so that between them they kept a moving record of both tens and units. When our number system has been thoroughly learned we are able to use it both for working and recording. We do not always use our own numbers for recording: we talk of four dozen boxes of matches rather than forty-eight, farmers count their sheep in scores, kippers are sold in pairs, the bag of a shoot is recorded as so many brace of partridges, and a carpenter probably has several gross of screws in his workshop. We do, however, use our familiar notation for calculating. The need for two men to count out forty-eight oranges, one to count units up to ten and the other to count the number of tens, illustrates a difficulty which children meet in their earliest attempts at adding numbers. To add four on to five, at this stage, involves counting up to five and then going on to count four more numbers. A child will often say "six" and stretch one finger out, say "seven" as he stretches a second finger out, "eight" with a third finger and "nine" with a fourth finger and give the correct answer, nine. This operation is possible so long as the number to be added is small enough for the number of fingers stretched out to be counted, at a glance, without a prolonged counting of fingers which would interfere with the main counting. A second stage, a little more mature than the other, involves keeping two sequences running in the mind at the same time, saying "five, and one makes six, and two makes seven, and three makes eight, and four makes nine". Arithmetically these are equivalent; one uses fingers as "props", and the other is completely verbalized, but both correspond to the scheme,

$$
\begin{array}{ccccccccc}
 & & & & & 1 & 2 & 3 & 4 \\
1 & 2 & 3 & 4 & 5 & 6 & 7 & 8 & 9
\end{array}
$$

in which the counting is continued from the first number for as many units as there are corresponding to the number to be added. This difficulty of keeping in the conscious mind two sets of things is a common characteristic of many arithmetical processes, and much of our writing out of calculations is designed to enable us to keep two trains of thought going without muddling them. For addition, there are two ways of overcoming the difficulty: one is to learn the combinations of numbers up to ten and the other is to draw up a reference table. No one can ever hope to make much progress in arithmetic until the simple additions are known, but this does take time and familiarity with the numbers, and, until the additions are known and the response is automatic and reliable, it is valuable for children to have a handy table by them.

Adding four on to five is done by counting on a further four numbers after five, namely, 6, 7, 8, 9. We could set this out

$$
\begin{array}{c|cccc}
 & 1 & 2 & 3 & 4 \\
\hline
5 & 6 & 7 & 8 & 9
\end{array}
$$

the figure on the extreme left telling us the number we are counting *from*, the last figure on the top row telling us how many we had counted *on*, and the figure under the 4 giving us the answer.

A whole table of this sort, in which each row begins one number farther ahead each time, may be drawn up:

	1	2	3	4	5	6	7	8	9	10
0	1	2	3	4	5	6	7	8	9	10
1	2	3	4	5	6	7	8	9	10	11
2	3	4	5	6	7	8	9	10	11	12
3	4	5	6	7	8	9	10	11	12	13
4	5	6	7	8	9	10	11	12	13	14
5	6	7	8	9	10	11	12	13	14	15
6	7	8	9	10	11	12	13	14	15	16
7	8	9	10	11	12	13	14	15	16	17
8	9	10	11	12	13	14	15	16	17	18
9	10	11	12	13	14	15	16	17	18	19

To find the sum of 5 and 4, find 5 on the extreme left, 4 right at the top, and then 9 is level with the 5 and below the 4.

ADDING

We are all so familiar with our numbers that we rarely pause to think just what they do for us. When we say that six plus nine plus eight equals twenty-three, our figures

$$6+9+8=23$$

not only add ●●●●●● ●●●●●●●●● ●●●●●●●● to give ●●●●●●●●●●●●●●●●●●●●●●● but they also arrange them tidily for us and give the sum in the form

which is two tens and three.

CARRYING

When we add 26 + 38 the sum of the units 6 and 8 is given to us directly in the convenient form of 14, that is, one ten and four:

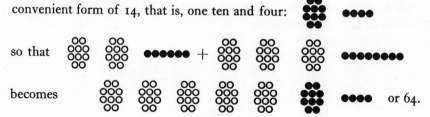

SUBTRACTING

The mechanics of our tens notation is flexible enough for us to use 14 for either

●● ●●●● or ●●●●●●●●●●●●●● at will.
●●●
●●

Thus, when we wish to subtract 26 from 64, we are asking:

"If we remove ⦿⦿ ⦿⦿ oooooo from ⦿⦿ ⦿⦿ ⦿⦿ oooo

what sort of pattern are we left with?"

To be able to take the 6 from the 4 we need to set out one group of ten as ten separate units; we indicate that one group of ten has been subtracted by printing it in *red* so that now we have to

remove ⦿⦿ ⦿⦿ oooooo from ⦿⦿ ⦿⦿ ⦿⦿ oooooooooooooo

and when we have done this we are left with the part printed in black in

oooooo oooooooo

which is obviously 38.

When we do this subtraction with figures, the translation into simple words of the operation illustrated with dots is "Six from four I replace by six from fourteen, which is *eight*. I have taken one of the tens (to replace four by fourteen) and there are two more tens to subtract, so three tens from six tens is *three* tens". This is modified when we talk to ourselves but is basically what many people say when they subtract.

Number Patterns

The Hindu-Arabic numerals serve the two very useful purposes of providing a means of recording numbers concisely and of enabling calculations to be performed with considerable efficiency. They are, however, number symbols based on a pattern of tens and there are many properties of numbers which are not effectively displayed by these symbols. We are used to seeing playing cards and dominoes which represent numbers by dots arranged in patterns, and arrangements of this type may be used to bring out regularities and sequences of numbers. The simplest, and by far the most important of the elementary classifications of numbers, is into *odd* and *even* numbers, and the arrangement of the patterns used to represent numbers in the form

o oo oo oo oo oo oo oo oo oo oo oo

brings out this difference.

The alternate odd numbers, with the extra dot which does not fit into the rectangular pattern, are obvious, and cards can easily be sorted into odd and even sets of numbers.

There are many other properties of numbers which can be illustrated in this sort of way, properties which become obvious in such a representation but which are not brought out at all in their representation by numerals. There is, for instance, nothing in the appearance of 8 or 7 to indicate that 8 is the product of factors, 2 × 4, whereas 7 has no factors. A classification of numbers which can be arranged as rectangles and those which cannot indicates the classification into "products" and "prime numbers".

RECTANGULAR AND PRIME NUMBERS

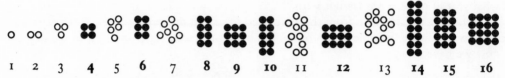

1 2 3 4 5 6 7 8 9 10 11 12 13 14 15 16

When a number is a rectangular number it can be arranged as a number of equal rows, thus *twelve* can be arranged as 3 rows of 4 or 6 rows of 2. This at once leads to the idea of multiplication, also to the idea of prime numbers. When a number can be arranged as a rectangle it is said to be the product of factors, thus:

3 and 4 are the factors of 12
or 12 is the product of 3 and 4

are both statements describing the rectangular arrangement.

SQUARE NUMBERS

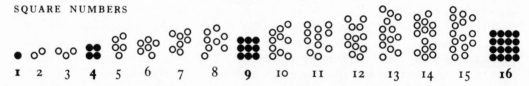

1 2 3 4 5 6 7 8 9 10 11 12 13 14 15 16

This arrangement illustrates first that square numbers have the same number of rows as they have columns, so that their two factors are equal: 9 is 3 × 3 and 16 is 4 × 4. It might also be noticed that the square numbers become progressively more separated as the sequence proceeds. Thus, 4 = 1 + 3, 9 = 4 + 5, 16 = 9 + 7. If it is observed that 3, 5, 7 are successive odd numbers, it might be expected that 16 + 9 would be the next square number and it may be verified that 25 is 5 × 5. Even without formal multiplication it is possible to count out twenty-five counters and arrange them in five rows of five. Anyone with an alert mind might ask why *odd* numbers are added each time and the little exercise of building up one pattern from the previous one illustrates this simply

To add one more to each of the three rows we add one set of three.
To add one more to each of the three columns we add another set of three.
To fill in the corner we add a single one; so we have added two threes and one for the

corner. The fourth figure shows what has been added, namely, *two* threes and a single *one*, which is necessarily an odd number. Next time we should add two fours and one for the corner, and the "one for the corner" we need each time gives us the typical one over of our odd-number pattern.

TRIANGULAR NUMBERS

Another sequence of numbers which occurs systematically is that of the triangular numbers.

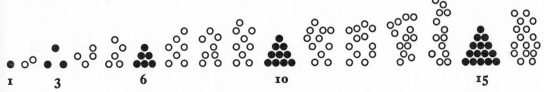

| 1 | 3 | 6 | 10 | 15 |

It is very easy to spot the pattern of their recurrence and to extend the sequence

1   3   6   10   15   .   .   .

These numbers are not very important at the elementary stage, but they form one of the regular sequences of the natural numbers and they will be mentioned again when series are discussed in Chapter 8.

Both the square numbers and the triangular numbers recur systematically but according to different laws. It is a matter of passing interest to wonder whether the two sequences are closely related in any way. If they are written out alongside one another

Square numbers   1   4   9   16   25   .   .   .
Triangular numbers   1   3   6   10   15   .   .   .

it might be noticed that the sum of two adjacent triangular numbers is always a square number. This is obvious when the number patterns are inspected:

Some numbers, such as five and seven, fit into none of these number sequences, others belong to several; 36 is even, it is a rectangular number, a square number and a triangular number, and there are many quite interesting patterns which can be made with 36 counters. *Five* does not fit into any of the sequences and the only meaningful arrangement is the one illustrating the fact that it is an *odd* number.

5
FIVE   ○○
     ○○
     ○

On cards given to children to stimulate thoughtful activity, one observes that a favourite arrangement for five is

5
FIVE   ○ ○
     ○○○

which is a pointless and misleading arrangement. It conveys no mathematical properties, opens up no trains of thought, and suggests a symmetry which corresponds to no property of the number. Such false patterning, suggesting that there is some purpose in making the arrangement, is quite barren of meaning and should be avoided.

GEOMETRICAL PATTERNS

Seven is a number which belongs to no special sequences, it is prime and somewhat barren of purely arithmetical interest. It is, however, a number that has found an important place in religious, mythological and superstitious imagery. As well as having seven days in a week, seven deadly sins and the sevenfold gifts imparted by the anointing spirit, happy people are in the seventh heaven, "seven for the seven stars in the sky", and there are seven-leagued boots, seven wonders of the world and seven Ages of man. From the seven circuits of the walls of Jericho to the "seven angels which had the seven vials full of the seven last plagues" in the Book of the Revelation (Ch. 21, v. 9), the Biblical imagery is full of sevens. One is interested to know why there is this widespread interest in *seven*. It is clearly not an arithmetical interest: these sevens are not added or multiplied, they are not seven in a sequence of five of these, six of those, seven of something else; these sevens stand alone in a context of rich imagery. Now although seven things can be arranged with six of them surrounding a central one, in a pattern symmetrical about twelve axes of symmetry, each one touching the central one and each of its neighbours, it does not lead to many arithmetical trains of thought but it does lead to several geometrical ideas of importance. The arrangement ●●● looks like the design for a jewel; it leads to the fitting together of equilateral triangles, to exploring the properties of hexagons; it is part of an endless pattern such as is seen with honeycombs and soap-bubbles, with butterfly eggs on leaves, and frog-spawn (Fig. 1.7).

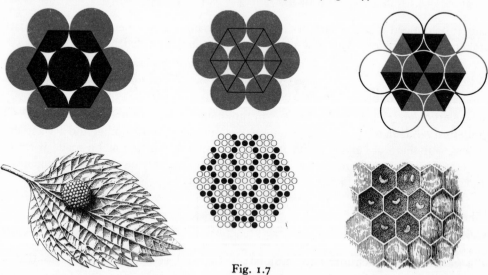

Fig. 1.7

PRODUCTS AND FACTORS

Of the number patterns discussed, by far the most important is that which distinguishes between rectangular numbers and prime numbers, for this leads to the combination of numbers to give products and the breaking down of numbers into factors and, ultimately, to the process of multiplication.

If 3 is added to 3 the result is 6 $\quad 3+3=6$

„ 3 „ „ „ 6 „ „ „ 9 $\quad 6+3=9$

„ 3 „ „ „ 9 „ „ „ 12 $\quad 9+3=12$

If we look at $\quad$ 3 $\qquad$ 6 $\qquad$ 9 $\qquad$ 12 $\qquad$ 15

we see that the numbers are arranged as groups of *three*, and each term consists of the previous term with one further group of three added to it. In saying that the factors of 12 are 3 and 4 we mean that 12 can be arranged as 4 groups of 3. This is written

$$3 \times 4 = 12$$

which is read as "three multiplied by four is equal to twelve".* On the other hand, it is frequently more convenient to read

$$3 \times 4 = 12$$

as "three times four is equal to twelve", more particularly when the multiplication arises in some context other than pure number; for instance, if I have four pennies, and four more pennies and then again four more pennies, I have in all three times four pennies, i.e.

$$3 \times 4 \text{ pennies} = 12 \text{ pennies}$$

which can most conveniently be read "three times four pennies equals twelve pennies".

It is not at all difficult to see that 12 can be thought of either as $\qquad$ or as so that 12 also belongs to the sequence

$\quad$ 4 $\qquad$ 8 $\qquad$ 12 $\qquad$ 16 $\qquad$ 20

and that $\qquad\qquad\qquad 4 \times 3 = 12$

which is read as "four multiplied by three is equal to twelve".

The particular relationship between the numbers can be expressed in a variety of ways, all of which are equivalent to one another in that they are all descriptive of the fact that three rows of four or four rows of three will give us twelve.

$3+3+3+3=12 \quad : \quad 3 \times 4 = 12 \quad : \quad 12 = 3 \times 4 \quad : \quad 12 = 3+3+3+3$

$4 + 4 + 4 = 12 \quad : \quad 4 \times 3 = 12 \quad : \quad 12 = 4 \times 3 \quad : \quad 12 = 4 + 4 + 4$

These basic facts of repeated addition, arranging in rectangular forms and the commutative law, $3 \times 4 = 4 \times 3$, are best understood by working with simple numbers and avoiding being side-tracked by the complications of tens and units, carrying figures, and setting out formal "sums".

---

* *See* p. 39 of *Mathematical Association's Report* on "The Teaching of Mathematics in Primary Schools" (G. Bell & Sons Ltd, 1955).

Numbers of Things

Some people find that numbers in themselves are interesting and will spend many happy hours enjoying working with number problems without relating their knowledge of number relations to actual objects. While it is obvious that no progress can be made in arithmetical and mathematical thinking until interest in numbers and some ability in handling them has been achieved, it is also clear that the counting and adding, combining, arranging and recording of numbers would, in the first place, hardly have developed as abstract ideas unless some system had been built up from experiences of handling objects and dealing with things of various shapes and sizes. As soon as we begin to attach numbers to objects and concern ourselves with quantities of things which have a material existence, we find that the simple ideas about whole numbers such as 1, 2, 3 . . . become greatly enriched.

CARDINAL AND ORDINAL NUMBERS

The whole numbers themselves are commonly used in two quite distinguishable ways, as cardinal numbers and as ordinal numbers. These usages are obvious from the two sentences, "There are *six* forms in the school" and "Angela Adams is in the *Sixth* form". The cardinal number *six* in the first of these two sentences refers to the group of forms as a whole and states that the group of forms at that school has six members. The ordinal number *sixth*, in the second of these sentences, refers exclusively to one form in the school and serves to distinguish it from the other forms. Similarly the cardinal number "fourteen" in the sentence "There are fourteen steps in this flight" refers to the flight as a whole and describes its contents, whereas the ordinal number "fourteen" in the sentence "The top step of the flight is number fourteen" refers to the one step, the top step, which happens to be the fourteenth. Although the usage is different, the two sentences give precisely the same information and the information will usually be obtained in the same way. In this instance I stand on the bottom step and say "one" and then move to the next step and say "two" and so on until I am standing on the top step where I say "fourteen". Having completed the ascent of the flight in this way I can then interpret the information obtained either in the cardinal form "There are fourteen stairs in this flight" or the ordinal form "The top step is the fourteenth" or "The top step is number fourteen". The ordinal form of the number is usually used when objects are placed in a particular order: thus, the year 1686 when Sir Isaac Newton published the first volume of his *Principia* comes before the year 1687 and the first volume comes before the second volume. The reader might like to sort out the ordinal and cardinal numbers by underlining the ordinal numbers in black and the cardinal ones in red in the sentence: "Henry VIII reigned for 38 years, and in the year 1533, which was the 24th year of his reign, he married the second of his six wives, Ann Boleyn, who bore him one child, Henry's second daughter, later to become Queen Elizabeth I."

CONTINUOUS AND DISCRETE QUANTITIES

As soon as we begin to apply arithmetic to material things, we observe that it is applied sometimes to continuous quantities and sometimes to separate objects. For instance, I can slide my hand up the banister rail but have to step up the stairs one by one. The distinction between continuous and discrete quantities is of fundamental importance throughout mathematics and the distinction should be thoroughly appreciated when ideas of division are first introduced to quite young children. I can find a point a quarter of the way up the banisters but I could not stand on a step a quarter of the way up a flight of fourteen stairs. I can divide the lemonade in a bottle equally between three children, but I cannot divide four dolls equally between the three children. If a farmer who owned a fifteen-acre field and fifteen cows left in his will both his land and his herd of cows to be divided equally between his two sons, each son should receive seven-and-a-half acres of land. They should also each receive seven cows, but the remaining cow, which cannot be divided between them, must be treated differently. It would probably be sold and the proceeds divided. The two calculations are:

$$\text{(i)} \quad 2\overline{)\,15}7\tfrac{1}{2} \qquad\qquad \text{(ii)} \quad 2\overline{)\,15}7, \text{ remainder } 1$$

This distinction should also be noted when we use various units. If we compare three lumps of sugar with a dollop of treacle which contains three teaspoonfuls of treacle, we see at once that there are three lumps—three separate, different lumps—but only one dollop of the treacle, which is compared with something quite distinct and separate from itself, in this instance the capacity of a teaspoon. There is an arbitrariness about this unit; instead of three teaspoonfuls, we might have equated it to ten saltspoonfuls. It is also unusual for a continuous quantity of any sort of material to consist of an exact number of unit parts; a cow, for example, might well give more than three gallons of milk a day but less than four gallons.

Other Number Systems

Had we been a race of people with four instead of five digits on each hand, we might well have developed a system of counting using eight and not ten as the base. There follow a number of examples which will give an idea of how such a system might be explored.

Jonathan Swift invented the fantasy of Gulliver's voyage to the Houyhnhnms, the race of horses which had developed a civilization and a language. Had he pursued his fantasy a little more deeply he might have thought about their arithmetic. Being ungulates with but a single toe on each forefoot, their number system would be likely to be based on *two* as ours is on *ten*. It would then have been to the Houyhnhnms that we should have looked for the invention of a *binary* system of counting. Binary and decimal equivalents are given in the following table:

Binary number	1, 10, 11, 100, 101, 110, 111, 1000, 1001, 1010 . . .
Decimal equivalent	1, 2, 3, 4, 5, 6, 7, 8, 9, 10 . . .

Today such a system is of the greatest importance because, in an electric circuit, a current may either be flowing or not flowing, so that a signal "1" or a signal "0" may be sent. The binary system is made up entirely of these two symbols and is the basis of the digital computers which are nowadays revolutionizing the performance of complex calculations.

As adults we have grown up using the tens notation and we take it for granted. We can, perhaps, recapture some of the difficulties which we must have overcome, as children, by playing with an alternative system. This exercise serves also to distinguish between properties which are common to more than one system and properties which are specific to the tens notation.

Imagine that instead of four fingers and a thumb, our hands had only four fingers. When we had counted up to eight on our fingers, we should then have used up all our digits and we should have eight as a complete "oct" just as now we have ten as a complete "ten". Eleven to us now is ten and one, written as 11. In an eights system, what we now know as nine would be a whole eight plus one and we should write this as 11. We need to invent a few names to go with the notation and the following table shows numbers in our tens system and their names alongside the same numbers in an eights system, with a systematic set of new names.

Tens System		Eights System		Tens System		Eights System	
1	one	1	one	24	twenty-four	30	throcty
2	two	2	two	25	twenty-five	31	throcty-one
3	three	3	three	26	twenty-six	32	throcty-two
4	four	4	four	27	twenty-seven	33	throcty-three
5	five	5	five	28	twenty-eight	34	throcty-four
6	six	6	six	29	twenty-nine	35	throcty-five
7	seven	7	seven	30	thirty	36	throcty-six
8	eight	10	oct	31	thirty-one	37	throcty-seven
9	nine	11	unoct	32	thirty-two	40	forocty
10	ten	12	twoct	33	thirty-three	41	forocty-one
11	eleven	13	throct				
12	twelve	14	fouroct	36	thirty-six	44	forocty-four
13	thirteen	15	fivoct				
14	fourteen	16	sixoct	46	forty-six	56	fivocty-six
15	fifteen	17	sevnoct				
16	sixteen	20	twocty	49	forty-nine	61	sisocty-one
17	seventeen	21	twocty-one				
18	eighteen	22	twocty-two	64	sixty-four	100	bisoctred
19	nineteen	23	twocty-three				
20	twenty	24	twocty-four	81	eighty-one	121	bisoctred and twocty-one
21	twenty-one	25	twocty-five				
22	twenty-two	26	twocty-six				
23	twenty-three	27	twocty-seven	100	hundred	144	bisoctred and forocty-four
24	twenty-four	30	throcty				

Some familiar properties remain, others are transformed. In both notations,

$$2 \times 10 = 20, \quad 10 \times 10 = 100, \quad 11 \times 11 = 121, \quad 12 \times 12 = 144.$$

The familiar property that a number whose digits add up to 9 or to a multiple of 9, transfers to 7—thus,

$$18 = 2 \times 9, \quad 1 + 8 = 9; \quad 27 = 3 \times 9, \quad 2 + 7 = 9, \text{ etc.}$$

showing the property of numbers divisible by nine in the tens notation—is replaced by

$$\text{sixoct} = 16 = 2 \times 7, \quad 1 + 6 = 7,$$
$$\text{twocty-five} = 25 = 3 \times 7, \quad 2 + 5 = 7$$
$$\text{throcty-four} = 34 = 4 \times 7, \quad 3 + 4 = 7, \text{ etc.}$$

in the eights notation.

The property, in the tens notation, that any number ending in o or 5 is divisible by 5, is replaced, in the eights notation, by the property that any number ending in o or 4 is divisible by 4.

As an exercise, write out a seven or a nine or a twelve notation, invent the necessary words and explore the characteristics of the notation comparing it with the tens notation. If you use twelve as a base you will need also to invent single symbols for the numbers which are ten and eleven in the tens notation.

Prove that in the eights notation the fourth power of every odd number ends in a 1 and the fourth power of every even number ends in a 0.

In the tens notation, the fifth power of every whole number ends with the same digit as the number itself. Show that this is true and say how much of this statement is true in the eights notation.

THE BINARY NOTATION

If instead of grouping in tens and writing 10 for ten, we group in twos and write 10 for two, we obtain the *binary system*. Three is two (10) plus one (1) = 10 + 1 = 11. Four is two (10) × two (10) = 100. Five is four plus one = 100 + 1 = 101 and so on.

Tens notation	Binary notation
1	1
2	10
3	11
4	100
5	101
6 (= 3 × 2)	110 (= 11 × 10)
7	111
8	1000
9	1001
10 (= 2 × 5)	1010 (= 10 × 101)
11	1011
12	1100
13	1101
14	1110
15	1111
16	10,000

EXERCISES

1. Translate the following into binary numbers and check the truth of these statements in the binary notation

$$3 + 12 = 15$$
$$5 \times 3 = 15$$
$$5 + 10 = 15$$
$$2 \times 2 \times 2 \times 2 = 16$$

2. Work out 63 in the binary system then add one and check that the answer is equal to 8 × 8.

2

Systems of Units

Units of Length

We have inherited our system of units from a long-distant past, from times when tools were not capable of very great precision and when men did most of their home-building work for themselves. If you put your thumb down on a ruler you will find that it is about an inch broad. The distance from the point of your elbow to the tip of your middle finger is called a "cubit" and is about eighteen inches in length, and the distance from the end of your nose to the tip of your fingers, when your arm is stretched out sideways from your shoulder, is almost exactly two cubits and is the length we now call a "yard". Check your own personal measurements and find out how nearly they agree with the primitive table of

$$18 \text{ thumbs} = 1 \text{ cubit}$$
$$2 \text{ cubits} = 1 \text{ yard}$$

Now, without bothering how long your own personal cubit is, as compared with standard rulers, try making use of your own personal measurements. The door of my room is one cubit and thirteen of my thumbs wide. I have measured this length out on the edge of a piece of cloth and then tried the cloth against the door; the error was less than half an inch. The edge of the table on which my typewriter stands is exactly two of my cubits long. There is a larger table in the room and I have measured a length of two cubits along one of its edges and then placed the smaller table alongside and compared the two lengths. I find that I have overestimated the two cubits along the edge of the longer table by about an inch when compared with the smaller table. I have been practising the use of my personal measurements for some time and I now find that I can use them with an error in consistency of about one in forty, although this error does depend upon the convenience of the position in which the lengths are placed. For cubits, table tops, the edges of sideboards and mantelpieces are convenient; for yards measured from nose to fingertips, rope, cloth and such-like materials are the most easily measured; and the sizes of books, foolscap envelopes and such objects are convenient for practising thumb-widths. When you have practised a few such lengths and have attained a fair degree of consistency, check these measurements with a standard ruler and get to know your own personal measurements. The cubit has been in use since the earliest times and we have records of the sizes of a number of ancient buildings and monuments whose remains still exist. From the recorded measurements of the pyramid of Khufu we know that the cubit used in the designing and building of that pyramid was 20·62 in. long. You can, therefore, get a reasonably accurate idea of how big an ancient Egyptian man was, by finding someone whose cubit is about 20·6 in.

The cubit is obviously an inconvenient measure for use on the ground, particularly for older people with rheumatism, and the foot is the obvious part of the body to use. Greek and Roman "feet" varied in length from a "foot" of 12·45 in. used in Athens, the

11·69-in. foot used in the construction of the Parthenon, to the Roman foot of 11·61 in. Measurements of distances at Stonehenge reveal a number of multiples of a unit of 11·68 in. and in medieval England a foot of 12·45 in. was in common use. A present-day size 10 shoe fits a 11·66 in. foot. The method of measuring a length by putting heel to toe and measuring in feet is reliable, and once you know the length of your feet you can use them for estimating with reasonable accuracy lengths of rooms, widths of flower beds, distances between rows of vegetables. The cubit has disappeared entirely from use and the simple table of lengths derived from personal measurements is

$$12 \text{ in.} = 1 \text{ ft}$$
$$3 \text{ ft} = 1 \text{ yd}$$

Out of doors the traditional units are the pole, the furlong and the mile. The word furlong is derived from "furrowlong". Various explanations are given of the origin of this distance. It has been suggested that it was the distance oxen could pull a plough before having to pause for breath (M. E. Bowman, *Romance in Arithmetic*), and for all but the first class runners, 220 yd is about as far as a man can continue an all-out sprint. The "furrowlong" became roughly standardized as the length of a strip in medieval fields. A ploughman behind a plough being pulled by oxen yoked to a pole will come to the end of a furrow and will then have to turn his oxen; the radius of the turning circle will depend upon the length of the pole and will be an important factor in the tidy ploughing of parallel strips. This length is fairly consistent and became known as the "pole" or "rod". The "rod" possibly refers to the stick or rod carried by ploughmen to encourage their oxen by lightly whacking them from the rear. A rod certainly seems rather a long length for such a stick, but a ploughman would be quite a distance behind his oxen. The rod or pole was one-fortieth of a furrow long. The area of a strip a furlong in length and a rod in width was called a rood. Present-day "allotments" as a rule are a rod in width. The other outdoor measurement of importance was the "mile", which is a variant of the Latin word *mille*, a thousand. Roman soldiers on the march with a stride of just over 31 in. marched at a thousand paces to the mile, a pace being "the distance between where the heel left the ground to that where the same heel descended in the next stride": in other words, a pace was two strides. A mile was equal to 8 furlongs, so the old outdoor measurements were simply

$$40 \text{ poles} = 1 \text{ furlong}$$
$$8 \text{ furlongs} = 1 \text{ mile}$$

So long as these were the rough and ready measures of the old home craftsmen and their wives, the seamstresses working with their homespuns and the labourer toiling in the fields, the two tables of personal measures and outdoor distances sufficed, but as trade developed and land tenure became subject to leases and deeds based on more or less accurate surveying, the need for legal standards of length became felt. The two separate tables of length

$$\left. \begin{array}{l} 12 \text{ in.} = 1 \text{ ft} \\ 3 \text{ ft} = 1 \text{ yd} \end{array} \right\} \quad \text{and} \quad \left\{ \begin{array}{l} 40 \text{ poles} = 1 \text{ furlong} \\ 8 \text{ furlongs} = 1 \text{ mile} \end{array} \right.$$

were united in the reign of King Edward I. It is worth noting that when these two tables are united to form a single table the number eleven turns up as a link between them.

$5\frac{1}{2}$ yd = 1 rod ($5\frac{1}{2}$ is half eleven), 220 yd = 1 furlong (220 = 20 times 11) and 1760 yd = 1 mile (1760 = 160 times 11). The "Statute for measuring Land", which is almost certainly of the late thirteenth century, states "five yards and a half make one perch, that is sixteen and a half feet, measured by the aforesaid Iron Yard of our Lord the King". This was confirmed in 1592 by a decree of Queen Elizabeth: "To avoide Doubts that may arise. A Myle is to conteyne Eight Furlongs, and everie Furlonge to conteyne Fortie Luggs or Poles, and every Lugg or Pole to conteyne Sixtene Foote and Halfe."*

Units of Weight

The tables of length were tidied up by Edward I, and there is little difficulty in seeing that the number 11, and various multiples, forms a link between two primitive tables. With our tables of weights, however, a variety of quite separate systems has left sundry items and, apart from legal units, a number of practices remain as vestiges of discarded tables of weight. The basis of our system of weights is the pound, abbreviated to lb. The word "pound" is derived from a Latin word *pondo* which itself is derived from *pendere* which means "to hang", and the abbreviation, lb, is from the Latin *libra*, a balance. The words themselves indicate quite clearly not only whence some of the standard weights came to us, but also the method of weighing. The Bible uses the expression "weighed in the balance" and Egyptian drawings show that balances have been used for several thousands of years. There have been several "pounds" at one time and another, for instance, the "Troy pound" used for weighing gold and precious stones and for coinage. The weights used by goldsmiths and for coinage still persist in the system called Troy weight, possibly named from the town Troyes, in France. The table was

20 pennyweights (dwt) = 1 oz (Troy)

12 oz (Troy)   = 1 lb (Troy)

This certainly agrees with something which is familiar: 240 dwt is the weight of 1 lb, so that the pound (Troy weight) was the weight of a pound's (money) worth of pennies. The word "ounce" and the word "inch" are both derived from the Latin word *uncia* meaning "one twelfth", so that the *twelve* Troy ounces in a pound have given us the word for an ounce. The division by two and by two again and by two again was a practice common in northern Europe at a time when the crude numerals scarcely allowed any other form of calculation to be accomplished in any easy way. This repeated sub-division into halves bequeathed to us our other ounce (avoirdupois) of which there are 16 to the pound. For higher weights such as the hundredweight, ton and stone we also retain bits from sundry sources. The hundredweight was probably, at some time, some-where, a hundred pounds, but the stone was the weight of the millers and over the centuries the millers were important and prosperous men. The hundredweight, with a bit over (like a baker's dozen), was modified to contain an exact number of stones and became 112 lb, or 8 stones, and the ton remained 20 of these 112-lb hundredweights, or 2240 lb.

So far as the general public is concerned, for small weights we use ounces and pounds and for larger weights we use stones, hundredweights and tons. Drams still seem to

---

* Quoted from *Romance in Arithmetic*, M. E. Bowman (U.L.P.), which contains many very interesting details of other units.

figure in the tables printed in school text-books, but few of the millions of children who have learned that 16 drams make one ounce can ever have made use of this fact in the last fifty years. The ordinary weights are still called "avoirdupois", a modernized form of a word which has been spelt in a variety of ways in England since Norman-French was a living language. A sixteenth-century spelling, "haberdepoyes" does suggest a direct Latin derivation from *habere*, used in the sense of goods or property, and the *pois* is the same as the French word *poids*, from the Latin *pendo*, I weigh. The meaning of the word was originally "goods sold by weight" as distinct from "goods sold by volume". It is convenient to think of the table as:

Table of Weights (Avoirdupois)

16 oz	= 1 lb		
112 lb	= 1 cwt	14 lb	= 1 stone
20 cwt	= 1 ton	8 stones	= 1 cwt
2240 lb	= 1 ton		

There is little point in complicating these tables.

Although these are the legal and official tables there remain practices which should be noted. Usually, for lighter articles, pounds and ounces are in general use, but for a number of goods the quantities made up are based on the stone as the basic unit. One can buy a stone of flour, or a seven pound bag; a smaller bag of flour weighs $3\frac{1}{2}$ lb and a small bag $1\frac{3}{4}$ lb. A quartern loaf weighs $3\frac{1}{2}$ lb (a quarter of a stone). Since the war, practice has been changing and many firms now market "self-raising flour" in 1-lb and 3-lb bags. The quartern and half-quartern units were, of course, derived from the stone by the process of successive divisions by 2.

In 1620, when the Pilgrim Fathers set sail for America, the prosperous millers of England had little cause to complain of their lot and no one with a vested interest in the "stone" sought freedom in New England. Those who did sail, straightforward, honest men, took with them the memory of the English pound and did not forget that the hundredweight was the unit for heavier weights. To them the word "hundredweight" suggested the number 100 rather than 112 and they established the American table of weights as 100 lb = 1 cwt and 2000 lb = 1 ton. There are no stones. American visitors to England are confused by the dials of English weighing machines and an American who weighs 148 lb in America is quite surprised to find he weighs 10 stones, 8 lb in England. An American battleship of 44,000 tons weighs 88,000,000 lb whereas a British battleship of 40,000 tons weighs 89,600,000 lb. In transatlantic dealings it is essential to specify whether weights are expressed in *long tons* (2240 lb) or *short tons* (2000 lb), and as a rough guide, if *long* tons are not quoted knock 10 per cent off the American weight before comparing it with the corresponding British weight. The American and British *pound* are identical.

The avoirdupois *pound* is the only legal pound in Britain nowadays. For special purposes, the Troy *ounce* and the Apothecaries' *ounce* are legal. Each of these is 0·06857 lb (avoirdupois) = 1·097 oz (avoirdupois). The general public are rarely concerned with these measures, but when they carry a prescription from a medical practitioner to a dispensing chemist the quantities of the ingredients are usually expressed in Apothecaries' measures, using the traditional symbols for these units.

Apothecaries' Weights

20 grains = 1 scruple ℈

3 scruples = 1 drachm ℨ

8 drachms = 1 ounce   ℥

Most people must have heard of the *carat*. This is a word (derived originally from the Greek word for a seed of the locust-tree) which is used in two different senses: a diamond may be weighed in carats, in which case a carat is $3\frac{1}{5}$ grains; a wedding ring may be a 22-carat gold ring, in which case a carat is a twenty-fourth part, so that 22-carat gold contains 22 parts of gold to 2 parts of alloy and 18-carat gold contains 18 parts of gold to 6 parts of alloy.

The word "scrupulous" comes to us from the word "scruple" and we get an interesting insight into the degree of accuracy of weighing in the fifteenth and sixteenth centuries from the use of this word. A scrupulous person would be one who was careful to weigh to the accuracy of a scruple, or a twenty-fourth of an ounce (apothecaries'). This is equal to 1·3 grammes. If you go to a laboratory, cut a piece of postcard or "tin" from the lid of a tin-can or some such suitable material so that it just balances against 1·3 grammes, and so make for yourself a weight of 1 scruple; you can then use it to check the weight of, say, an ounce of tobacco or a quarter of a pound of tea, or some such convenient commodity to see whether we live up to the standard of scrupulousness which in bygone days was so impressive that it led to the coining of a word. To do this, put a quarter of a pound of tea in one scale pan and a quarter-pound weight in the other, then put your scruple on one pan and then on the other pan and find out whether your scales are sensitive enough to record the difference made by a scruple. If they are sensitive enough, then you can say whether your quarter of a pound is accurate to within a scruple. If they are not sensitive enough, then you who use them are not scrupulous in your weighing, as judged by standards of four or five centuries ago.

The "grain", $\frac{1}{7000}$ lb (avoirdupois), is a standard unit in terms of which other official weights are defined, and is the same exactly in the United States of America and in Great Britain. An ounce (avoirdupois) is 437·5 grains, an ounce (Troy or Apothecaries') is 480 grains and a pound is 7000 grains. A scruple is 20 grains.

Units of Capacity

The British tables of capacity are very simple.

2 pints = 1 quart

4 quarts = 1 gallon (gal)

is all we need to know for liquid measure. Water Boards and oil companies quote volumes in millions of gallons and do not bother with larger units than the gallon. Gills are misleading since the north and south of England do not agree as to whether there are 2 or 4 gills to the pint. Milk is sold in "half-pint" bottles, and the unit "gill" is not much used nowadays.

The United States of America also have pints, quarts and gallons, and their table looks just like the British, but

1 gal (British) = 1·201 gal (U.S.A.)

Pecks and bushels are used for measuring the volumes of certain dry goods such as grain, peas, some fruits.

$$2 \text{ gal} = 1 \text{ peck}$$
$$4 \text{ pecks} = 1 \text{ bushel}$$

For small quantities of liquid the *fluid ounce* is used. Twenty fluid ounces = 1 pint. This unit is a convenient size for many quantities used in cooking and especially in preparing food for babies. Feeding bottles are usually graduated in fluid ounces.

A tablespoon, not quite full right up to the brim, holds half a fluid ounce.

A fluid ounce of water weighs one ounce avoirdupois.

Particular trades have their own special units such as the cran of herrings, the magnum of wine and so on, but these are not necessarily standard units legally defined. Some industries use measures of considerable historical interest which are worth a little study.

The Metric System

The first suggestions for starting a new and logical system of units and getting away from the inconsistencies of the traditional units, seem to have been made in France in the late seventeenth century. A French priest, Gabriel Mouton, of Lyons, proposed such a system as early as 1670, and it is he who seems to have introduced the idea of making the unit of length bear a specified relationship to the circumference of the Earth. Weights and measures are so important a part of the daily life of all who buy and sell, from the great wholesale houses to the individual housewife, that there is a tremendous resistance to change. It took the violence of the French Revolution to enforce the break with tradition which was necessary for the introduction of the metric system. It is now a legal system in almost every country of the world. The U.S.A. legalized its use in 1866 and Great Britain in 1897.

The official standards have changed slightly since the initial definitions by the French Revolutionary government in 1791. The first unit to be defined was the *metre*. The arc of a great circle from the Equator to the North Pole was declared to be 10,000,000 metres in length. At once the contrast is apparent between the homely thumb's breadth and foot, and the division of a great and extremely inaccessible distance by an exceedingly large number. The fractions one-tenth, one-hundredth and one-thousandth of a metre were to be designated by Latin prefixes, deci-, centi-, milli-, and multiples of a metre, ten, hundred, thousand, by Greek prefixes deka-, hecto-, kilo-. The metre, thus defined, happened to be just over a yard long and the kilometre about five-eighths of a mile. It was to be a feature of the system that the different types of unit should be derivable from one another. The unit of weight was called the *gramme* and was the weight of one cubic centimetre of distilled water at a temperature of 4°C weighed in a vacuum. Logically it would have been expected that the cube of the unit of length would have been used to define the unit of weight, but a cubic metre of water weighs about a ton and is somewhat large as a basic unit, so the weight of a millionth of this was chosen for the gramme. For capacity the unit chosen was the *litre*, a thousand cubic centimetres or a thousandth of a cubic metre.

The French Revolution occurred at a time somewhat before very great precision in measurement had been achieved, and the current standards are not identical with those of 1791. The present metre, which is significantly different from the $\frac{1}{10,000,000}$ part of the Earth's meridional quadrant, is officially defined as the length of a platinum-iridium bar, made in 1889, kept at the International Bureau of Weights and Measures at Sèvres, France. Similarly, the official international kilogramme is the mass of a platinum-iridium standard kilogramme, also constructed in 1889 and kept at Sèvres. Since 1889, standards of accuracy of measurement have improved still further and the official kilogramme is now known to be 1·000028 times the mass of a thousand cubic centimetres of water, at the standard conditions. The *litre* is not now defined as 1000 cubic centimetres but as the volume of a kilogramme of water under the standard conditions. This slight discrepancy is of no practical importance to the retail traders and the "man in the street", but it is within the limits of accurate scientific measurement and is of some significance in some experimental work. The metric system has been adopted in most civilized countries, but there are considerable difficulties in the way of replacing the standard usage of inches and pounds in the British Isles and the United States of America. Every screw in Britain is made to British Standard specifications, and most of these are based on $\frac{1}{64}$ of an inch as the standard for British screw threads. Any suggestion that we abandon our present units and adopt metric units exclusively would involve a protracted plan to replace all machinery, all nuts and bolts, all standard threads, all gas pipes and water pipes and electrical gear to standards of different specification. Factories would have to be re-tooled, and yet supplies of spares by the million would be needed for maintenance of existing machinery. Such a change might have been possible before the Industrial Revolution; it would still be possible now, but only as a very long-term plan with an indefinite transitional period. It must be borne in mind that metric units have been permitted in Britain since 1864 and have been legalized for use in trade since the Weights and Measures (Metric System) Act of 1897, but we have not moved very far towards adopting metric standards.

Metric Equivalents

1 cm	= 0·394 in.	1 in. = 2·54 cm
1 m	= 1·094 yd = 39·4 in.	1 yd = 0·9144 m
1 km	= 0·621 mile	1 mile = 1·61 km
1 kg	= 2·204622 lb	1 lb = 0·4536 kg
1 tonne	= 2204·6 lb = 0·984 tons	1 ton = 1·016 tonnes
1 litre (l)	= 0·2200 gal	1 gal = 4·546 l

EXERCISES

1. Get to know your own personal measurements:

    thumb — how near to an inch is the width of the ball of your thumb?

    foot — in measuring out, heel to toe, how do you have to place your feet in order to measure fairly accurately in feet?

    cubit — how long is your cubit?

    yard — in measuring out cloth, rope, etc., where should you hold your hand for nose to end of thumb to be a yard?

    Know also how high your eyes are above the ground.

2. Measure a standard brick. First estimate the height of a wall by eye, then count the number of courses of bricks and estimate the height from this, then measure the height with a tape measure or ruler.

3. Estimate the length of a wall by eye, then count the number of bricks in its length and estimate the length from this, then measure the length with a tape measure.

4. Weigh a pan or a jug, put a pint of water into it and check that the weight has increased by a pound and a quarter. Then add eight tablespoonfuls of water and check that the weight of water is now a pound and a half.

5. "From Ushant to Scilly is thirty-five leagues." Measure the distance from Ushant to Scilly from a map, in miles, and calculate how many miles in a league.

Money Units

The units of length, weight and capacity are all derived in a similar way. Some measure is chosen in quite an arbitrary fashion and a carefully constructed "standard" is made legal by Act of Parliament, that legal standard being retained as a permanent unchanging standard of comparison. If convenient, some other unit could be chosen and made into a permanent replacement of the previous system, as was done when the metric system was introduced in France. The two very important sets of units of money and time, however, are established quite differently.

The pound, shilling and penny have been in use in England since early Anglo-Saxon times and, compared with most European currencies, they have been extremely stable. "12 pence = 1 shilling; 20 shillings = £1" have been the money tables for a great many generations; and the minted coin, one penny, has scarcely changed for two hundred years in appearance and not changed at all in its value relative to the shilling or the pound. The difference between money as a unit of measurement and the units of length, weight or capacity, is that the thing money measures, value, is not a fixed and unchanging characteristic of a body as are its weight and volume. The penny and the pound have been English money units for fifteen hundred years but their value has fluctuated in relation to commodities, and the money measures of different commodities have fluctuated relative to one another.

Our coinage has a very long history. Writing about the Anglo-Saxon period, well before the Norman conquest, Dorothy Whitelock, in Volume II of the Pelican *History of England*, says:

> ... "mancus" was a weight of gold of about 70 grains, and was considered equivalent to thirty silver pence; a "mark" was a Danish weight made up of eight "ores", and there were two systems current in relating it to the native coinage, for we find on some occasions 20 pence reckoned to an "ore" of silver, and on others 16; the shilling referred to in our records is not usually a coin, but merely a unit of count, denoting 20 pence in early Kent, fourpence in Mercia and early Wessex, fivepence in Wessex in later times; a pound, then as now, contained 240 pence. But all references to money are misleading unless one bears in mind the high purchasing power of the Anglo-Saxon penny (a silver coin), and it is well to remember that 30 pence was the legal price of an ox, fourpence or fivepence that of a sheep.

This extract illustrates very well the need to think separately about the actual system of coinage and about its purchasing power.

COINAGE

The actual words "pounds", "shillings" and "pence" and the symbols £ s d illustrate the ancient history of our coinage which dates back to the Roman invasion of Britain, survived the Anglo-Saxon, Norse and Norman invasions and did not succumb to the inflations of the 1920's which destroyed the German mark and pfennig and the French centime.

£ is the initial letter of the Roman *libra* a pound, "pound" is the Old English "pund" related to the German *pfund*, and the dash through the middle of the L is a relic of the Gothic script from which German script developed and which survived in Britain until the Second World War in the titles of newspapers.

d is the initial letter of the Roman *denarius* which was a small silver coin. Ironically this word derives from a Latin word, *deni*, meaning "of ten" and would be quite appropriate in a decimal system of coinage. Penny is an Anglo-Saxon word, *pening* in Old English, with the same root as the German *pfennig*.

s is the initial letter both of the English word shilling and the Latin word *solidus* for an old Roman coin introduced by the Emperor Constantine. The stroke / means "solidus" or "shilling", and 7/6d should be read as "seven shillings and sixpence", the stroke indicating shillings, and the d, pence. When writing down a sum of money the stroke has this very precise meaning and it is wrong to think of it as just a haphazard mark separating the 7 and the 6 in 7/6d. It should never be used between pounds and shillings, as in £8/7/6 which might reasonably be read as eight pounds shillings seven shillings and six. In contexts other than money, the stroke has many legitimate uses—for example, in commercial practice, filing systems employ such references as JM/KP/FWL/17, and fractions such as $\frac{4}{5}$ are sometimes more conveniently printed 4/5—but in these contexts the stroke has no reference whatsoever to shillings, although it is called a solidus. A sum of money may be written correctly in the form £8 7/6d, but when all denominations are used it is more tidily written as £8—7s—6d. On cheques the lines between the figures prevent the insertion of additional figures by any unscrupulous person who may be tempted to tamper with them.

From an arithmetical point of view the twelve and the twenty involved in the relationships between coins are not only an annoyance to school children and shoppers, but on a large scale involve designing calculators and accounting machines specifically for this purpose. With a decimal system of coinage, such machines could be used as all-purpose calculating machines and their added versatility would give far better returns for the capital expended on their purchase. With the introduction in 1957 of the new £5 note, in the style of the pound and ten shilling notes, a minor adjustment in the value of one penny could have given us a complete decimal system. Already we have

10 shillings = 1 ten-shilling note
10 ten-shilling notes = 1 five-pound note

and if one penny were increased in value by one sixth, we could have a table

10 pennies = 1 shilling
10 shillings = 1 ten-shilling note
10 ten-shilling notes = 1 five-pound note.

The penny has already been given this value in Kenya and at the beginning of 1961

South Africa adopted a similar system, basing it on the old ten shilling note which is the new unit of currency and called a "Rand". The change in the value of a penny which would be all that was involved, would restore it to the purchasing power it had in about 1950 and this does seem a reform which could be carried through at the present time with little upset.

Banks deal simply in money, but in most other contexts money units enter into calculations with other units. Drapers sell materials at prices such as 7/11d for 1 yd. Greengrocers sell potatoes at 3d for 1 lb; eggs may be sold at 4/– for a dozen eggs, so that in most everyday money transactions both money units and other units are involved. Such calculations are referred to in the paragraphs on combined units (*see* Chapter 6), where such quantities as shillings per pound, miles per hour, man-hours and similar combinations are discussed.

There is little difficulty in understanding money calculations when they are presented in isolation, but although the relations of 12 pennies to one shilling and 20 shillings to one pound may be easily understood, there are, in the actual calculations, some difficulties which can be eased by careful consideration of the procedure and the design of the setting out. It is largely because of our need to be able to deal with money that multiplication tables in England are carried to 12 × 12 and do not stop at 10 × 10.

PURCHASING POWER

Some interesting facts about the changing values of money may be obtained by looking through old arithmetic books. For instance, an old book, *Revision Papers in Arithmetic*, gives the question:

Find from the following returns for February 1912 the average earnings of a worker per week in each of the trades specified. Give each result to the nearest halfpenny.

	Number of workpeople	Earnings in one week (£)
Cotton	125,074	123,245
Woollen	27,722	26,102
Linen	47,442	28,108
Hosiery	20,883	17,143

The reader might try to find out present-day average rates and give some estimate of the degree of inflation in the last half-century.

From the same book we find eggs sold in 1912 at 15d per dozen. Beer was bought at £2 5s 0d for a 36-gallon barrel and sold at 6d a quart. Oranges cost 5/– a hundred. Gas was sold at 3/7d per 1000 cubic feet.

Another text book, not dated, gives prices of:

> 7d a quart for milk
> 2¼d per loaf for bread
> 1/2d per lb for mutton
> 2½d per lb for granulated sugar
> 1/9d per dozen for eggs
> 1/6d per lb for "back" bacon
> 1/2d per lb for butter

A little research will enable the reader to estimate the approximate date when this book was written.

3

A Closer Look at Multiplication and Division

THE MULTIPLICATION $3 \times 5 = 15$ can be understood in terms of a pattern of dots, and simple multiplications as far as $10 \times 10 = 100$ can be performed from memory. Beyond this we rely upon a routine way of setting out calculations, the working being written in some form such as

$$
\begin{array}{r}
324 \\
13 \\
\hline
3240 \\
972 \\
\hline
4212 \\
\end{array}
$$

Once the routine has been established, multiplication becomes a mechanical process presenting little difficulty, but it is interesting to analyse what is going on behind this compressed and efficient computation.

MULTIPLICATION TABLES

Facility in arithmetic can be attained only after the preliminary counting of small groups, proper to the infants' school, has been followed by diligent learning of tables. This is a discipline which must be accepted by both teacher and class and it should always be backed by patient and sympathetic encouragement from parents. The work has to be done by the children; parents and teachers each have contributions to make in finding ways of making this discipline as entertaining, interesting and palatable as possible. Complete mastery of tables takes some time and it is wise to keep a table available for reference for as long as it is needed.

	1	2	3	4	5	6	7	8	9	10	11	12
0	0	0	0	0	0	0	0	0	0	0	0	0
1	1	2	3	4	5	6	7	8	9	10	11	12
2	2	4	6	8	10	12	14	16	18	20	22	24
3	3	6	9	12	15	18	21	24	27	30	33	36
4	4	8	12	16	20	24	28	32	36	40	44	48
5	5	10	15	20	25	30	35	40	45	50	55	60
6	6	12	18	24	30	36	42	48	54	60	66	72
7	7	14	21	28	35	42	49	56	63	70	77	84
8	8	16	24	32	40	48	56	64	72	80	88	96
9	9	18	27	36	45	54	63	72	81	90	99	108
10	10	20	30	40	50	60	70	80	90	100	110	120
11	11	22	33	44	55	66	77	88	99	110	121	132
12	12	24	36	48	60	72	84	96	108	120	132	144

Fig. 3.1

Such a table of reference is the more valuable for having been made by the person who is to use it. The building up of the table is simple in the extreme. Let us take the table of *threes* as an example. We put 3 at the top to indicate that it is the table of threes that we are building, and a line under it to separate it from the body of the table. As usual we start with zero and write o under the 3. To nothing we add one three and write 3 under the o. To this 3 we add another three, making 6, which we write under the 3. To 6 we add another three, making 9, and we write 9 under the 6, and so on. When all the numbers up to twelve have been treated in the same way, the set of columns can be combined into a single table (Fig. 3.1).

The numbers on the left indicate the number of times successive additions have been made to the zero which is the first entry in each column. By finding, say, 5 at the very top of a column and 6 on the extreme left, the entry 30 in the 5-column and the 6-row indicates that "six times five is thirty". The sooner this table is memorized the better.

COMPOUND MULTIPLICATION

Once we are concerned with multiplications outside the range of the memorized tables, the work has to be set down on paper and calculated by the usual standard procedure. It is interesting to analyse just how much work is condensed into the simple arrangement

$$
\begin{array}{r}
324 \\
13 \\
\hline
3240 \\
972 \\
\hline
4212
\end{array}
$$

To begin with we must remember that the Hindu-Arabic numerals are organized so that 324 means 300+20+4 and 13 means 10+3. The product is the sum of the products of the *actual values* of each of the digits of 324 by the *actual values* of each of the digits 13.

We may think of 324 as written out on three cards $\boxed{300}$ $\boxed{20}$ $\boxed{4}$

fitted one behind the other to look like $\boxed{3|2|4}$

and the multiplier, 13, as $\boxed{10}$ $\boxed{3}$ looking like $\boxed{1|3}$

so that all the operations

$$
\begin{array}{rcl}
\boxed{300} \times \boxed{10} &=& 3000 \\
\boxed{20} \times \boxed{10} &=& 200 \\
\boxed{4} \times \boxed{10} &=& 40 \\
\boxed{300} \times \boxed{3} &=& 900 \\
\boxed{20} \times \boxed{3} &=& 60 \\
\boxed{4} \times \boxed{3} &=& 12 \\
\hline
&& 4212
\end{array}
$$

have to be performed and the sub-products added.

This amount of writing is cut down by doing all the multiplication by 10 in one line

$$\begin{array}{r} 324 \\ \times \quad 10 \\ \hline 3240 \end{array}$$

and the multiplication by 3 in one line

$$\begin{array}{r} 324 \\ \times \quad 3 \\ \hline 972 \end{array}$$

and merely adding the sub-products, giving a form of solution which is written out

$$\begin{array}{r} 324 \\ 13 \\ \hline 3240 \\ 972 \\ \hline 4212 \end{array}$$

The key point in writing this out is the placing of the first figure written in the solution

$$\begin{array}{r} 324 \\ 13 \\ \hline \end{array}$$

The 4 is multiplied by a figure in the tens column so the answer will be a number of *tens* and must be placed in the tens column

H.	T.	U.
3	2	4
	1	3
	4	

After this it is straightforward to continue and put in the 2 and the 3

TH.	H.	T.	U.
	3	2	4
		1	3
3	2	4	

then when multiplying by 3, the 4 units multiplied by the 3 units will give twelve units or 1 ten and 2 units, so we put down the 2 in the units column and "carry" the "ten" as a 1 in the tens column, then we say 2 multiplied by 3 is 6 and 1 to carry makes 7 and finally $3 \times 3 = 9$

TH.	H.	T.	U.
	3	2	4
		1	3
3	2	4	
	9	7	2
4	2	1	2

When we add, we say "2 plus 0 = 2, 2 down in the units column; 4 plus 7 = eleven, 1 down in the tens column and carry one; $1 + 9 + 2$ is equal to 12, 2 down in the hundreds column and carry one; $1 + 3 = 4$."

Among schoolchildren learning mathematics, the mistakes which are found consist of:

(a) those arising from faulty knowledge of tables. This can be cured only by referring to a printed table until the tables up to 10×10 are known accurately;

(b) placing numbers in wrong columns. The only remedy is to go through the rules of procedure again, paying attention to the design of the layout of the solution. Junior School arithmetic paper, ruled in squares, is useful for ensuring this;

(c) faults of addition, usually arising from carelessness with carrying. If carrying mistakes are still being made it is as well to go back to the beginner's practice of writing-in a small carrying figure until the tendency to make mistakes has been overcome;

(d) serious misconceptions arising from a lack of understanding of what is being done. There is no panacea for these faults and they must be diagnosed individually. This group of difficulties may be illustrated by one example of an answer produced by a person aged 18.

$$
\begin{array}{r}
38 \\
\times\ 12 \\
\hline
16 \\
3 \\
\hline
46 \\
\hline
\end{array}
$$

The procedure adopted was to multiply the figures in the units column together, $2 \times 8 = 16$, and write this down as 16; then to multiply the figures in the tens column together and write this answer, $3 \times 1 = 3$, in the tens column.

The cause of the error was a muddling of "addition" and "multiplication" procedures.

In addition, the units are all added together and their sum put at the bottom; the tens are then added together and their sum put at the bottom, in the tens column; at no stage are digits in the units column and digits in the tens column added together, except when there is a carrying figure in the answer.

In multiplication, the units figure multiplies the units, tens and hundreds, if any; then the tens figure multiplies the units, tens and hundreds, etc.

The mistake arose because the student thought that in multiplication only units multiplied units, only tens multiplied tens, and that the columns were kept separate as in addition. The removal of this misconception involved going right back to the beginnings of multiplication.

DIVISION

The idea of division is easily understood when put in practical terms. Taking two illustrations: (1) A pack of 52 cards has to be divided between four people. The method is to make four piles, putting a card on each pile, in turn, until the pack is used up. We then count and find that there are exactly 13 cards in each pile: $52 \div 4 = 13$. (2) We could also mark off 52 equal divisions on the edge of a strip of paper, fold it and fold it again to make four equal sections of the paper, open it out again, and count that there are 13 divisions in each section (Fig. 3.2).

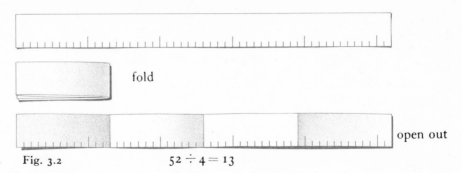

Fig. 3.2 $52 \div 4 = 13$

The numerical process of division is the reverse of multiplication. A series of attempts is made to find out what must multiply a number to produce a particular answer. The idea of making an estimate, and then a better estimate to bring it nearer to the required answer, and persisting with this process of successive approximations, is one that requires a certain maturity of thought. This is why long division is often baffling to children with a mental development much below that of an ordinary eleven-year-old. The process may be taught mechanically before this mental age has been attained, but then, since the working *is* mechanical, in the face of difficulties it may break down. The immature child, moreover, lacks the resourcefulness which comes with understanding. In the following paragraph we shall try to examine carefully the long division process.

THE NATURE OF THE WORKING OF LONG DIVISION

A typical long division is set out like this:

$$
\begin{array}{r}
463 \\
32 \overline{)\ 14816} \\
128 \\
\hline
201 \\
192 \\
\hline
96 \\
96 \\
\hline
\end{array}
$$

This is a condensed calculation containing only the figures essential for a practised person to obtain the answer. The reduction of writing to a minimum is very desirable from the point of view of reaching an answer efficiently and quickly but it does obscure the precise nature of some of the steps.

The first question we ask ourselves is, "What is the first figure of the answer and where do we put it?" In the example the first figure is 4 and it is put in the position above the 8 so that it signifies "four hundred".

Few people carry the thirty-two-times table in their heads and in order to simplify the analysis the table of multiples of 32 from 32×1 to 32×9, from 32×10 to 32×90 and from 32×100 to 32×900 is written out. Since in long division we start with the largest number and work through to the smallest, the table is set out with the largest multiples of 32 at the top and the smallest multiples at the bottom of the column on the left-hand side of the page.

If the first question we ask ourselves is re-phrased in the form, "Between which of the multiples of 32, tabulated below, does 14816 lie?" or, more briefly, "Where does 14816 fit?" we can see from the left-hand column that the answer is, "Just above 12800", since the next multiple, 16000, is too big. The whole calculation may be described in the following steps:

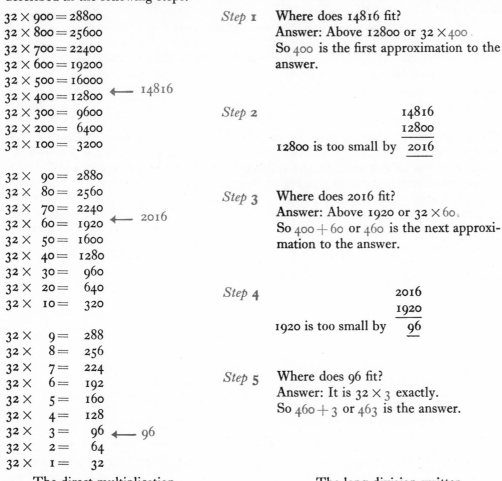

$32 \times 900 = 28800$
$32 \times 800 = 25600$
$32 \times 700 = 22400$
$32 \times 600 = 19200$
$32 \times 500 = 16000$
$32 \times 400 = 12800$ ← 14816
$32 \times 300 = 9600$
$32 \times 200 = 6400$
$32 \times 100 = 3200$

$32 \times 90 = 2880$
$32 \times 80 = 2560$
$32 \times 70 = 2240$ ← 2016
$32 \times 60 = 1920$
$32 \times 50 = 1600$
$32 \times 40 = 1280$
$32 \times 30 = 960$
$32 \times 20 = 640$
$32 \times 10 = 320$

$32 \times 9 = 288$
$32 \times 8 = 256$
$32 \times 7 = 224$
$32 \times 6 = 192$
$32 \times 5 = 160$
$32 \times 4 = 128$
$32 \times 3 = 96$ ← 96
$32 \times 2 = 64$
$32 \times 1 = 32$

Step 1   Where does 14816 fit?
Answer: Above 12800 or 32×400.
So 400 is the first approximation to the answer.

Step 2
$$\begin{array}{r} 14816 \\ 12800 \\ \hline \end{array}$$
12800 is too small by 2016

Step 3   Where does 2016 fit?
Answer: Above 1920 or 32×60.
So $400 + 60$ or 460 is the next approximation to the answer.

Step 4
$$\begin{array}{r} 2016 \\ 1920 \\ \hline \end{array}$$
1920 is too small by 96

Step 5   Where does 96 fit?
Answer: It is 32×3 exactly.
So $460 + 3$ or 463 is the answer.

The direct multiplication of 32 by 463 looks like this:

The long division written in full looks like this:

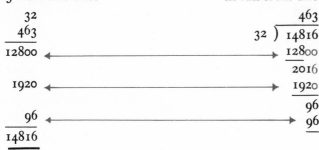

$$\begin{array}{r} 32 \\ 463 \\ \hline 12800 \\ 1920 \\ 96 \\ \hline 14816 \end{array}$$

$$\begin{array}{r} 463 \\ 32 \overline{)\ 14816} \\ 12800 \\ \hline 2016 \\ 1920 \\ \hline 96 \\ 96 \\ \hline \end{array}$$

The long division process is simply that of finding the multiples of 32, in order, which, when added, give 14816. When the multiplication and division are set alongside each other, it is clear that the long division method "finds" the multiples of 32, such as 12800, and then the multipliers 400, 60 and 3, which give these multiples. These multipliers provide, in order, the figures in the answer. The answer to a division is called a "quotient".

With long division it is convenient to use arithmetic paper printed in squares (Fig. 3.3) so that there is no difficulty in keeping numbers in the correct columns; this is especially important when "bringing down the next figure" involves entering the figure in a column after quite a number of lines of working, such as the final 2 in Fig. 3.3.

A simple long division is set out in Fig. 3.3. It is suggested that beginners and, in fact, any who have not thoroughly mastered the multiplication tables, would find it helpful to write out the multiples of the divisor, from $32 \times 1 = 32$, $32 \times 2 = 64$, up to $32 \times 9 = 288$ and write them in a column to the left of the long division so that they can be referred to during the long division calculation. This is a great help in the early stages, when mastery of the long division process is being built up, but it is a "prop" which should be dispensed with as soon as possible.

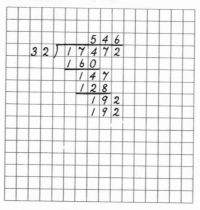

Fig. 3.3

EXERCISES

The exercises which follow have been carefully graded so that complications are introduced one at a time. After working them through, the reader might care to make a list of difficulties arising in successive questions.

31) 7471   29) 6989   32) 13536

31) 13082   29) 11948   26) 10244

34) 10098   39) 11896   37) 329448

4

Extending the Number System

Negative numbers and fractions

If I have some objects in front of me OOO I can count them and say "there are five objects". The number "five" is a simple description of the number of objects in the group, similar to a statement that "grass is *green*"; it stimulates no activity and produces no consequences. "Paint that door green", however, is a sentence which sets me collecting brush and paint pot, and a painting operation in motion. Of such a nature is the command $3 + 5$ which, in operational language, means "add five to that three". The result of painting the door is a green door. The result of adding the five is 8. If the owner of the door thinks it looks awful now it is green, a new command, "Scrape off that green paint", may be given, and armed with blowtorch and scraper I remove the green paint. If I want the 3 back I can erase out the added 5 by taking it away again and I am left with 3. This instruction is written in the form $8 - 5$.

The reversibility of an operation is most important in the understanding of mathematical operations. There is a relationship between 3, 5, 8, which can be expressed in four different ways:

$$5 + 3 = 8, \quad 8 - 3 = 5, \quad 3 + 5 = 8, \quad 8 - 5 = 3$$

These four statements, which we meet as children, express four different operational procedures but they correspond to a single arithmetical fact. When mature enough to make general statements, we can understand that if m is understood to mean "any number", n to mean "another number" and p to mean "the sum of m and n", then

$$m + n = p, \quad p - n = m, \quad n + m = p, \quad p - m = n$$

are four statements such that if one of them is true, then all are true; and such that each of the four statements gives the same information about the three numbers m, n and p.

If I have eight pennies on the desk in front of me and then I take eight pennies away, I have nothing left. This is written as

$$8 - 8 = 0$$

Teachers of young children are well aware that "nothing", or "zero", has to be introduced very carefully in the early stages of arithmetic. Logically the statement $8 - 8 = 0$ is obtainable as the reverse of the process

$$0 + 8 = 8$$

and read as meaning "if eight is added on to nothing the answer is eight". Now a great deal of imagination is required to *start* by having nothing. It is far simpler to start with something, take it away and become aware that there is nothing left. Children's rhymes, such as the "Ten little Indian boys" or the "Ten green bottles hanging on the wall", begin with ten little Indian boys and by the time they reach the stage of "then there

35

were none" the children have become quite Indian-boy minded and will feel the nothing-ness left by the disappearance of the last little Indian boy. On the other hand, it is an unusual experience for anyone to begin with the idea of nothing and build up on that feeling. It can be contrived; although I do not habitually look in my hat and observe that there does not seem to be a rabbit in it, a skilful conjuror can coax me into looking into a hat to make sure that it contains no rabbit and, thus prepared, I wait for one to appear. Provided the patter is skilfully carried through, the appearance of the rabbit in a pre-viously empty hat can really be described by the equation

$$0 + 1 = 1$$

The idea that the starting point of number and counting is zero, has to be built up carefully and deliberately, because it is not natural for young children to begin counting 0, 1, 2, 3, . . . The role of zero as the proper starting point of number operations is a basic concept in the understanding of number.

DIRECTED NUMBERS

It is possible to start with any ordinary whole number and to add another whole number to it and the result will be an ordinary whole number. *This is always true.*

The same cannot be said about subtraction. If we think of 3, 5 and 8 as numbers of things then, $8 - 5 = 3$ is a simple statement, meaningful in the simplest way. The subtraction $5 - 8$ cannot be carried out at all so long as we are using the numbers as cardinal numbers referring to countable objects. If, however, we think of the numbers as operational and consider the statement

$$+5 - 8 = -3$$

and give it the meaning "the operation of adding five and then subtracting eight is equivalent to subtracting three", then there is little difficulty in understanding what is meant.

"Add five" is an instruction and not a number. If we start at 0 and add five to it we obtain a number and we should have to agree that the *number* $(+5)$ means "the number obtained by adding five to zero".

$$0 + 5 = +5$$

"Subtract five" is an instruction and not a number. If we start at zero and count backwards from zero we obtain a number (-5) and we agree that the *number* (-5) is obtained by subtracting five from zero.

$$0 - 5 = -5$$

There is nothing very difficult about this idea. If we tell a ten-year-old boy that the war was over twelve years ago, he can readily understand that the war was over two years *before* he was born and obtain the answer by the calculation

$$10 - 12 = -2$$

where it is understood that -2 means $0 - 2$, the 0 referring to his age when he was born and the -2 meaning two years before that.

Julius Caesar invaded Britain in 55 B.C. What was the date of the 2000th anniversary of this invasion?

We are only in the year 1960 now, yet it is not a foolish question to ask about the 2000th anniversary of an event. 2000 years ago could be written as the year -40 A.D.

In order, therefore, that the process of subtraction can hold good for all numbers, it is necessary to extend the numbers 1, 2, 3, 4, . . . backwards, first to include 0, and then to -1, -2, -3, . . .

The system of all integers may be set out

$$\ldots -6, -5, -4, -3, -2, -1, 0, +1, +2, +3, +4, +5, +6, \ldots$$

with positive numbers to the right and negative numbers to the left.

Adding a positive number means moving to the right, subtracting a positive number means moving to the left.

Adding a negative number, which means making the quantity *more negative*, means moving to the left.

Subtracting a negative number, which means making the quantity *less negative*, means moving to the right.

Moving to the right three units, or $+3$, can, therefore, be done in two ways:

$$+3 = +(+3) = -(-3)$$

Moving to the left three units, or -3, can, therefore, be done in two ways:

$$-3 = -(+3) = +(-3)$$

Another way of conveying the idea of directed numbers is to draw a circle somewhere near the middle of a room to represent 0. Facing the window is the positive direction and $-$ means "about-turn". Begin by facing the window and carry out the orders

$$+(+7)+(-3)$$

and the distance you will be from 0 will be 4 paces in the positive direction from 0. This means that

$$+(+7)+(-3) = +4$$

Again begin by facing the window and carry out the orders

$$+(+7)-(+3)$$

You will *face the window, step forward seven paces* then *about-turn, step forward three paces*
$\qquad +$ $\qquad\qquad (+7)$ $\qquad\qquad\qquad -$ $\qquad\qquad\qquad (+3)$

and you will be *four paces nearer the window than* 0.
$\qquad\qquad (+4)$

Finally, begin by facing the window and carry out the orders

$$+(+7)-(-3)$$

You will *face the window, step forward seven paces* and then you will *about-turn* and
$\qquad +$ $\qquad\qquad (+7)$ $\qquad\qquad\qquad\qquad\qquad -$

step backwards three paces and you will be ten paces towards the window from 0, showing
$\qquad (-3)$

that $\qquad\qquad\qquad\qquad +(+7)-(-3) = +10$

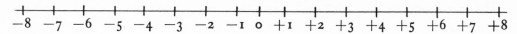

$$-8 \quad -7 \quad -6 \quad -5 \quad -4 \quad -3 \quad -2 \quad -1 \quad 0 \quad +1 \quad +2 \quad +3 \quad +4 \quad +5 \quad +6 \quad +7 \quad +8$$

This array can be extended indefinitely in both directions to show the collection of *all* integers.

Multiplication, Division and Fractions

If two numbers such as 7 and 8 are multiplied together the answer is another number, 56. It is always true that if two positive whole numbers are multiplied together the answer is another positive whole number. The commutative law holds for multiplication as it does for addition, $7 \times 8 = 56$ and $8 \times 7 = 56$.

The process of arranging 56 objects in groups of 8 and counting that there are 7 such groups is called "division" and written

$$56 \div 8 = 7$$

A somewhat different procedure, that of dividing the 56 objects into 8 groups and then counting that there are 7 in each group, is also written

$$56 \div 8 = 7$$

The same arithmetical operation arises in two different ways. The 56 zeros below

OOOOOOOOOOOOOOOOOOOOOOOOOOOOOOOOOOOOOOOOOOOOOOOOOOOOOOOOOO

grouped in eights

OOOOOOOO OOOOOOOO OOOOOOOO OOOOOOOO OOOOOOOO OOOOOOOO OOOOOOOO

fills seven groups, but the same 56 zeros

OOOOOOOOOOOOOOOOOOOOOOOOOOOOOOOOOOOOOOOOOOOOOOOOOOOOOOOOOO

arranged in eight groups

OOOOOOO OOOOOOO OOOOOOO OOOOOOO OOOOOOO OOOOOOO OOOOOOO OOOOOOO

gives seven in each group.

Both operations are written as $56 \div 8 = 7$.

The statements
$$7 + 7 + 7 + 7 + 7 + 7 + 7 + 7 = 56$$
$$8 + 8 + 8 + 8 + 8 + 8 + 8 \quad = 56$$
$$7 \times 8 = 56$$
$$8 \times 7 = 56$$
$$56 \div 8 = \quad 7$$
$$56 \div 7 = \quad 8$$

all express, in different ways, the same essential relationship between the three numbers 7, 8 and 56. Division may, in this way, be looked upon as being a reverse process to multiplication.

FRACTIONS

It is possible to start with any ordinary whole number and to multiply it by another ordinary whole number and the product will be an ordinary whole number. *This is always true.*

The same cannot be said about division. If we consider the numbers 3, 4 and 12, then

$$12 \div 4 = 3$$

is a straightforward statement which can be verified very easily by dividing a collection of twelve objects into four groups of three objects in each group.

The division $\qquad\qquad\qquad 4 \div 12$

cannot be carried out so long as we are thinking of the numbers as cardinal numbers referring to whole, indivisible objects, such as cows or chairs. Now although there are such things as cows and chairs which cease to be cows or chairs when they are cut up, there are other things, such as lengths of string, years, pints of water, train-loads of people or cakes of soap which can be so divided. Whether a unit be a length of string, a year or a cake, if it is divided into five parts, each part is called one fifth and written $\frac{1}{5}$ (Fig. 4.1).

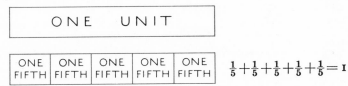

Fig. 4.1

A quantity twice the size of one-fifth arises in two ways; it may arise by first dividing a unit into fifths and taking two of these fifths (Fig. 4.2).

Fig. 4.2

or it could arise by dividing *two units* by *five* (Fig. 4.3).

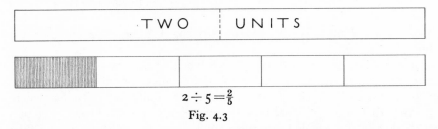

Fig. 4.3

If two units are divided by five the answer is seen to be exactly the same quantity as that obtained by dividing a unit into fifths and taking two of these divisions.

$$2 \div 5 = 2 \times \tfrac{1}{5} = \tfrac{2}{5}$$

In much more familiar terms it can be shown by changing shillings and florins* into pennies and counting them out that, as *one penny* is *one twelfth* of *one shilling*, then two of

* One florin equals two shillings or 24 pennies.

these pennies can be described by saying

twopence = two twelfths of one shilling.

But, if a florin is divided into twelve equal parts, each part contains twopence

twopence = one twelfth of two shillings.

Similarly, pieces of string or tape may be cut up and measured in inches or feet or yards and it is very easy to demonstrate that

one yard divided by twelve = three inches = three times one foot divided by twelve.

$$3 \quad \div \quad 12 \quad = \quad \tfrac{3}{12} \quad = \quad 3 \quad \times \quad \tfrac{1}{12}$$

It is also very easy to show that three inches can be obtained by dividing a foot into four equal parts (Fig. 4.4).

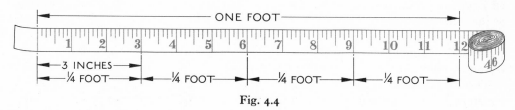

Fig. 4.4

This at once leads on to the important relationship

$$\tfrac{3}{12} = \tfrac{1}{4}$$

Since *three* inches can be obtained by dividing *one* foot by *four* or by dividing *two* feet by *eight* or by dividing *three* feet by *twelve*, we obtain the following arrangement:

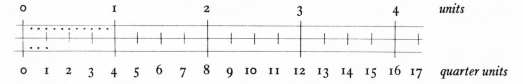

Each of the small units is obtained by dividing 1 by 4, or 2 by 8, or 3 by 12 or, symbolically: $\tfrac{1}{4} = \tfrac{2}{8} = \tfrac{3}{12} = \tfrac{4}{16} = \ldots$

We have names, one, two, three, . . . for labelling the units but we now find that in order to enable us to write down the result of dividing any number by any other number, there are positions between the units, which arise quite naturally, for which we need names. In verbal language, if each unit is divided into two equal parts, each part is called a half. If each unit is divided into three equal parts, each part is called a third; if each unit is divided into four equal parts each part is called a quarter; and after that these special names are obtained simply by adding "-th" to the root of the ordinary number word, five—fifth, six—sixth, seven—seventh, . . .

Two of these *fifth parts* are called *two-fifths, three* of these *fifth parts* are called *three-fifths* and so, in order to refer to these quantities, we need two number words to describe them and we also need some convention which will allow *two* figures to be used to provide a symbol to stand for a *single* entity.

The convention for labelling such parts is the familiar $\frac{1}{5}$, $\frac{2}{5}$, $\frac{3}{5}$ . . . notation, called vulgar fractions. Now that it is in general use it seems an obvious convention, and the facility with which it lends itself to such operations as cancelling, multiplication and change of units commends it. It is surprising to learn how late in the development of arithmetic this apparently simple notation was introduced and it is even more surprising to study some of the extremely complicated methods of working with sub-divisions which were in use before vulgar fraction notation became available.

Until a notation became available which allowed both numerator and denominator of the fraction to be indicated in some form of composite symbol, it was only possible to specify either the one or the other. From earliest times two systems have been in use. One system was employed by the ancient Egyptians as early as 1700 B.C. The Rhind Papyrus which has been dated between 1700 B.C. and 1600 B.C. contains calculations by an Egyptian priest, Ahmes, who expressed all fractions as the sum of fractions with *one* as the numerator. Thus, "$\frac{4}{9}$" could only be written as $\frac{1}{3}+\frac{1}{9}$ and so on. The sole exception was two-thirds, for which there was a special sign. Ahmes calculated the area of a circle and obtained a value which amounts to $(\frac{2}{3}+\frac{1}{9}+\frac{1}{81})$ times the square of the diameter, equivalent to a value for π of 3·1605, quite a good approximation.

The *Encyclopædia Britannica* illustrates the hieroglyphic notation (Fig. 4.5) for the equation

$$x\left(\tfrac{2}{3}+\tfrac{1}{2}+\tfrac{1}{7}+1\right)=37$$

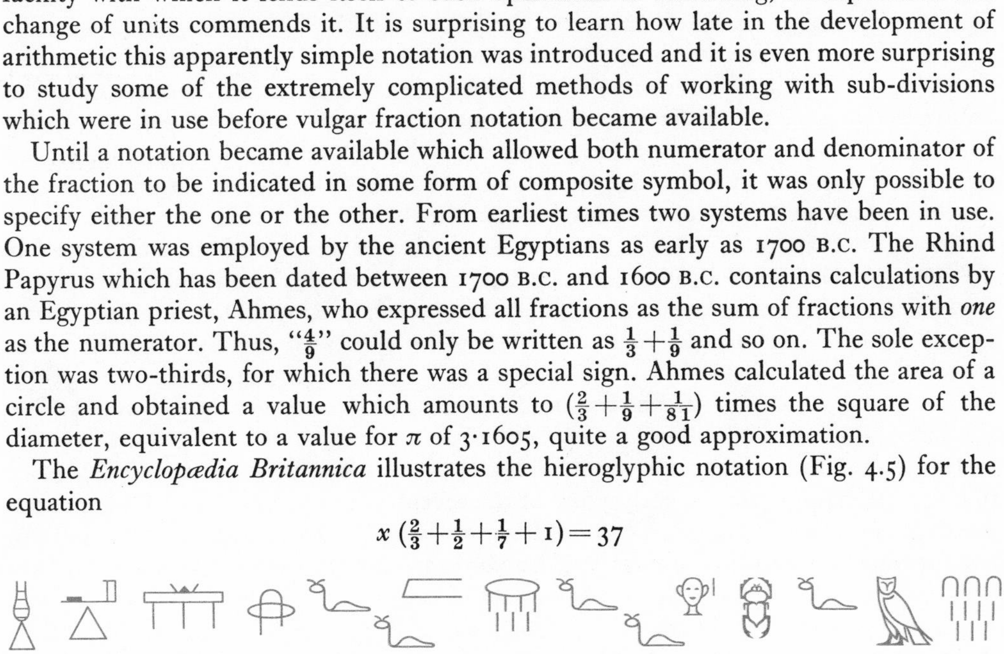

Fig. 4.5

from which it is easy to recognize the forms for the fractions  $=\frac{1}{7}$.

This practice of expressing a fraction as a series of fractions with one as the numerator was taken over by the Greeks who used it until about the end of the fifth century A.D. It is possible to obtain very good approximations in this way. For example, you might like to check the error in writing $\frac{1}{4}+\frac{1}{7}+\frac{1}{9}+\frac{1}{10}+\frac{1}{20}$ for $\frac{17}{26}$ and show that it is correct to about one in five thousand.

The other system in early use was to express fractions in terms of a standard denominator. One such denominator, 60, was used by the Babylonians and came down to Europe via the Greeks and continued in use until about the sixteenth century A.D., leaving us with the legacy of "60 seconds make a minute, 60 minutes make an hour" for time measurement and the similar "60 seconds = 1 minute, 60 minutes = 1 degree" for angular measurement; another such denominator, 12, was used by the Romans and has left us with the vestiges of a duodecimal system in our 12 pence = 1 shilling, 12 inches = 1 foot, and in the tradition of selling things in dozens and grosses. W. W. Rouse Ball, in his *A Short Account of the History of Mathematics*, quotes the great thirteenth-century mathematician known as Fibonacci (or sometimes as Leonardo of Pisa) as giving a value for the root of the equation $x^3+2x^2+10x=20$, the number 1·22′ 7″ 42‴ 33⁗ 4ᵛ 40ᵛⁱ. This means (in our notation) $1+\frac{22}{60}+\frac{7}{3600}+\frac{42}{216000}+$ . . . . where successive denominators 60, 60 times 60, 60 times 60 times 60, are used to give minutes, seconds, thirds and so on.

The number 60 was the basis of the number system of the Babylonians. It is possible that 360 was an early guess at the number of days in a year and that the maps of the heavens divided the arc of the celestial great circle, the Ecliptic, into 360 equal parts, each corresponding to a day's motion of the Sun across the Celestial Sphere. Once the number 360 had been thought of, it must have seemed to be so wonderful a number that the great creator would certainly have given it some place in the architecture of the universe, for the list of the factors of 360 is marvellous to recite: 2, 3, 4, 5, 6, 8, 9, 10, 12, 15, 18, 20, 24, 30, 36, 40, 45, 60, 72, 90, 120, 180. What other number but 360 (and its multiples such as 720) can display such a profusion of factors? Even after the year was known not to consist of exactly 360 days the division of a circle into 360 degrees remained the practice. This gives the equilateral triangle an angle of 60° and it was this division which led the Babylonians to develop a number system based on 60. It persisted for so many centuries because the wealth of factors, comprising all the simple numbers except 7 and 11, enabled so many fractions to be expressed exactly in minutes and seconds.

The Roman system of twelfths was used in much the same way: 2. 3' 5'' would mean $2 + \frac{3}{12} + \frac{5}{144}$.

The system of successive powers of a number as successive denominators was applied to a decimal notation in the early years of the seventeenth century. The Dutch mathematician and military engineer, Simon Stevinus, in 1585 used a notation 25⓪ 3① 7② 9③ for what we should write as 25·379; Napier in an essay in 1617 used 25,3' 7'' 9''' to stand for 25·379, using a decimal base instead of the base of 60 which this notation had previously implied; and in the tables published by Briggs in the same year, 1617, the decimal notation as we know it today first appeared, the number $25 + \frac{3}{10} + \frac{7}{100} + \frac{9}{1000}$ being written 25·379.

The vulgar fraction notation developed from the first of the early systems of dealing with fractions, where there were different denominators, as soon as it became possible to indicate some numerator other than unity. A Hindu astronomer, Bhaskara, born in 1114, is known to have used a notation equivalent to $\frac{3}{4}$ for three-quarters. By the time this idea had reached Europe, through the Arabs, a line had been drawn between the numbers. However, as late as the seventeenth century any of the forms 3-4, 3/4 or $\frac{3}{4}$ were being used. It seems that the decimal notation and the vulgar fraction notation began to be used consistently at about the same time and were in fairly general use by about 1650. There is still no international agreement about the form and position of a decimal point; what is written as 3·1416 in Britain would be 3.1416 in the U.S.A. and 3,1416 in France.

There are today these two notations available for inserting numbers in between the whole numbers (Fig. 4.6).

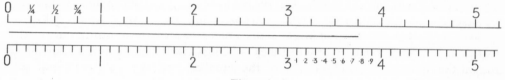

Fig. 4.6

The length of the line between the two scales can be expressed either as $3\frac{3}{4}$ units or as 3·75 units. The result of any division may be expressed in one or other of these ways.

The introduction of the idea of negative numbers and the interpolation of fractions between the whole numbers have made the number system very much more complete. Subtractions and divisions may now be performed without the qualification that these operations are possible only under certain conditions. Before we leave the simple numbers, a few comments on the two basic numbers o and 1 need to be made.

THE NUMBER ''O''

As a *cardinal* number, o is a difficult concept to understand, but as it means there are no objects present (e.g. that a box is empty), it is rarely used in this context in isolation from other statements. The meaning is clear when it is so used.

As an *ordinal* number, o is the position from which the numbering starts. For instance, the five seconds *before* the hour are used for the purpose of checking the time on clocks, and the British Broadcasting Corporation broadcasts six "pips", the first exactly five seconds before the hour and the last pip at the hour. The passage of those five seconds can be counted by saying, at successive pips, nought one two three four five.

In *addition*, the addition of o does not alter the number, $5 + o = 5$. In the same way $o + 5 = 5$.

Subtraction of o from a number does not alter its value, $5 - o = 5$. Subtraction from o leaves a negative number, $o - 5 = -5$.

Multiplication of a number by o gives the answer o. If I have a pocketful of sixpences, put my hand in my pocket but do not take anything out of it, I have nothing in my hand. This obvious and trivial statement merely serves to illustrate the statement $6 \times o = o$.

Multiplication of o by any number gives the answer o. If I put nothing on the table and then I put nothing on the table again and then I put nothing on the table again, altogether I have put nothing on the table, so that $o \times 3 = o$.

Division of o by any number gives the answer o. If I have nothing in my hand and I share it between four people, then each share will be nothing, $o \div 4 = o$.

N.B. *Division* by o leads to difficulties. As a simple example of ordinary division I may suppose that I have 12 pennies in my pocket and that I take out 4 pennies and then another 4 pennies and another 4 pennies. I can do this three times because $12 \div 4 = 3$.

If again I begin with 12 pennies and this time I take out 3 pennies, then another 3 pennies, another 3 pennies and another 3 pennies, I can do this 4 times because $12 \div 3 = 4$.

If again I start with 12 pennies and now I take out nothing, I put my hand in again and take out nothing, again I put my hand in and take out nothing, there is no limit to the number of times which I can do this and there is no answer in simple numbers to the division $12 \div o$.

It is sometimes convenient to be able to record that something can be continued without there being any limit to the number or any end to the process and for this purpose a special symbol has been introduced, namely ∞.

THE NUMBER "1"

Multiplication by 1 leaves a number unchanged. If I select *one* group of *ten* objects, I shall have *ten* objects $10 \times 1 = 10$.

Multiplication of 1 by a number gives that number. If I pick up *one* object, then I again pick up *one* object, and do this *ten* times, I shall have picked up *ten* objects $1 \times 10 = 10$.

Division of a number by itself leaves the answer 1. If I have 12 pennies in my pocket and I take out 12 pennies, I can do this once: $12 \div 12 = 1$.

Division of a number by 1 leaves the number unchanged. If I have 12 pennies in my pocket, I take out 1 and then one again and then one again and so on until I have taken them all out, I shall have extracted 1 penny twelve times: $12 \div 1 = 12$.

Division of 1 by a number involves the breaking of the unit into a fraction $1 \div 12 = \frac{1}{12}$. This is mere tautology and can only be read as saying that "when *one* is divided by *twelve* the result is the twelfth part of *one*".

DIVISION BY A FRACTION

Division arises when a question such as "How many *two*s are there in *eight*?" is asked. To find how many twos there are in eight the process is that of dividing *eight* by *two*: $8 \div 2 = 4$.

To the question "How many *halves* are there in *eight*?" the answer is again that of dividing, but now it is dividing eight by a *half* instead of by two. The answer obtained is

$$8 \div \tfrac{1}{2} = 16.$$

1	2	3	4	5	6	7	8
UNIT	UNIT	UNIT	UNIT	UNIT	UNIT	UNIT	UNIT
half	half	half	half	half	half	half	half	half	half	half	half	half	half	half	half
1	2	3	4	5	6	7	8	9	10	11	12	13	14	15	16

Fig. 4.7

Since there are two halves in one, there will be eight times two halves in eight, that is to say sixteen halves in eight (Fig. 4.7).

$$16 \times \tfrac{1}{2} = 8$$

which is equivalent to $\qquad 8 \div \tfrac{1}{2} = 16$

Now since $\qquad 8 \times 2 = 16$

it follows that the process of *dividing* 8 by $\frac{1}{2}$ gives an answer which is equal to that obtained by *multiplying* 8 by 2.

There is nothing in the argument above which would not hold good if the 8 units had been divided by one-third, in which case each of the units would have contained three-thirds and the whole eight, twenty-four.

We have already seen, on page 39, that

$$2 \div 5 = \tfrac{2}{5} \quad \text{and that} \quad 2 \times \tfrac{1}{5} = \tfrac{2}{5}$$

so that we now have both *dividing by N is equivalent to multiplying by* $\dfrac{1}{N}$

and *dividing by* $\dfrac{1}{N}$ *is equivalent to multiplying by N*, where N can be any whole number.

There remains the case of dividing by a quantity such as $\frac{2}{3}$. The verbal expression "How many two-thirds are there in four?" is equivalent to the symbolic expression $4 \div \frac{2}{3} = ?$

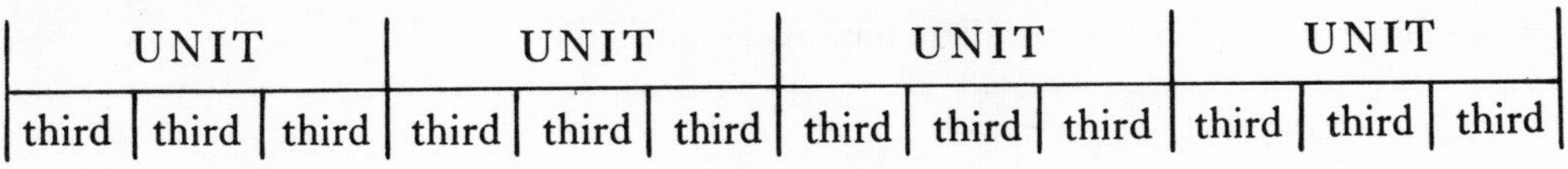

UNIT			UNIT			UNIT			UNIT		
third	third	third	third	third	third	third	third	third	third	third	third

Fig. 4.8

There are 12 *thirds* in 4, i.e. $4 \div \frac{1}{3} = 12$, or $4 \times 3 = 12$ (Fig. 4.8).

If now we take divisions which are double the length, we shall have half the number in the whole length, so that $4 \div \frac{2}{3} = 6$ or $4 \div \frac{2}{3} = 4 \times 3 \times \frac{1}{2} = 4 \times \frac{3}{2}$ (Fig. 4.9). We thus

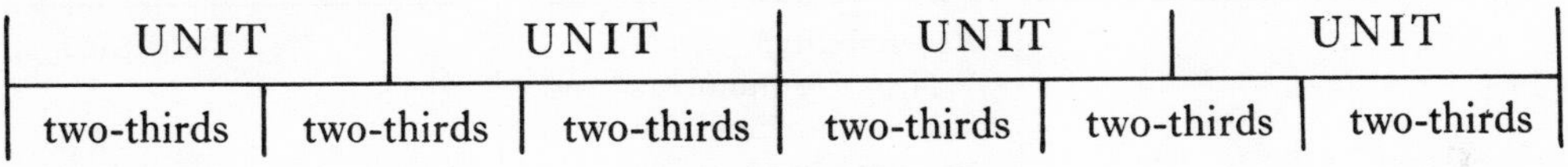

UNIT		UNIT		UNIT		UNIT	
two-thirds	two-thirds	two-thirds	two-thirds	two-thirds	two-thirds		

Fig. 4.9

arrive at the rule: To *divide* by a vulgar fraction, *invert* it and *multiply*. This may be expressed in more homely language: To *divide* by a vulgar fraction, *turn it upside down* and *multiply*.

In the working above, we have demonstrated that this rule gives the correct answer in only one particular case. No attempt has been made to prove this as a general proposition. It would be pleasing if students who have done much Algebra would turn to any standard Algebra text-book and look through the formal proof of this as a general proposition. Those who have done little formal Algebra may, at this stage, be content to accept the fact that the proposition may be proved in the general case.

PRODUCTS, QUOTIENTS AND FRACTIONS

The simple arrangement of dots  illustrates that a relationship exists between the three numbers "three", "five" and "fifteen". This relationship may be expressed in all the following ways

(a) $3 + 3 + 3 + 3 + 3 = 15$

(b) $5 + 5 + 5 = 15$

(c) $3 \times 5 = 15$

(d) $5 \times 3 = 15$

(e) $15 \div 5 = 3$

(f) $15 \div 3 = 5$

(g) $15 \times \frac{1}{5} = 3$

(h) $15 \times \frac{1}{3} = 5$

(i) $3 \div \frac{1}{5} = 15$

(j) $5 \div \frac{1}{3} = 15$

The reader is invited to compose ten short paragraphs which would give ten short stories such that each one illustrated each of the ten relations, setting the calculations in an appropriate context.

Adding and Multiplying Processes

In this chapter we have seen that once the concept of negative numbers has been introduced, adding and subtracting processes may be performed without such qualifications as "4 may be subtracted from 9 but not from 3". We have also seen that zero plays a basic role in the definition of such numbers. Similarly, we have noted that multiplication and division processes can be extended to all pairs of real numbers once fractions have been introduced, and that unity plays a basic role in the definition of fractions. There is a dualism between the two sets of operations which, at this stage, may be illustrated by setting out examples in two parallel columns (Fig. 4.10).

Addition and Subtraction		*Multiplication and Division*
$3 + 4 = 4 + 3$	Commutative Law.	$3 \times 4 = 4 \times 3$
$3 + 0 = 3$	Adding zero and multiplying by unity leave unchanged.	$3 \times 1 = 3$
$-5 + 5 = 0$	Reversibility: Negative numbers and fractions defined by zero and unity respectively.	$\frac{1}{5} \times 5 = 1$
$3 + (4 + 5) = (3 + 4) + 5$ That is, $3 + 9 \quad = 7 + 5$	Associative Law.	$3 \times (4 \times 5) = (3 \times 4) \times 5$ $3 \times 20 \quad = 12 \times 5$
$0 - (-6) \quad = 6$	Minus a negative number gives a positive number. Dividing by a reciprocal gives the integral number.	$1 \div \frac{1}{5} = 5$
$8 - (+2 - 3) = 8 + (-2 + 3)$ $= 8 + 3 - 2$	Minus in front of a quantity changes minus to plus and plus to minus. Division by a fraction changes numerator to denominator and vice versa.	$8 \div \frac{2}{3} = 8 \times \frac{3}{2} = 8 \times 3 \div 2$

Fig. 4.10

DECIMAL FRACTIONS

Some manufactured goods are packed in 1-lb packets or 7-lb bags or 5-gallon drums, but most of the things that are measured are not whole numbers of units nor exact simple fractions of a unit. Some measurements are approximately rough and ready; for others the tolerance which can be allowed is extremely small. For instance, when a gardening periodical says that lettuces should be thinned out to nine inches apart, an inch more or less would not matter very much and "nine inches" may be taken as meaning "somewhere between 8 and 10 inches". On the other hand, the long propeller-shaft in a ship is constructed so that it will rotate very rapidly without vibration, with no tendency to "whip". A 30-ft shaft must be turned in a machine shop to an accuracy limited only by the precision by which its straightness and its diameter can be measured. Instruments capable of measuring to a ten-thousandth of an inch are available in such machine shops.

There is an appropriate degree of accuracy for most measurements. Our number system is based on *ten* and, in practice, it turns out to be a most suitable number for the purpose of recording successive orders of accuracy.

To the question, "How tall are you?" it would be appropriate to answer 65 inches, giving the answer to the nearest inch. Differences in amount of hair and height of heels would make any more accurate estimate of height unreliable.

A door has to fit in a door-frame well enough to keep out draughts, but there must be sufficient clearance for it not to rub against the door-frame under various climatic conditions and it would be appropriate to measure its width to within a tenth of an inch.

If the "catch" on a door, where it fits into the brass plate on the door-frame, is not quite in the right place, either the door will rattle whenever there is any wind blowing, or the catch will not slide into position when the door is closed, in which event it can be eased by a little filing so that it just fits, and the tolerance here is something of the order of a hundredth of an inch.

When a motor-car manufacturer says that the tappet clearance should be three-thousandths of an inch, he expects the mechanic, after grinding in a valve, to adjust the tappets to an accuracy of a thousandth of an inch.

To this practice of measuring progressively to degrees of accuracy, each degree being ten times more accurate than the one before, corresponds a notation which enables arithmetical work with such fractional quantities to be carried out with no more difficulty than work with whole numbers. This is illustrated by measuring the rod shown below more and more precisely.

Now when we write down 3·242 in. the number is written so that the 3, the 2, the 4, etc., are figures written in an order such that their actual value depends upon

How long is this rod?

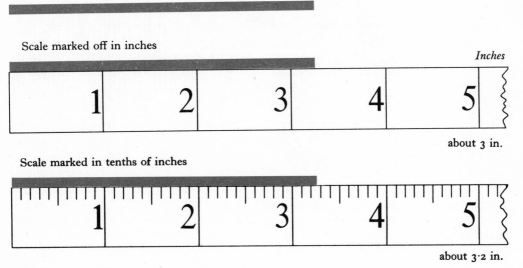

Scale marked off in inches

Inches

about 3 in.

Scale marked in tenths of inches

about 3·2 in.

Scale marked in hundredths of inches and
used with a magnifying glass

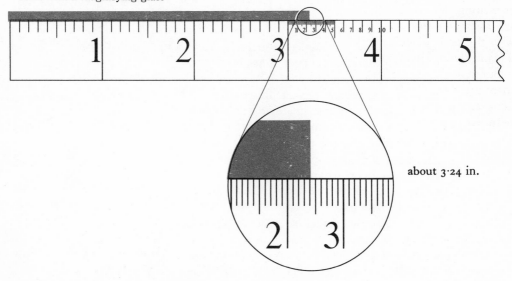

about 3·24 in.

A scale finely engraved in thousandths of an inch would not be usual on a ruler of this type, but if such a scale were available, a microscope would be needed to read it. The diagram below illustrates this further magnification.

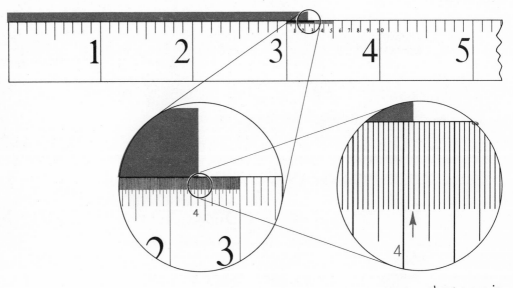

about 3·242 in.

their place in the number, and the place value of any figure is just ten times the place value of the figure on its right. Since this is exactly what happens with our ordinary way of writing out whole numbers, arithmetical operations with these subdivisions which are less than unity are just the same as those with numbers greater than unity. Numbers with the same place value must be kept under one another in addition or subtraction. This is assured by keeping the decimal points in the same vertical line.

Suppose that paper on which a book is printed happens to have a thickness such that there are a hundred pages to the inch. Part 1 of the book has 125 pages, part 2 of the book 243 pages; if the two parts were bound together how thick would the book be between covers?

$$\text{Vol. 1 contains 125 pages each } \tfrac{1}{100} \text{ in. thick}$$

$$125 = 100 + 20 + 5$$

100 hundredths of an inch	$=$ 1 in.
20 hundredths of an inch is $\tfrac{2}{10}$ in.	$=$ 0·2 in.
5 hundredths of an inch	$=$ 0·05 in.
$\overline{125}$ hundredths of an inch	$=$ $\overline{1·25}$ in.

Thickness of paper in Vol. I $\quad = \quad$ 1·25 in.
Thickness of paper in Vol. II $\quad = \quad$ 2·43 in.
$$\overline{3·68} \text{ in.}$$

Just to make sure that we understand the meaning of these figures in their particular places, let us look at 3·68 in. actual size (Fig. 4.11).

Fig. 4.11

These figures are drawn the exact height of the quantities they represent and you can see their respective contribution to the number 3·68.

Addition, subtraction and carrying figures are just as with whole numbers; the only rule is *keep decimal points under one another*.

Each place in the multiplier to the *right* of the o between two figures serves the same purpose in decimal fractions as it does with whole numbers; it preserves the place value. The simple subtraction

$$
\begin{array}{r}
2857{\cdot}7582 \\
1637{\cdot}7361 \\
\hline
1220{\cdot}0221 \\
\hline
\end{array}
$$

illustrates this point.

MULTIPLICATION

The procedure here is much the same as for multiplication with whole numbers. The decimal point needs placing with care, and the meaning of the answer should be considered. As with whole numbers we begin by multiplying by the left-hand figure of the multiplier, in this case 2, giving 62832. We then multiply by the figure to the right of the 2, namely 7, and start by putting the first figure of this product one column to the right of the first figure of the previous line. This is precisely the same procedure as for multiplication using whole numbers.

$$
\begin{array}{r}
3{\cdot}1416 \\
2759{\cdot}08 \\
\hline
6283{\cdot}2 \\
2199{\cdot}12 \\
157{\cdot}080 \\
28{\cdot}2744 \\
0{\cdot}251328 \\
\hline
8667{\cdot}925728 \\
\hline
\end{array}
$$

There remains the placing of the decimal point. This may be done in two ways. Either count up the decimal places in the two numbers being multiplied together; 3·1416 has *four* places, 2759·08 has *two* places and the product 8667·925728 has *six = four + two* places. If you do it this way you can ignore the decimal point throughout the multiplication and insert it only in the answer. The other way of fixing the decimal point is by noting that the 2 which is the first multiplier is *three* places to the left of the units figure 2759·08 and so the first figure of the first product is *three* places to the left of the 6.

There is really nothing wrong with the answer 8667·925728, regarded as the product of the two numbers which are *exactly* 3·1416 and 2759·08. It is, all the same, an answer which requires some analysis, if its implications are to be understood. If, for instance, it is to be a number of yards, then it would indicate a distance of nearly five miles. The sixth place of decimals represents a millionth of a yard or about $\frac{1}{30000}$ of an inch. One may ask whether it is possible in any circumstances to measure a distance as great as this to an accuracy of this order. The number, in itself, is unrealistic in any context. Secondly, a number such as 2759·08 is given to six figure accuracy. Multiplying it by what looks like an approximation to π has converted it to a number given to ten figure accuracy. Is this possible; if not, why not?

Teachers often find that children have extreme difficulty in grasping the simple fact that if, in any calculation, one figure is known to only "three figure accuracy", then the answer can be known only to this degree of accuracy, however precisely other elements in the calculation may be known. If, for example, the diameter of a pipe is measured with calipers to the nearest hundredth of an inch and is found to be 1·23 in., to this level of accuracy, the 1·23 might have been 1·234 or 1·232 or 1·230, etc. but, since we have not a measuring instrument which will provide us with the accurate figure in the thousandths of an inch, we can say only that the diameter is 1·23 in. to the nearest hundredth of an inch and that the next figure is quite unknown. We might indicate this statement symbolically by writing for the diameter in inches 1·23???. . . where the actual figures in the third, fourth, etc., places of decimals are unknown. If, from this information, we calculate the circumference in the ordinary way by multiplying by $\pi = 3·14159.$ . . we proceed as follows

$$
\begin{array}{r}
1·23???? \\
3·14159\cdots \\
\hline
3·69???? \\
0·123???? \\
0·0492???? \\
0·00123???? \\
0·000615???? \\
0·0001107???? \\
\hline
3·86????????? \\
\end{array}
$$

The addition in the third place of decimals is $0+0+1+9+3+?$, which is $13+?$. All we can say of this is that it is more than 10, so that there will certainly be 1 to carry but that we do not know the actual figure to put in this place because one of the items is unknown. Thus, although the 3·14159. . . can be known to as many places of decimals as are useful, the product cannot be known more accurately than to the number of figures in the least-accurately known component of the calculation. This is a general application, true for addition, subtraction and division as well as for multiplication.

CONTINUITY

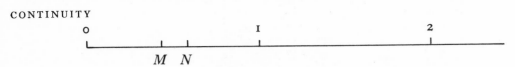

If M and N (above) are two unequal numbers, and they are expressed in decimals, then, after a finite number of places, the figures will begin to differ. There is no limit to the number of decimal places that may be filled, therefore *however small the difference between* M *and* N, *an infinite number of intermediate numbers may be inserted.*

For example if $M = 0·142857142857142857. . .$
                       $N = 0·142857142862594413. . .$

then any numbers
$$P = 0 \cdot 142857142858???? \ldots$$
$$0 \cdot 142857142859???? \ldots$$
$$0 \cdot 142857142860???? \ldots$$
$$0 \cdot 142857142861???? \ldots$$

will lie between M and N. Since any of these numbers may be continued to an infinite number of places, there is no limit to the number of distinct and separate numbers which may be inserted between M and N. This argument is just as valid if the numbers first differ in the tenth place, the millionth place or the million millionth place of decimals.

Rational and Irrational numbers

A number is defined as being a *rational* number if it can be expressed in the form $\frac{m}{n}$, where m and n are ordinary whole numbers, i.e. integers. Thus,

$$\frac{1}{27}, \frac{1066}{1485}, \frac{17321}{14142}, \text{ are rational numbers.}$$

Many numbers which are not rational numbers can be calculated to an unlimited number of places of decimals by properly defined procedures. Of these the simplest is the square root of 2. There is a standard method of extracting square roots which may be carried on indefinitely. Any reader who was taught this method will recall this working for $\sqrt{2}$:

```
                    1· 4   1   4   2   1 ...  etc.
              |  2·00  00  00  00  00
         1    |  1
        24    |  1 00
              |    96
       281    |     4 00
              |     2 81
      2824    |     1 19 00
     28282    |     1 12 96
              |        6 04 00
              |        5 65 64
    282841    |          38 36 00
              |          28 28 41
              |          10 07 59 ...
```

which gives the square root of 2 as an interminable non-recurrent decimal. Although it is in fact interminable and non-recurrent, and therefore irrational, this cannot be assumed in the first place. There is, however, a simple proof that it is not rational.

We begin by stating that *if $\sqrt{2}$ is rational, then it can be expressed as a vulgar fraction* with whole numbers for numerator and denominator.

Let this vulgar fraction, *in its lowest terms*, be $\frac{m}{n}$, so that

$$\sqrt{2} = \frac{m}{n} \quad . \quad . \quad . \quad . \quad . \quad . \quad . \quad . \quad (1)$$

where m and n have no factor in common (since we assume that the fraction is in its lowest terms).

Squaring equation (1) gives

$$2 = \frac{m^2}{n^2}$$

or

$$2\,n^2 = m^2 \quad . \quad . \quad . \quad . \quad . \quad . \quad . \quad (2)$$

The left-hand side of this equation contains 2 as a factor, therefore the right-hand side must contain 2 as a factor. This can be so only if m is *even*.

If m is even it can be written in the form

$$m = 2\,p \quad . \quad . \quad . \quad . \quad . \quad . \quad . \quad . \quad (3)$$

where p is a whole number.

Squaring equation (3) gives

$$m^2 = 4\,p^2 \quad . \quad . \quad . \quad . \quad . \quad . \quad . \quad (4)$$

Substituting for m^2 in equation (2) gives

$$2\,n^2 = 4\,p^2$$

or

$$n^2 = 2\,p^2$$

The right-hand side contains 2 as a factor, therefore the left-hand side must contain 2 as a factor. This can be so only if n is even.

We have, therefore, shown that $\sqrt{2}$ could be expressed in the form $\frac{m}{n}$ provided that m and n were both even, in which case $\frac{m}{n}$ could be cancelled by 2. This contradicts the assumption that $\sqrt{2}$ may be expressed as a factor $\frac{m}{n}$ *in its lowest terms* and we must, therefore, conclude that this assumption is false.

Since, therefore, $\sqrt{2}$ cannot be expressed in the form $\frac{m}{n}$, when m and n are positive whole numbers $\sqrt{2}$ cannot be rational.

Similar arguments hold for $\sqrt{3}$, $\sqrt{5}$, $\sqrt{7}$, etc.

Another irrational number is π, which is equal to the sum of an infinite series.

$$\pi = 4\{1 - \tfrac{1}{3} + \tfrac{1}{5} - \tfrac{1}{7} + \tfrac{1}{9} - \tfrac{1}{11} + \ldots \textit{ad inf.}\}$$

This has recently (March, 1957) been calculated to 10,000 places of decimals by G. E. Felton, on a Ferranti "Pegasus" computor. The first 250 places are

3·1415926535897932384626433832795028841971693993751058209749445923078164062862089986280348253421170679821480865132823066470938446095505822317253594081284811174502841027019385211055596446229489549303819644288109756659334461284756482337867831652712019091...   etc.

There is no *practical* value in knowing π beyond about ten places of decimals but it is of some interest to mathematicians to have an irrational number such as π worked out at length. There are a number of interesting questions which arise: for instance, "Are all the digits uniformly distributed?" or "Is there any pattern in the distribution of digits?" Since π has no particular association with 10, a number system based on 10 would not be expected to favour any particular digit and, from the list of figures given for the first 250 places you can count how nearly each digit, 0, 1, 2, 3, 4, 5, 6, 7, 8, 9 occurs twenty-five times and how many times each digit occurs in each successive group of fifty. It is only since computing machines have been developed that such questions could be asked and answered to considerable numbers of places.

5

Time and the Calendar

THE TWO basic periods upon which our system of time-keeping depends are the year and the day. These are determined by two quite distinct motions. The year depends only upon the time the earth takes to travel round the sun in a roughly circular path, with a radius of about 93,000,000 miles and an average speed of about 66,000 miles an hour.

The day depends principally upon the time taken for the earth to rotate about its axis (Figs. 5.1 and 5.2).

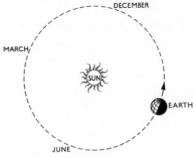

Fig. 5.1

The Year is the time taken for the *Earth* to complete its 580,000,000 mile journey round the sun. (The *Tropical Year*, used in calculations in connexion with calendars, is measured from the passage of the sun across the equator at the instant of the *Equinox* in March, to the next March Equinox.)

Fig. 5.2

The Day depends upon the time taken for the *Earth* to rotate about its axis. (The Earth actually rotates on its axis in 23^h 56^m $4 \cdot 1^s$. The remaining 3^m 56^s is accounted for by the distance it has moved in its orbit round the sun.)

These two motions of moving along in its orbit and of spinning about its own axis are independent motions and, unfortunately for time-keeping purposes, the number of days in a year happens to be 365·242196 . . .

There are pronounced variations in the length of the day during the course of a year, and for practical reasons the duration of the year rather than that of a day has to be used for the regulation of time. The latest official definition of a second is that adopted by the General Assembly of the International Astronomical Union in 1955, viz:

$$1 \text{ second} = \frac{1}{31,556,925 \cdot 975} \text{ of the Tropical year 1900.}$$

This gives an accuracy of about a second in 3000 years and it is claimed that new devices which will permit time to be measured to this degree of accuracy are available.

If we leave the regulation of clocks to the experts and content ourselves with checking them with the broadcast time-signals we shall have a straightforward set of relationships in which exactly

$$60 \text{ seconds} = 1 \text{ minute}$$
$$60 \text{ minutes} = 1 \text{ hour}$$
$$24 \text{ hours} = 1 \text{ day}$$

and either $365 \text{ days} = 1 \text{ year}$

or $366 \text{ days} = 1 \text{ leap year}$

according to a set of rules which are described later.

This would be fairly easy to understand and work with if we had not inherited a series of traditional complications.

The first of these is that our clocks are all 12-hour clocks and they have to go through two cycles of times for each natural cycle of one day. At the beginning of 1946, when such a large number of people had grown accustomed to the use of 24-hour time in the Forces, it might have been acceptable if 24-hour time had been introduced for railway time-tables and for the B.B.C. and for postal telegraph working, but the chance was missed and popular resistance to change will now delay any such reform for generations. The principal function of a clock is to imitate the rotation of the earth, so that by looking at the hands we can tell "the time of day", that is, the "relative position of the sun".

From these diagrams it is clear that a twenty-four hour clock is simply one in which, if 24 is to the north and 12 to the south, the hour-hand would point in the direction of the sun. Put in other words, time of day is the angle the sun's meridian has turned through since midnight. However, this simple picture is obscured because we have inherited a division of the day into two periods of twelve hours, which is much older than rotating clocks and clockwork. Our clocks go round twice as fast as the one illustrated and we indicate time before noon by the initials a.m., or "ante meridiem", and past noon by the initials p.m., or "post meridiem".

The second complication is the month. We can hardly blame ourselves for the natural difficulties which arise from the existence of the moon; its most interesting monthly performance of increasing through the crescent stage, to the hunchback gibbous stage, to the beautiful round full moon, and then decreasing to extinction, could hardly be ignored. The duration of this cycle is 29·53059 days, an awkward number which is not an exact number of days. Nor is the year an exact number of months; one year is 12·36813 months, so that 12 months is quite a bit short of a year and 13 months is too long. Since, in nature, months and years do not keep in step, no ingenuity in naming

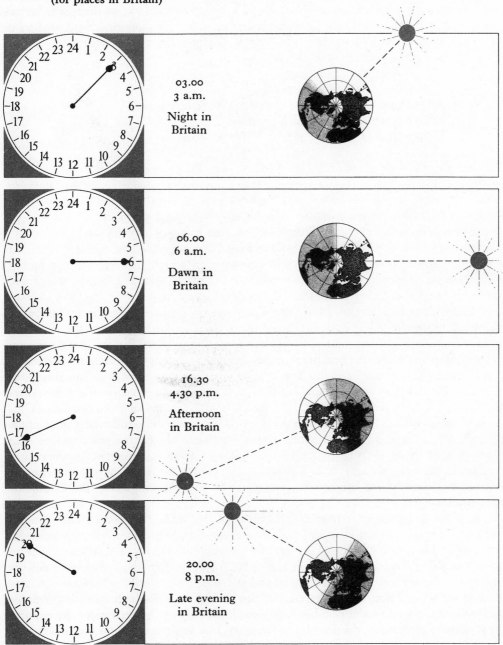

Fig. 5.3

The relationship between a 24-hour clock and the movement of the sun relative to the earth (a slight modification of the position of the shadow could be made to illustrate winter or summer conditions).

them could make them do so. We have preserved a convention, worked out by Sosigenes and introduced by Julius Caesar in 45 B.C., by which the year is divided into twelve parts, mostly containing 30 or 31 days, called months (i.e. moonths), but which are never in step with any cycle of the actual moon. Our months have given rise to a jingle of which there are a number of local variants:

> "Thirty days hath September, April, June and November
> All the rest have thirty-one, excepting February alone,
> With twenty-eight days each common year,
> Leap year coming once in four, February then has one day more."

There is also the anomaly that the *ninth* month is called *Sept*ember and so on until the *twelfth* month which is called *Dec*ember. These months of ours have little to do with the moon, but the treatment of February and the invention of the leap year is important. Sosigenes based his calendar on the duration of a year as 365·25 days. Four years of 365 days would be four times a quarter of a day, that is, one whole day too short, so one day was added every fourth year to keep the calendar in step. He had, himself, inherited a tradition from earlier times, probably Etruscan, in which the actual lunar month played a most important part. Civic officials, the pontifices, watched for the new moon, and when it appeared they proclaimed the beginning of a new month from the steps of the Capitol. The first day of the month was named Kalendae, the "callings", whence our word, "calendar". The days after a full moon were counted back from the Kalendae of the next month, so that February 23rd would be the sixth day before the Kalends of March. After the pontifices had been abolished and the Julian calendar introduced, the nomenclature "Kalendae" for the first days of the purely conventional Julian months was retained and the extra day was inserted in leap years by repeating February 23rd, that is, by having two "6th days before the Kalends" or "bis-sextus calendas". Thus derives the adjective "bissextile" for a leap year. For two thousand years our months have borne no relation to the actual moon, but they are useful sub-divisions of a year: holiday time is July (named after Julius Caesar) or August (named after Augustus Caesar), January and February are wintry months, May and June are warmer and gardens are bright with flowers. The months are worth the arithmetic they involve.

The third complication introduced is the seven-day week. 7 is not a factor of 29·53 nor of 365 or 366, and weeks fit into neither months, nor calendar months, nor years nor leap years. The week, of course, is essentially a religious division of time, perpetuating the six working days and the Jewish Sabbath, "for in six days the Lord made Heaven and Earth, the sea and all that in them is, and rested the seventh day: wherefore the Lord blessed the seventh day, and hallowed it". The week and the Sabbath are fully preserved in the Christian tradition of worship, being modified only by the keeping of the Sabbath by Christians on Sunday, the first day of the week, in commemoration of the resurrection of Christ on Easter Sunday. Our religions are very much interwoven in our calendars: even ancient pagan names survive; one can turn up a Christian calendar and find those most holy days of Easter week referred to as the Tuesday, Wednesday, Thursday before Easter, using names identifying the days with the worship of those thoroughly pagan deities Tiw, Woden, Thor and Frigga, Sunday itself being the day for Sun worship.

Calendars and Dates

The   7 days in a week

29·530588 days in a lunar month

365·242195 days in a year

are incompatible numbers, and there are neither a whole number of weeks nor a whole number of lunar months in a year. The shortest cycle which contains a whole number of years and a whole number of lunar months is 19 years, which is within about 2 hours of 235 lunations.

$$
\begin{array}{ll}
& 29·530\ 588 \\
365·242\ 195 & 235· \\
19 & \overline{5906·117\ 6} \\
3652·421\ 95 & 885·917\ 6 \\
3287·179\ 755 & 147·652\ 9 \\
\overline{6939·601\ 705} \text{ days in 19 years} & \overline{6939·688\ 1}\quad \text{days in 235 lunations}
\end{array}
$$

6939·688 days in 235 lunations

6939·602 days in 19 years

0·086 day difference

$$
\begin{array}{l}
0·086 \text{ day} \\
24· \\
\overline{1·72} \\
0·34 \\
\overline{2·06}\ \text{hours}
\end{array}
$$

All these complications of times of day and calendars need worry no one living in Britain who is either Christian or Atheist. The sensible way of finding out what day of the month the first Saturday in August will be is to use a calendar, and if you are going away for a three-weeks' holiday you can always count it out on the calendar or in a diary. "What day of the week will your birthday be next year?" is a question best answered from a diary. The dates of the beginning and ending of summer-time concern everyone, but the newspaper and radio give ample notice of this. There are licences for motor cars, and you might like to ponder why the dates on which "Quarterly" licences expired were March 24th, June 30th, September 30th, December 31st.

For all British citizens the beginning of the "Income-Tax year" on April 6th is an interesting date with a history worth the telling, but other dates concern the Christian calendar and interest the irreligious only in so far as a secular parliament has chosen legal Bank Holidays to coincide with some of the Church's festivals. For Jews and Moslems, however, life is not so simple.

JEWISH CALENDAR

The Jewish year follows both a solar cycle which determines the years and a lunar cycle which determines the months. Jewish months really are lunar months, and 12 lunar months, that is, 354·37 days, is nearly 11 days short of a year. Jewish years have 12 months, with a thirteenth month intercalated in the 3rd, 6th, 8th, 11th, 14th, 17th and 19th years of the nineteen-year cycle. By Jewish reckoning, the year 5719, or the 19th year of the 301st lunar cycle since the Creation, began in September 1958. The Spring equinox falls in the month Nissan, and the feast of the Passover is between the 15th and 22nd of Nissan. Since full moon is halfway through the month, or $14\frac{3}{4}$ days after the beginning of the month, the Passover immediately follows the full moon after the Spring equinox.

MOSLEM CALENDAR

The Moslems keep a year which is tied completely to the moon and ignores the sun. Alternate months have 30 and 29 days (thus averaging 29·5 days) with an extra day put in every 32 years to make up the 29·53 days in a month. Thus, the "year" begins at different seasons, retrogressing through the seasons every $32\frac{1}{2}$ years. The ninth month of the Moslem year, Ramadan, the month of fasting throughout Islam, will move from March 1959, through February, January, December, etc., back to March again in 1991, beginning eleven days earlier each year.

GREGORIAN CALENDAR

When Julius Caesar introduced the Julian calendar in 45 B.C. it was based on the assumption that the length of a year was $365\frac{1}{4}$ days.

$$
\begin{array}{ll}
365\text{·}25 & \text{days} = \text{length of a Julian Year} \\
365\text{·}2422 & \text{,,} \ = \text{length of an actual (Tropical) year} \\
\hline
0\text{·}0078 & \text{,,} \ = \text{difference}
\end{array}
$$

This error of 0·0078 day a year is equivalent to an error of 1 day in 128 years or 3 days in 384 years. This is so nearly equal to 3 days in 400 years that by omitting 3 leap years every 400 years the calendar can be made to be correct to within an error of a day every 4000 years. By the sixteenth century A.D. the errors accumulating since 45 B.C. amounted to about $12\frac{1}{2}$ days and the changes then recommended by Ghiraldi of Naples and Christopher Clavius of Rome to Pope Gregory XIII were that the century years 1600, 2000, 2400 in which the number of centuries was divisible by 4 should continue to be leap years, but the other century years 1700, 1800, 1900, 2100, 2200, 2300, . . . etc., should be common years, thus providing for the required removal of three leap years every 400 years; also that 10 days be removed from the calendar. The removal of 10 days to bring the calendar back into line with the seasons put the Vernal Equinox on March 21st or 22nd, whereas the traditional Quarter Day had been the "Feast of the Annunciation" or "Lady Day" on March 25th.

A Brief issued by Pope Gregory XIII ordered that October 5th, 1582 should be followed by October 15th, 1582, that the beginning of a year should be counted from January 1st, and that the years 1700, 1800, 1900, 2100, 2200, 2300, . . . etc., should no longer be leap years. It also embodied revised instructions for finding the date of Easter. Now 1582 was less than thirty years after the reign of Bloody Mary, the spouse of the hated Philip of Spain, and the memory of the English Christians who had been murdered by the agents of the Inquisition was still fresh. It is not surprising, therefore, that there was no disposition to follow the lead of Rome. However, within 170 years arithmetical common sense proved stronger than sectarian squabbles, and by 1750 an Act was passed in the British Parliament introducing the new-style calendar during the year 1752. Between 1582 and 1752 there had been a leap year in 1700 in England but no leap year in the countries which had accepted Gregory's calendar, so there were then eleven days' discrepancy between the two calendars. These were absorbed by decreeing that September 2nd, 1752 should be followed by September 14th, 1752 and that the beginning of the legal year should be January 1st instead of March 25th. The same provisions applied to Scotland, except that Scotland had adopted January 1st as New Year's Day as early as 1600.

Thus, in quoting any historical documents between 1582 and 1752 it is necessary to specify which calendar was being employed. For example, a date referred to as "February 3rd, 1684" in England would be "February 3rd, 1685" in Scotland, and "February 14th, 1685" in those parts of Europe under Papal jurisdiction, but as in England for other parts of the Continent. The Germanic states changed to the new-style calendar in 1700 by an agreement reached at the Diet of Regensburg.

INCOME TAX YEAR

Until 1752 the legal year had run from Lady Day to Lady Day (March 25th) and despite calendar changes the Treasury just went on balancing annual accounts at yearly intervals. Since the calendar had omitted September 3rd, 4th, 5th, 6th, 7th, 8th, 9th, 10th, 11th, 12th, 13th, 1752, March 25th, 1753 was only 354 days after March 25th, 1752. In order to include 365 days of income and expenditure in his annual accounts the Chancellor of the Exchequer did not have them ready until 365 days after March 25th, 1752, that is, on April 6th, 1753. Thus, he added March 26th, 27th, 28th, 29th, 30th, 31st, April 1st, 2nd, 3rd, 4th, 5th, 1753, to make up for those dropped out the previous September, and we have just gone on like this, being taxed on incomes earned during the year beginning April 6th and finishing April 5th.

EASTER

The Jewish Passover is fixed to follow the full moon in the month Nissan, and Nissan is the month in which the Vernal Equinox (March 21st) occurs. St. Luke, Chapter 22, describes how Jesus ate the Passover with his disciples before going to Gethsemane. The Last Supper, the Agony in the Garden and the Crucifixion were at the time of the full moon following March 21st. The hurry to remove the Body of the Crucified Christ from the Cross before the beginning of the Jewish Sabbath (Saturday) fixes the Crucifixion on a Friday.

The Church has sought to preserve this sequence in the commemoration of Easter, the most holy days of the Christian year. The considerable arithmetic involved in the calculation of the dates of this annual festival is set out in great detail in the preface to the *Book of Common Prayer*.

6

Working with Simple and Compound Units

BEFORE WE discuss working with the great variety of units which are in common use we should recognize the difference between pure numbers and quantities.

Pure Numbers and Quantities

When we talk about "three", or see the figure 3, or we write $5 - 2 = 3$ in a context in which these numbers are not associated with any particular things or measures, we refer to them as "pure numbers" or simply "numbers". When numbers are associated with things or with units they are "quantities". Thus, "30 apples" is a quantity of apples, "7 pints" is a quantity of water or milk, and "8 feet" is a quantity called a length.

Pure numbers may be added, subtracted, multiplied or divided according to the ordinary rules of arithmetic without any complications or reservations. For instance, there is a relation between the three *pure numbers* 5, 8 and 13 which may be expressed in any of the forms

$$5 + 8 = 13 \qquad 8 + 5 = 13 \qquad 13 - 5 = 8 \qquad 13 - 8 = 5$$

and, more generally, if p, q and r are three *pure numbers*, then if one of the following relations is true, all four will be true:

$$p + q = r \qquad q + p = r \qquad r - p = q \qquad r - q = p.$$

Quantities may be added or subtracted only if they are of the same kind and expressed in the same units. Thus, if I have 5 apples and buy another 8 apples, I shall have 13 apples, and the relations

$$5 \text{ apples} + 8 \text{ apples} = 13 \text{ apples}, \qquad 8 \text{ apples} + 5 \text{ apples} = 13 \text{ apples}$$
$$13 \text{ apples} - 8 \text{ apples} = 5 \text{ apples}, \qquad 13 \text{ apples} - 5 \text{ apples} = 8 \text{ apples}$$

all express the same relation between 5 apples, 8 apples and 13 apples.

On the other hand, at the time of writing, there are in my house 5 apples and 8 rooms. In no meaningful way can these be combined to give 13 of anything. Apples and rooms are quantities of quite a different kind, but the same situation holds when we are dealing with things of the same kind but expressed in different units. If I have £5 and 8 shillings, then I can do no more than say that I have £5 + 8s. In no sense is it possible to say that I have 13 of anything.

The idea of a pure number is probably understood by most people, but it is not easy to describe in simple terms. One way of describing how we arrive at the idea of a pure number would be to suppose that we have 8 plates and some knives and some apples. If on each plate I place an apple and a knife, and I put the plates, each with an apple and a knife, on a table, then on that table there will be 8 plates, 8 apples and 8 knives. The number 8 is something quite distinct from the plates, apples and knives; it is an abstraction; it is what is common to the particular collections of plates, apples and knives. The fact that the number 8 can be detached from the plates or apples is of fundamental importance because purely abstract calculations can be performed and the results used to give information about any sorts of objects. The purely numerical statement $5 + 8 = 13$ illustrates a rule for combining these abstract ideas of fiveness and eightness independently of any material context. In particular contexts, this statement can tell us that if a sow has 5 piglets in one litter and 8 in another, she will have had 13 piglets altogether, or that if one cement mixer mixes 5 tons of concrete and another mixes 8 tons of concrete, they will have mixed 13 tons of concrete altogether.

So far we have referred to numbers and quantities only in relation to addition and subtraction when the distinction between them is simple and clear cut. In the sum $5 + 8 = 13$ all the terms are pure numbers, and in the sum 5 apples $+$ 8 apples $=$ 13 apples all the terms are quantities of apples. When we are concerned with multiplication and division we are confronted with quite a different situation.

MULTIPLICATION

If I put 3 apples on a table and then another 3 apples on the table, I shall have put 6 apples on the table altogether. This statement may be set out either as

$$3 \text{ apples} + 3 \text{ apples} = 6 \text{ apples}$$

or as

$$2 \times 3 \text{ apples} = 6 \text{ apples}$$

where the 2 is a pure number and the 3 apples and the 6 apples are quantities of apples. The 2 indicates that the action of putting 3 apples on the table is done *twice*, and repeating an operation is not a quantity; I could have taken 3 knives twice or 3 plates twice, the twice being something quite distinct from apples, knives or plates. Similarly, I can mark off a four-inch length along the edge of a piece of paper and then another four-inch length and then another four-inch length so that the total distance between the beginning and end marks would be twelve inches. I take four inches three times, and the whole operation can be set out in the form

$$3 \times 4 \text{ inches} = 12 \text{ inches}.$$

As before, the 3 is a pure number. These statements can be expressed as

a pure number $\times$ a number of units $=$ a number of the same units

| 3 | $\times$ | 4 in. | $=$ | 12 in. |
| 2 | $\times$ | 3 apples | $=$ | 6 apples |

DIVISION

When we are considering division in the context of quantities we have to distinguish between two quite separate operations. If we have 28 apples we may wish to give the same number of apples to each of 4 people and we shall find that we can give 7 apples to each person. This operation consists of dividing the *quantity* (28 apples) by the *number* 4, and is written

$$\frac{28 \text{ apples}}{4} = 7 \text{ apples}$$

This operation is properly described as division.

On the other hand, we may wish to put the 28 apples into bags so that each bag contains 7 apples, and we ask how many times this can be done. The answer is the pure number 4. The calculation is set out in the form

$$\frac{28 \text{ apples}}{7 \text{ apples}} = 4$$

This operation is quite distinct from the previous one, which was described as division, and it is best classified as ratio.

RATIO, RATE AND PROPORTION

When we are talking about pure numbers we may use the word division to describe the operation which may be set out in the form

$$\frac{28}{7} = \frac{4}{1}$$

On the left-hand side of this equation we have divided numerator and denominator by the number 7 which is a common factor. This is the process usually referred to as "cancelling".

When we look at the *ratio*

$$\frac{28 \text{ apples}}{7 \text{ apples}}$$

we see that the common factor 7 may be cancelled, giving

$$\frac{\overset{4}{\cancel{28}} \text{ apples}}{\underset{1}{\cancel{7}} \text{ apples}} = \frac{4 \text{ apples}}{1 \text{ apple}}$$

Both numerator and denominator are expressed in the same units and their ratio is the pure number $\frac{4}{1}$ or 4. This next step amounts to

$$\frac{4 \cancel{\text{ apples}}}{1 \cancel{\text{ apple}}} = \frac{4}{1}$$

and this simplification of the ratio is so closely analogous to the operation with pure numbers which we call "cancelling" that it is convenient to say: "if the same unit occurs in both the numerator and denominator of an expression it may be cancelled".

A *ratio* is a comparison of two quantities expressed in the same units. If one length is 28 inches and another length is 7 inches, the ratio of these two lengths is as 4 is to 1. This statement is written

$$\frac{28 \text{ in.}}{7 \text{ in.}} = \frac{4}{1}$$

RATE

If a person walks 28 miles in 7 hours, his *rate* of walking is

$$\frac{28 \text{ miles}}{7 \text{ hours}}$$

In this case the units are different and although numerator and denominator have a numerical common factor of 7, which may be cancelled, leading to the slight simplification

$$\frac{\overset{4}{\cancel{28}}\ \text{miles}}{\underset{1}{\cancel{7}}\ \text{hours}} = 4\ \frac{\text{miles}}{\text{hours}}$$

there is no common element in the units, miles and hours, and no further reduction of the expression is possible. The rate $\dfrac{\text{miles}}{\text{hour}}$ is read as "miles per hour" and may be regarded as a compound unit since it is a unit of velocity and it is compounded of units of length and time.

A *rate* is a comparison of two quantities expressed in different units. Other examples of rates are prices of commodities such as $\dfrac{9\text{d.}}{\text{lb}}$ which is read as "ninepence per pound", wages such as $\dfrac{£10}{\text{week}}$, read as "£10 per week", or density of population such as $\dfrac{10\ \text{inhabitants}}{\text{acre}}$, read as "ten inhabitants per acre".

PROPORTION

When rates or ratios are compared, the comparison is a proportion. With pure numbers, the relation

$$\frac{84}{3} = \frac{56}{2}$$

may be read in the form "84 is to 3 is the same proportion as 56 is to 2".

With ratios, a relation such as

$$\frac{84\ \text{miles}}{56\ \text{miles}} = \frac{3\ \text{hours}}{2\ \text{hours}}$$

is a way of writing down the statement that "the distances travelled are in the same proportion as the times taken".

With rates, the relation

$$\frac{84\ \text{miles}}{3\ \text{hours}} = \frac{56\ \text{miles}}{2\ \text{hours}}$$

could also be interpreted as implying that "the distances travelled are proportional to the times taken", but it would usually be taken to mean that "the velocity is the same in each case".

Compound Units

Many nouns serve as units for particular purposes. The first sentence of this paragraph could be described as an "8-word sentence". Anything we wish to study which involves comparison of quantities needs to have some units defined. For instance, in reading this paragraph one person might glance at the first half of a line and then shift his glance to the second half of the line and take in the whole line in two glances, while another person might take three glances over the line. Anyone studying reading habits might define rate of reading in terms of a compound unit such as $\frac{glances}{line}$ (glances per line) or, possibly, $\frac{words}{glance}$ (words per glance).

Such units often have to be used for some purposes, but they are of limited usefulness and validity. In the example just used, we might observe that lines of print vary in length and size of type, and to compare performances under different reading conditions one would need to make allowances for these differences. As far as possible all measurements are expressed in terms of a very few highly standardized units. For general purposes, in Great Britain, we reduce all our working to the units of the foot, pound and second, bringing in other units, such as money, only when absolutely necessary. For purposes of expressing measurements and constants in the physical sciences, the standard units are the centimetre, gramme and second (the c.g.s. system), but the centimetre and gramme are quite small quantities for many measurements, and, particularly with engineers, the larger units of the metre, kilogramme and second (the m.k.s. system) are in general use. Not all scientific measurements can be expressed in terms of these units only, and one further standard unit has to be introduced for electrical measurements.

AREA

The compound unit, which children probably meet first, is the unit of area. Area is, in itself, a single, simple concept: the amount of surface which a figure or a body has. Any standard area could be used as a unit, and one could say that the area of this page was equal to the area which could be covered by 80 postage stamps. It is much more useful, however, to relate the unit of area to the unit of length, and the usual unit of area is "the area covered by a square inch", that is, by a square each of whose sides is one inch in length. For larger areas the square foot or the acre may be used; in the metric system a square centimetre or an *are* are standard units (1 *are* = area of a square whose side is 10 metres long).

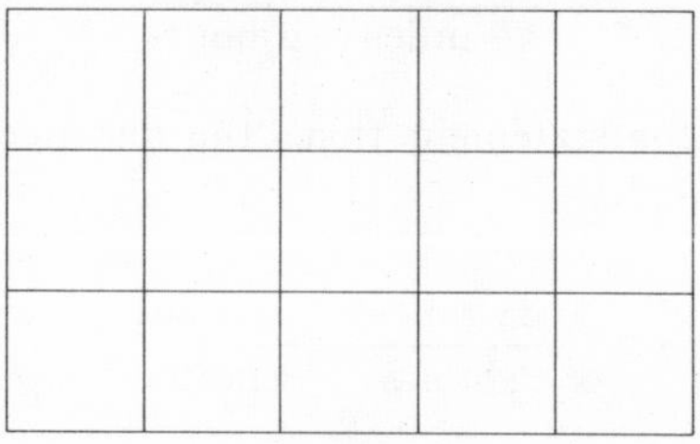

Fig. 6.1

In Fig. 6.1, each of the smaller portions is a square one centimetre high and one centimetre wide and it is called a "square centimetre".

The area of the figure is the number of square centimetres which fits into it. This number is obtained by counting the number of squares in each row and multiplying this by the number cf rows. There are five square centimetres in each row and three rows, giving

$$area = 3 \times 5 \text{ square centimetres}$$
$$= 15 \text{ square centimetres.}$$

Whatever the unit of area chosen, the finding of the area of a figure is simply the counting of the number of units of area it contains. This is straightforward enough, but with awkwardly-shaped areas the actual job of counting squares is not always simple. In some cases it is easier to cut up a figure and rearrange the parts to simplify the counting.

For instance, a triangle

can be cut into three parts

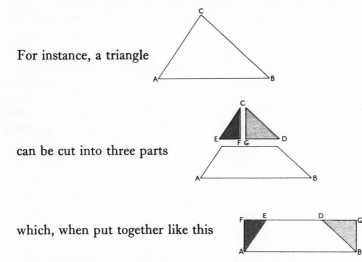

which, when put together like this

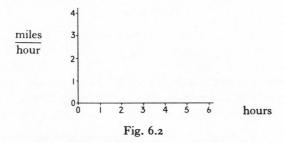

form a rectangle whose area may be calculated very easily.

As long as we are concerned only with the simple task of finding areas, this is all that need be said about the task, but once we have progressed beyond the lower forms of a secondary school and have begun to let lengths represent other quantities, we need to think a little more carefully about the nature of area. We notice, to begin with, that the area of a rectangle (3 cm) wide and (5 cm) long is 15 square centimetres. If we form the product

$$(3 \text{ cm}) \times (5 \text{ cm})$$

we obtain $3 \times 5 \times \text{cm} \times \text{cm}$ or 15 cm^2. A rule for finding the area of a rectangle is to multiply together length and width and interpret centimetre $\times$ centimetre, or cm^2, as "square centimetres". The importance of this step becomes apparent when, for instance, we draw a graph *representing* "time" horizontally and "speed" vertically (Fig. 6.2).

$$\frac{\text{miles}}{\text{hour}}$$

Fig. 6.2

If such a graph is used to represent a journey at $3 \dfrac{\text{miles}}{\text{hour}}$ for 5 hours, this will give a simple rectangle (Fig. 6.3).

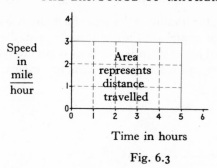

Fig. 6.3

We see that the number of squares per row is equal to the number of hours represented and the number of rows represents the number of miles per hour, so the area *represents* $\left(3\dfrac{\text{miles}}{\text{hour}}\right) \times (5 \text{ hours})$ or 15 miles. Thus, the area under a "velocity-time" graph *represents* the *distance* travelled.

As soon as height and width are used to represent other quantities we must be prepared to accept a form of statement

$$\text{unit of area} = (\text{unit of height}) \times (\text{unit of width})$$

for without such a form of the definition for a unit of area, the progress to the use of integral calculus would not be possible.

EXAMPLE

Fig. 6.4 shows the speed at which a man walked during a period of just over seven hours while on holiday. He spent half an hour for lunch. Estimate how far he walked.

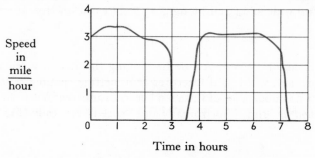

Fig. 6.4

Velocity-time chart of a seven-hour walk with half an hour break for lunch.

About $18\frac{1}{2}$ square centimetres are included under the graph, and each centimetre horizontally represents one hour and each centimetre vertically represents one mile/hour, so that each square centimetre, which has an area of 1 cm $\times$ 1 cm or 1 cm², represents $1\dfrac{\text{mile}}{\text{hour}} \times 1$ hour. If one walks at one mile per hour for one hour the distance travelled will be one mile, so 1 cm² of area represents 1 mile. The $18\frac{1}{2}$ cm² will, therefore, represent a total journey of about $18\frac{1}{2}$ miles.

MAPS

The form of representation met with every day in the use of maps, plans and charts is a simple matter when restricted areas are drawn to scale. Difficulties arise in the representation of the whole world, where a spherical surface is represented on a plane.

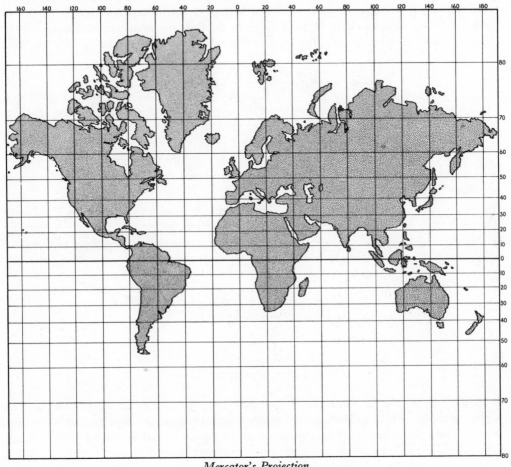

Mercator's Projection
Shapes preserved, areas distorted

Fig. 6.5

Some distortion in this representation is inevitable and it is only the form of the distortion which is under control. For some purposes shapes are important, and in maps such as Mercator's (Fig. 6.5) shapes are retained, locally, by using at every point equal horizontal and vertical scales. This leads to a very considerable distortion of size, so that in latitude 60°

$$\text{vertical scale} = 2 \times \text{equatorial scale}$$
$$\text{horizontal scale} = 2 \times \text{equatorial scale}$$
$$\text{Area} = 2 \times 2 = 4 \times \text{area scale at equator.}$$

Thus, Mercator represents a spherical surface on a plane and retains shapes locally undistorted at the expense of distortion of the size of different localities, the distortion of areas increasing as distance from the equator increases, and in latitude 60°N or S this distortion of area is four times too big.

For some purposes, such as comparisons of population or distribution of crops, it is more important to preserve areas undistorted than it is to retain the precise shapes of countries. Various maps have been devised to do this; for instance, Mollweide's map (Fig. 6.6) is an equal-area map, preserving area relations at the expense of shapes. This

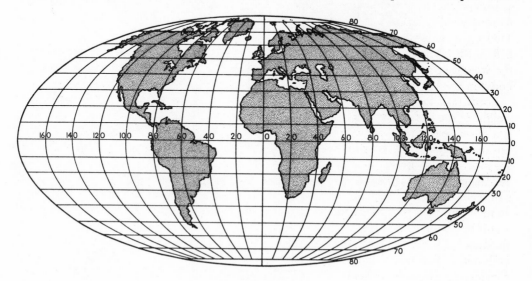

Fig. 6.6

Mollweide's Projection
Areas preserved, shapes distorted

is done by decreasing the vertical scale and increasing the horizontal scale as we move to higher latitudes. Thus, in latitude 60°, north–south distances are represented by lengths 0·7727 times the corresponding distances at the equator, and east–west distances are represented by lengths which are 1·294 times corresponding distances at the equator.

Since area has been defined as the product, length × breadth,

$$
\begin{aligned}
\text{Area represented} &= (0\text{·}7727 \times \text{N–S distance}) \times (1\text{·}294 \times \text{E–W distance}) \\
&= 0\text{·}7727 \times 1\text{·}294 \times (\text{N–S distance}) \times (\text{E–W distance}) \\
&= \qquad 1 \qquad \times \text{area on globe} \\
&= \text{area on globe}
\end{aligned}
$$

WEIGHT AND MASS

In the remaining portion of this chapter, the abbreviation for "pound" will be written Lb when it stands for "pound-weight" and lb when it means "pound-mass". The distinction between weight and mass was made clear in the seventeenth century by Sir Isaac Newton, but by this time the word *pound* had been in use for a thousand years or more and Newton coined no other word to replace it as the unit of weight, so that "pound" could be retained, without ambiguity, as a unit of mass. In everyday language we are not worried very much by having only one word to describe two different quantities, but it is essential that they are easily distinguishable when used in expressing precise relationships in properly-defined systems of units. A pound-mass is a unit used for describing the amount of matter in a body and it depends, ultimately, only upon the total number of atoms in the body. A pound-weight is a unit of force used for describing the force with which a body is pulled downwards in the Earth's gravitational field, and so it depends both on the mass of the body and on the strength of the gravitational field. A body would contain the same amount of matter whether it were on the Earth or the Moon, that is to say, mass is an invariant property of a body; but, as the gravitational field at the surface of the Moon is only about one sixth of that at the surface of the Earth, the weight of a body on the Moon would only be one sixth of the weight of the same body on the Earth.

Force may be measured directly by suspending a body from a spring balance. The weight of the body is the force which stretches the spring, and the amount of stretching is a measure of the force. The idea of force is simple to understand because, by picking up an object and holding it, we can feel our muscles supporting the weight. In the absence of any direct sensory appreciation, we have to form a concept of mass by abstracting some factor which is common to a variety of experiences. If a table-tennis ball were thrown at a window it would almost certainly bounce off without hurting the window, but if a golf ball were thrown at a window it would probably break the glass; a golf ball would stretch the spring of a spring balance more than a table-tennis ball; if the two balls were placed on a table and were blown at through drinking straws, the table-tennis ball would move off much more quickly than the golf ball. We arrive, after considering a number of such experiences, at the idea that a more massive body is harder to set in motion, but, once moving, is harder to stop than a less massive body, and that equal forces acting on the bodies will not have equal effects. Newton defined mass precisely by saying that, if a body is free to move, a force acting on it will cause it to accelerate. The quotient, $\dfrac{\text{force}}{\text{acceleration}}$, he defined as the "mass" of the body. A particular and especially important case is that of a body which is released at some height above the ground and allowed to fall freely. Its weight is the force which acts downwards on the body, causing it to fall with an acceleration due to gravity, which is usually called g. It is an experimental observation that, in the absence of air resistance, bodies fall with an acceleration of $32 \cdot 2 \dfrac{\text{ft}}{\text{sec}^2}$ in England. A body of weight w will have a mass, m, such that

$$w = m.g$$

When I buy a pound of apples, the weight of the apples is 1 pound-weight (written 1 Lb) and its mass is 1 pound-mass (written 1 lb). From the above equation we have

$$1 \text{ Lb} = 1 \text{ lb} \times g = 1 \text{ lb} \times 32 \cdot 2 \, \frac{\text{ft}}{(\text{sec})^2}$$

$$\text{or} \quad 1 \text{ Lb} = \frac{32 \cdot 2 \text{ lb ft}}{(\text{sec})^2}$$

A counsel of perfection requires that whenever we use the pound as a unit of weight, or of force, we refer to the "pound-weight", leaving the word "pound", standing alone, or the "pound-mass", for the unit of mass. Unfortunately, some text-books which stress this usage themselves use "foot pound" as the unit of work instead of "foot pound-weight", and, although correct, a sentence which begins "A body of weight 28 pound-weight . . ." is clumsy and somewhat tautological. The best convention I have come across, making the distinction between the two units quite clear with the minimum of writing and fuss, is that already described, where Lb means *pound-weight* and lb means *pound-mass*. This is incorporated in the "Stroud" system of units which is quite well known and those who consistently use it include the Applied Mechanics Department of the Royal Naval College, Greenwich. Unfortunately, neither the "Stroud" system nor any other system is used universally, and many clumsy and sometimes ambiguous systems are still in use.

PRODUCTS OF SIMPLE UNITS

(*a*) *Area* is the simplest of the quantities for which the unit is the product of two units multiplied together. The unit, which is called the *square inch*, is written in², where

$$1 \text{ in}^2 = 1 \text{ in.} \times 1 \text{ in.}$$

(*b*) *Labour*. Many units in everyday use are the *products* of other units. If 20 men in a factory each work for 40 hours, the amount of work to be paid for is obtained by multiplying these two quantities:

$$20 \text{ men} \times 40 \text{ hours} = 800 \text{ man-hours.}$$

The *man-hour* is a unit of work in everyday use.

(*c*) *Units of Electricity*. The power used by electric fires or cookers is measured in kilowatts (kW). If a cooker using 2 kW of electricity is kept switched on for 3 hours, the number of units of electricity used is

$$2 \text{ kilowatts} \times 3 \text{ hours} = 6 \text{ kilowatt-hours}$$
$$\text{or} \qquad 2 \text{ kW} \quad \times 3 \text{ h} \quad = 6 \text{ kWh.}$$

A *kilowatt-hour* is the unit of electricity recorded on the meter and it is the measure of the electrical consumption paid for.

(*d*) *Energy*. If a crane lifts a weight of 60 Lb through 20 feet, the energy expended is

$$20 \text{ ft} \times 60 \text{ Lb} = 1200 \text{ ft Lb.}$$

The foot-pound wt. (ft Lb) is the unit of energy for mechanical work.

RATES

Whenever the word "per" appears in an expression containing units it is an indication that the compound unit being used is a rate and is of the nature of one unit divided by another.

(a) *Speed*. If a train travels at a uniform speed and goes 60 miles in one hour its speed is

$$\frac{60 \text{ miles}}{1 \text{ hour}} \quad \text{or} \quad 60 \frac{\text{mile}}{\text{hour}}$$

The unit of speed is the rate, $\frac{\text{mile}}{\text{hour}}$. This is read as "miles per hour", and for the convenience of printers and with due regard to the appearance of a printed page, it is usually printed as mile/hr. As with other rates, it is advisable to keep to the fractional form when the unit is being used in the course of calculations.

An alternative unit for speed, involving a smaller distance travelled and a shorter time, is ft/sec (read as feet per second). If a body moves 20 ft in 5 seconds, its speed will be given by

$$\text{speed} = \frac{20 \text{ ft}}{5 \text{ sec}} = \frac{\overset{4}{\cancel{20}} \text{ ft}}{\underset{1}{\cancel{5}} \text{ sec}} = 4 \frac{\text{ft}}{\text{sec}}$$

(b) *Cost*. If 2s. 4d. is charged for 7 lb of potatoes, the cost of potatoes is

$$\text{cost} = \frac{28 \text{d.}}{7 \text{ lb}} = \frac{\overset{4}{\cancel{28}} \text{d.}}{\underset{1}{\cancel{7}} \text{ lb}} = 4 \frac{\text{d.}}{\text{lb}}$$

which is read as fourpence per pound and written 4d. /lb.

(c) *Density*. The mass of 1 cubic foot of water is 62·5 lb. The density of water is given by

$$\text{density} = \frac{62 \cdot 5 \text{ lb}}{1 \text{ ft}^3} = 62 \cdot 5 \frac{\text{lb}}{\text{ft}^3}$$

where $\frac{\text{lb}}{\text{ft}^3}$, read as pounds per cubic foot and usually printed as lb/ft³, is the unit of density in the British system of weights and measures.

Using the metric system, a cubic centimetre of lead has a mass equal to 11·3 gramme. The density of lead is 11·3 g/cm³.

(d) *Silk Thread*. A healthy silkworm can be expected, on an average, to produce 450 metres of silk thread. A measure of the thickness of the thread can be made by weighing the cocoon. This led to a method of expressing thicknesses of threads which has also been applied to synthetic threads such as nylon. When the unit was established, a small French weight of $\frac{1}{20}$ gramme, the denier, was in use, and cocoons were weighed in deniers. The unit now used for silk and nylon is the denier, defined as

$$1 \text{ denier} = \frac{\frac{1}{20} \text{ gramme}}{450 \text{ metre}} = \frac{1}{9000} \frac{\text{g}}{\text{m}}$$

so that 15-denier stockings are woven from thread of a thickness such that

$$15 \text{ deniers} = \frac{15}{9000} \frac{\text{g}}{\text{m}} = \frac{1}{600} \frac{\text{g}}{\text{m}}$$

which can be read as "15-denier thread has a thickness such that 600 metres of thread will have a mass of one gramme" or "the density of 15-denier thread is one sixhundredth of a gramme per metre".

(e) *Density of Population.* This could be measured either by counting the number of people who live in an acre or the number per square mile, and could be expressed in units people/acre or people/mile^2.

A book of reference gives the density of population in 1926 for various countries as

> Cultivated areas of Egypt, 1047 people/mile^2
> England and Wales,   668 people/mile^2
> Germany,   350 people/mile^2
> India,   177 people/mile^2.

Units such as these are quite often met with in geography books but some effort is required to appreciate their significance in human terms. It is bad arithmetic as well as bad geography to work in units which convey only a vague impression. An exercise which any thoughtful person interested in social problems should carry out, sometime, would be to take a block of two or three acres with a number of streets, count the number of houses and flats in the area, take samples of the number of people living in each house, measure the total area included in the survey (e.g. the whole area inside the broken line in Fig. 6.7) and calculate the density of population.

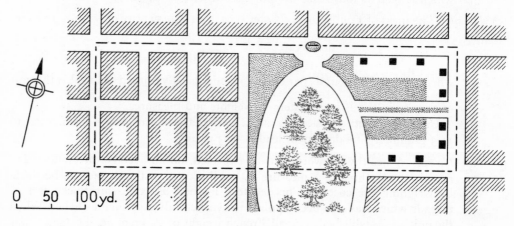

Fig. 6.7

If this exercise is carried out in the closer-packed part of a town, in a suburban area and in a rural area, some concept of the meaning of the units population/acre or population/mile^2 will be obtained.

Working with Compound Units

A contractor with 25 men who each work a 40-hour week has available 25 × 40 man-hours per week, that is, 1000 man-hours per week.

$$\text{Available labour} = 1000 \, \frac{\text{man-hr}}{\text{week}}$$

This is the sort of quantity which will be used in calculations which have to be made when estimating building costs, time required to complete various stages of construction where different groups of people are required for clearing a site, digging foundations, putting in concrete, laying bricks, etc.

If each man is paid 9/– for each working hour, then

$$\text{rate of pay} = \frac{9\text{s.}}{\text{man-hr}}$$

$$\text{labour force} = \frac{1000 \text{ man-hr}}{\text{week}}$$

$$\text{labour costs} = \frac{1000 \text{ man-hr}}{\text{week}} \times \frac{9\text{s.}}{\text{man-hr}}$$

$$= \frac{9000\text{s.}}{\text{week}} = \frac{\pounds 450}{\text{week}}$$

This calculation amounts simply to saying that the total wages are equal to the amount of work paid for multiplied by the rate of pay, calculated on a weekly basis. Notice that when the same unit appears both in the numerator and the denominator, it may be cancelled by a procedure akin to that of cancelling ordinary fractions. If used consistently, the units look after themselves.

The cost of 7 yards of material at 8/– per yard is a simple calculation which would usually be done mentally, but, for practice purposes, we can set it out in the following way:

$$\text{price} = \frac{8\text{s.}}{\text{yard}}$$

$$\text{amount bought} = 7 \text{ yd}$$

$$\text{total cost} = \frac{8\text{s.}}{\text{yd}} \times 7 \text{ yd}$$

$$= 56\text{s.}$$

$$= \pounds 2 \ 16\text{s. od.}$$

where, in this case, the unit of length can be cancelled, leaving only the unit of money, the shillings, in the answer.

The unit of *power* is a slightly more complex unit. Power is defined as the rate of doing work, so it takes the form *work done per second*. Work is itself measured in compound units, being equal to a force multiplied by a distance, and is expressed in ft Lb or ft Tons.

The common unit of power is the *horsepower* which is the rate of working of 550 ft Lb of work per second, that is,

$$1 \text{ h.p.} = \frac{550 \text{ ft Lb}}{\text{sec}}$$

To calculate the power required for a lift which raises a load of 3 Tons (Ton means ton-weight) through 100 feet in 15 seconds, we proceed as follows:

$$\text{Power required} = \frac{100 \text{ ft} \times 3 \text{ Ton}}{15 \text{ sec}}$$

$$= \frac{300}{15} \frac{\text{ft Ton}}{\text{sec}}$$

$$= 20 \frac{\text{ft Ton}}{\text{sec}}$$

Since 1 Ton = 2240 Lb, this quantity may be expressed in ft Lb/sec, giving

$$\text{Power required} = 44{,}800 \frac{\text{ft Lb}}{\text{sec}}$$

but

$$1 \text{ h.p.} = 550 \frac{\text{ft Lb}}{\text{sec}}$$

so that the ratio

$$\frac{\text{power required}}{1 \text{ h.p.}} = \frac{44{,}800 \frac{\text{ft Lb}}{\text{sec}}}{550 \frac{\text{ft Lb}}{\text{sec}}}$$

$$= \frac{44800}{550}$$ (The units are the same in numerator and denominator and may be cancelled.)

$$= \frac{81 \cdot 45}{1}$$

giving

$$\text{power required} = 81 \cdot 45 \text{ h.p.}$$

CHANGE OF UNITS

A note-book which costs 2 shillings could also be described as costing 24 pennies. Such a change of units presents few difficulties, and there is no need to use any elaborate procedure for this conversion. Some complicated formulae need very careful handling to convert them from one system of units to another, and it is convenient to use a very simple example to explain a system of conversion which is particularly helpful with the more difficult compound quantities.

In terms of value, (1 shilling) and (12 pence) are equal and interchangeable quantities. When two quantities are *equal* their *ratio* is unity. Thus:

$$\frac{1 \text{ shilling}}{12 \text{ pence}} = 1 \quad \text{and} \quad \frac{12 \text{ pence}}{1 \text{ shilling}} = 1$$

This is the "pure number", *one*, and not a quantity. Any number or quantity may be multiplied or divided by *one* without altering it. Thus, if the price, 2 shillings per book, is multiplied by the second of the two unit ratios which express the relation between shillings and pence:

$$\frac{2\text{s.}}{\text{book}} \times \frac{12\text{d.}}{1\text{s.}}$$

the s. (shillings) cancels top and bottom, leaving

$$\frac{2 \times \text{12d.}}{\text{book}}$$

or 24 pence per book.

Any change of units can be expressed in the form of a unit ratio. The equality 1 *inch* = 2·54 *cm* can be expressed in either of the forms

$$\frac{\text{1 in.}}{\text{2·54 cm}} = 1 \text{ or } \frac{\text{2·54 cm}}{\text{1 in.}} = 1$$

and so any quantity may be multiplied by 1 in./2·54 cm or by 2·54 cm/1 in. without altering its value. Unit ratios such as these are, therefore, *conversion factors* which may be used for the purpose of changing units. The ratios will be placed in brackets, so that any ratio such as

$$\left\{\frac{\text{60 min}}{\text{hour}}\right\}, \ \left\{\frac{\text{hour}}{\text{60 min}}\right\}, \ \left\{\frac{\text{metre}}{\text{3·28 ft}}\right\}, \ \left\{\frac{\text{kilowatt}}{\text{1·34 h.p.}}\right\}, \ \left\{\frac{\text{6·25 gal}}{\text{ft}^3}\right\}$$

is equal to the "pure number" *one* and may be used as a conversion factor.

EXAMPLES

Water is flowing at the rate of 1000 *cubic feet an hour. Express this in gallons per minute.*

We begin by writing the rate of flow in the form

$$\text{Rate of flow} = \frac{\text{1000 ft}^3}{\text{hour}}$$

If this is multiplied by the unit conversion factor $\dfrac{\text{hour}}{\text{60 min}}$, the *hour* will cancel top and

bottom, but since we have only multiplied by the number *one*, the actual quantity we are calculating, the rate of flow, will remain unaltered. We can then multiply by the conversion factor for changing cubic feet to gallons, and the whole calculation looks like this:

$$\text{Rate of flow} = \frac{\text{1000 } \cancel{\text{ft}^3}}{\cancel{\text{hour}}} \times \left\{\frac{\cancel{\text{hour}}}{\text{60 min}}\right\} \times \left\{\frac{\text{6·25 gal}}{\cancel{\text{ft}^3}}\right\}$$

$$= \frac{\text{6250 gal}}{\text{60 min}}$$

$$= 104\text{·}1 \text{ gal/min}$$

which is read as 104·1 gallons per minute.

Every conversion factor has an inverse; the relation between hours and minutes may be expressed either as

$$\left\{\frac{\text{60 min}}{\text{hour}}\right\} = 1 \text{ or } \left\{\frac{\text{hour}}{\text{60 min}}\right\} = 1$$

and for each calculation we have to decide which form is required. This is a very simple decision to make, since the function of the conversion factor is to cancel away the unit from which we wish to convert. In the example given, the rate of flow, $\dfrac{\text{1000 ft}^3}{\text{hour}}$, had the unit *hour* at the bottom so we choose the form of the conversion factor which has *hour* at the top.

Material costs 8 shillings a yard. Express this in francs per metre, given that £1 = 14 francs and 1 yard = 0·9144 metre.

The price, 8 shillings per yard, may be written in the form

$$\text{price} = \frac{8\text{s.}}{\text{yd}}$$

so for these units to be cancelled, the conversion factors must have the shillings below the line and the yards above the line. Choosing them in this way the calculation takes the form

$$\text{price} = \frac{8\text{s.}}{\text{yd}} \times \left\{ \frac{14\ \text{fr}}{20\text{s.}} \right\} \times \left\{ \frac{1\ \text{yd}}{0\cdot9144\ \text{m}} \right\}$$

$$= \frac{8 \times 14}{20 \times 0\cdot9144}\ \frac{\text{fr}}{\text{m}}$$

$$= 6\cdot12\ \text{fr/metre.}$$

Petrol costs 5 shillings per gallon. Express this in marks per litre, given that £1 = 11·6 marks and 1 gallon = 4·456 litres.

$$\text{price} = \frac{5\text{s.}}{\text{gal}} \times \left\{ \frac{11\cdot6\ \text{mk}}{20\text{s.}} \right\} \times \left\{ \frac{\text{gal}}{4\cdot546\ \text{l}} \right\}$$

$$= \frac{11\cdot6}{18\cdot2}\ \frac{\text{mk}}{\text{l}}$$

$$= 0\cdot64\ \text{mark/litre.}$$

Before travelling abroad a few preliminary calculations need to be made. Usually the answers need not be calculated to any great degree of accuracy, but one needs to have a fair idea of costs and the time likely to be taken over journeys. Suppose my car does about 35 miles to the gallon and I usually average about 28 miles per hour for cross-country journeys and I intend to motor from Boulogne to St. Nazaire, I can find from a map that

Boulogne   –   Rouen = 180 km

Rouen   –   Alençon = 150 km

Alençon   –   Rennes = 140 km

Rennes – St. Nazaire = 100 km

Work out the approximate cost, in English money, of the motor spirit required and the time likely to be taken for the journey.

The reader is left to find the cost of petrol in France, the current rate of exchange and the conversion factors for the units of distance and capacity.

ENERGY UNITS

In any book of mathematical tables or any text-book on Mechanics, the following statements will be found:

1 British thermal unit (B.t.u.) = 778 ft Lb

1 kilowatt-hour (kWh) = 2655000 ft Lb.

These simple statements are of very great importance for two different reasons. The first is that they form a link between three sets of units originally defined independently of one another, and the other reason is that they throw light upon industrial and social problems, national aspirations and the problems facing countries concerned with standards of living and industrial development.

The British thermal unit is a unit of heat. It is the heat required to raise one pound (lb) of water through 1° Fahrenheit.

The foot-pound (ft Lb) is a unit of mechanical work and is the work done in raising one pound-weight (Lb) vertically upwards through 1 ft.

The kilowatt-hour (kWh) is a unit of energy, or work, and is the "unit of electricity" recorded on domestic electricity meters.

It is a matter of general knowledge that when coal is burned in a steam engine, mechanical work can be done by the engine. The first relation given above is the numerical one linking the amount of heat generated and the amount of mechanical work it can do. With electric kettles and electric motors it is also common knowledge that electrical energy can be converted into either heat energy or mechanical energy, and the second of the equations gives the numerical relation between electrical energy and mechanical energy.

By means of these relationships, units of temperature and heat are brought into the system of units defined by the legal pound-mass, foot and second. In the metric system a similar equation brings the degree centigrade into the centimetre, gramme, second system. Electrical units are also brought into the system of units defined by standards of length, mass and time.

In an ordinary domestic electricity supply the voltage is usually 230 or 240 volts (V). The current flowing through the apparatus is measured in amperes (A). An electric kettle holding a quart may consume current at the rate of 10 amperes, so that the rate at which energy is being used is 240 volts *times* 10 amperes, or 2400 watts (W). If electricity is consumed at this rate for one hour, the total energy consumption would be 2400 watt-hours or 2·4 kilowatt-hours (kWh) or 2·4 "units of electricity".

An electric drill is rated at 0·95 A at 240 V; the rate at which it uses electricity is

$$0.95 \text{ A} \times 240 \text{ V} = 228 \text{ W}.$$

In an hour it would use 228 watt-hours of electricity or 0·228 kilowatt-hour. One kWh costs about a penny, so the electric drill would use about a farthing-worth of electricity in an hour. The amount of mechanical work equivalent to 0·228 kWh is 0·228 × 2655000 ft Lb. This is 605,000 ft Lb of work for about a farthing.

The units which are most commonly met with in electricity are the

> *ohm* (Ω) which is the unit of resistance
> *volt* (V) which is the unit of electromotive force
> *ampere* (A) which is the unit of current
> *watt* (W) which is the unit of power.

These are not independent units and they are connected by the equations

$$A = \frac{V}{\Omega} \quad \text{or} \quad V = A \times \Omega$$

---

* One English penny approximately equals one U.S. penny, and a farthing is ¼ of a penny.

and
$$W = V \times A = \frac{V^2}{\Omega}$$

and are related to the ft, lb, sec units by the equation
$$W = 2655 \, \frac{\text{ft Lb}}{\text{hr}}$$

Thus, although there are these four units in common use, only one of them can be defined independently. In addition to the standard units of length, mass and time, the whole subject of electrical measurement involves the introduction of only one further arbitrarily chosen unit.

Muscle Power. In a casual sort of way we know that electricity can be used to produce mechanical work and that steam engines can convert the heat of burning coal into mechanical energy. We know that it is easier to get a crane to lift a sack of coal than to struggle to lift it by muscle power. We rarely stop to work out just how much work can be expected from our muscles and how this compares with other forms of energy. The calculations which follow help us to think precisely about these things, and the numerical relationships reveal some surprising facts.

Just how much work is it reasonable to expect a fit man to be able to do and what is it worth? If we think of a navvy at work with a 30 pound sledge-hammer we should, I think, agree that it is asking about as much as a fit man could be expected to do if he were to lift the sledge-hammer to shoulder height and let it fall from there with a regular rhythm, striking one blow every six seconds, and to keep up this rate of working for an hour. It would not be over-generous to let him have four two-minute rests in the hour. Under these conditions, how much work would he do?

Each blow involves raising the 30 pound hammer through 5 feet.

Work done per blow = 150 ft Lb.

He works at the rate of one blow per 6 seconds or 10 blows per minute, so that:

Work done per minute = 1500 ft Lb.

He works for an hour, less 8 minutes of rest periods, so he works for 52 minutes, giving:

Total work done = 52 × 1500 ft Lb
= 78,000 ft Lb of work.

It seems reasonable to take this as somewhere about the limit of human output of mechanical work in an hour.

After working as hard as that it would not be unnatural for the man to stop for a while and have a tea-break. We can picture him boiling up half a pint of water (Fig. 6.8) and

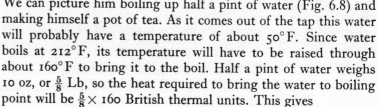

making himself a pot of tea. As it comes out of the tap this water will probably have a temperature of about 50°F. Since water boils at 212°F, its temperature will have to be raised through about 160°F to bring it to the boil. Half a pint of water weighs 10 oz, or $\frac{5}{8}$ Lb, so the heat required to bring the water to boiling point will be $\frac{5}{8} \times 160$ British thermal units. This gives

Energy used in boiling water = 100 B.t.u.

Fig. 6.8

From the equation at the beginning of this section, 1 B.t.u.$=778$ ft Lb, we see that

$$\text{Energy needed to raise } \tfrac{1}{2} \text{ pt} \atop \text{of water to boiling point} = 77,800 \text{ ft Lb.}$$

In terms of energy we can, therefore, say that about the limit of human energy output in one hour is just about the same as the energy needed to bring half a pint of water to the boil.

In some areas of Great Britain, at the time of writing, the charge for electricity is $5\tfrac{1}{2}$d. per unit for the first hundred units used in three months and 1d. a unit for the rest.

$$1 \text{ unit} = 1 \text{ kWh} = 2,655,000 \text{ ft Lb}$$

From this we see that, at the rate at which energy can be bought from electricity undertakings, the value of the mechanical energy which a man can do in an hour, or the heat energy required to boil half a pint of water is $\frac{78000}{2655000}$ of a penny, or just less than a thirtieth of a penny.

No working men are called upon to keep up this rate of working, but the calculation shows that in the economics of manual labour, a wage of 5s. an hour is justified if the pay is for 4s. $11\tfrac{1}{2}$d. worth of skill and less than a halfpenny for work done by the "sweat of the brow". If instead of using the price of electricity we had used prices of gas or petrol, we should have arrived at very much the same monetary valuation of mechanical energy.*

With these calculations in mind we can begin to think more rationally about standards of living, capital investments and the problems besetting countries which have not developed their power production. We remember from the stories of our grandparents, that two generations ago wages were pitifully low. When most labouring was done by muscle power the output was inevitably very small compared with that possible with even modest mechanical aids and it was very expensive, even at the low wages paid in those days.

Today, if you see a labourer working hard at a job where mechanical aids could be introduced, the appropriate comment ought to be: "What an extravagant employer, paying for muscle power at the rate of 5s. an hour (or 150s. per kWh) when he could get it done at 1d. per kWh by using electrical power." Such a comment is quite appropriate in England, where few districts are not supplied with power from the grid and no district is far enough from a petrol pump to make the use of an internal combustion or diesel engine difficult.

If, however, one turns to such places as Ghana, Nigeria or India there is a very different situation. In each of these countries power stations are hundreds of miles apart and millions of pounds will have to be invested in power stations and transmission lines to bring electric power to even a small fraction of the working population; oil fuels are not readily available.† The working populations cannot compete with those of more mechanized countries and so cannot raise the money for the capital expenditure involved.

---

† Much capital investment in internal combustion engines, diesels and oil-fired equipment is required initially, and until such equipment is available a transport and storage organization making oil fuels *locally* accessible will not develop. In the first-named place, such fuel is probably the most easily transported and most flexible source of power.

* See pages 25–27 regarding English monetary units. Briefly, one English penny (1d.) approximately equals one U.S. cent.

The only possible way to raise the standard of living in these countries is for countries which have achieved power production to invest capital in those which have not. But if the undeveloped countries become industrialized, will not their manufactured goods, produced by low-paid factory labour, swamp those of the older countries with high standards of living? This is a fear that is often expressed; but some economists, on the contrary, point out that the industrialization of a country leads it to import, as well as to export, far more. To go further into this is not possible here; what one can say with certainty is that the power-hungry countries of the world are determined to remedy their situation, and some may well resort to force, in sheer desperation. This will not produce their power stations, but poverty and rational behaviour are not always to be expected to go hand in hand. A study of foot-pound, kilowatt and horsepower will help one to understand the belligerent reaction of Egypt when she felt thwarted over the Aswan dam power project and will help to an assessment of the needs of the power-hungry countries.

BUYING ENERGY

From the example already worked out about the navvy and the cup of tea, it will be obvious that heating uses up energy extravagantly. The various means of converting stored energy into mechanical energy vary in their efficiency, energy being lost in the conversion process mainly in the form of heat. A petrol engine loses energy because much heat is generated, and an elaborate cooling system has to be incorporated to dispose of the unwanted heat. A high proportion of the energy in coal is wasted in dissipated heat which goes up the chimney or is lost at the surface of the boiler. The human body is kept at a temperature usually much above that of the surrounding atmosphere, and energy is being lost all the time in the form of heat transferred from the surface of the skin to the air. In addition, various other losses are inevitable. A motor car engine has auxiliary components such as an oil pump for keeping moving parts lubricated under pressure, and a dynamo for generating electric current; the human body has internal muscular activity to keep the heart pumping supplies of manifold ingredients to all parts of the body via the blood stream. The efficiency of conversion of stored energy into mechanical energy by machines, motors and living creatures varies considerably. An electric motor runs at a cooler temperature than a petrol engine, a steam engine or the bodies of men, horses or bullocks, and is very economical, but, as against this, vast quantities of energy are lost up the chimneys of power stations in generating electricity. In discussing the cost of buying the raw material of energy it must, therefore, be borne in mind that much is irretrievably lost, dissipated into the atmosphere through surface radiation and convection.

In measuring energy the metric unit, the *calorie*, is usually used. The *calorie* is defined as the heat required to raise 1 gramme of water through 1°C. The relation between the British unit and the metric unit is

$$1 \text{ B.t.u.} = 252 \text{ calories.}$$

The calorie is a very small unit and for many purposes a unit 1000 times as big is used. This is the heat required to raise 1 kilogramme of water through 1°C. Care is needed in distinguishing between the calorie taught in Physics lessons and the Calorie used in Domestic Science lessons and Diet-tables. The distinction made in all carefully written science books is that the large Calorie is spelt with a capital C and the small calorie with a lower case c. Thus,

$$1 \text{ Calorie} = 1000 \text{ calories}$$

but unfortunately many women's magazines which include articles about cookery refuse to take the trouble to make this distinction clear to their printers. To link the calorie and Calorie with the mechanical unit, we have

$$1 \text{ calorie} = 3 \cdot 09 \text{ ft Lb}$$
$$1 \text{ Calorie} = 3090 \text{ ft Lb.}$$

Most reference books quote the calorific content of materials in calories per kilogramme (kg) or Calories per kilogramme, and most of the materials we buy in England we know in cost per lb or per ton. Some arithmetic is, therefore, involved in converting from one system to another, and until we go over to the metric system it is necessary to be able to use the conversion factor obtained from

$$1 \text{ kg} = 2 \cdot 204 \text{ lb.}$$

I have, therefore, left the calorific content as obtained from various tables as they were quoted and I give the (1957) costs as they are usually met.

EXAMPLES

Compare the cost of buying energy in the following forms:

Bacon	6000 Calories per kilogramme	@	4/6d. per lb (63¢ per lb).
Bread	1200 Calories per lb	@	6d. per lb (7¢ per lb).
Butter	8000 Calories per kg	@	3/6d. per lb (49¢ per lb).
Cheese	4000 Calories per kg	@	2/6d. per lb (35¢ per lb).
Coal	5000 Calories per gramme	@	£8 os. od. per ton ($20.00 per ton).
Electricity	@ 1d. per kWh (about 1¢ per kWh)		
Flour	3640 Calories per kg	@	8d. per lb (9¢ per lb).
Gas	@ 1/9d. per Therm, where 1 Therm=100,000 B.t.u. (24¢ per Therm).		
Ham	3750 Calories per kg	@	4/6d. per lb (63¢ per lb).
Lard	8800 Calories per kg	@	1/8d. per lb (23¢ per lb).
Milk	700 Calories per kg	@	8d. per pint (1 gal of milk weighs 10¼ lb) (9¢ per pint).
Petrol	18,600 B.t.u. per lb	@	4/10d. per gal (specific gravity= 0·725) (67¢ per gal).
Potatoes	700 Calories per kg	@	3d. per lb (3¢ per lb).
Sugar	4100 Calories per kg	@	10d. per lb (11¢ per lb).

In working out the various costs it is not convenient to find the cost of the Calorie as this is a very small unit. The cost per 10,000 Calories is simpler.

In setting about the calculations we have to combine two rates—the cost, which may be given in shillings/lb, and the calorific value, which may be given in Calories/kg. Their combination will require the use of one or more conversion factors to bring them all to the same units, which may conveniently be pence per 10,000 Calories.

What is the cost of buying energy in the form of lard?

$$\text{Cost of lard} = \frac{20 \text{ d.}}{\text{lb}}$$

$$\text{Calorific value} = \frac{8800 \text{ Calories}}{\text{kg}} \text{ or } \frac{1 \text{ kg}}{8800 \text{ Cal}}$$

$$\text{Conversion factor} = \left\{ \frac{2 \cdot 204 \text{ lb}}{1 \text{ kg}} \right\} = 1$$

$$\text{Cost of energy} = \frac{20 \text{ d.}}{\text{lb}} \times \frac{1 \text{ kg}}{8800 \text{ Cal}} \times \left\{ \frac{2 \cdot 204 \text{ lb}}{1 \text{ kg}} \right\}$$

$$= \frac{2 \cdot 204 \text{ d.}}{440 \text{ Cal}}$$

$$= \frac{1 \cdot 002 \text{ d.}}{200 \text{ Cal}}$$

$$= \frac{50 \cdot 1 \text{ d.}}{10{,}000 \text{ Cal}}$$

The cost of buying energy in the form of lard is 4/2d. per 10,000 Calories.

For *coal* the information is that a kilogramme gives 5000 Calories,

$$\text{Cost of coal} = \frac{160 \text{ s.}}{\text{ton}}$$

$$\text{Calorific value} = \frac{5000 \text{ Cal}}{\text{kg}} \text{ or } \frac{1 \text{ kg}}{5000 \text{ Cal}}$$

$$\text{Conversion factors are } \left\{ \frac{1 \text{ ton}}{2240 \text{ lb}} \right\} \text{ and } \left\{ \frac{2 \cdot 204 \text{ lb}}{1 \text{ kg}} \right\}$$

$$\text{Cost of energy} = \frac{160 \text{ s.}}{1 \text{ ton}} \times \frac{1 \text{ kg}}{5000 \text{ Cal}} \times \left\{ \frac{1 \text{ ton}}{2240 \text{ lb}} \right\} \times \left\{ \frac{2 \cdot 204 \text{ lb}}{1 \text{ kg}} \right\}$$

$$= 0 \cdot 315 \frac{\text{s.}}{10{,}000 \text{ Cal}}$$

$$= 3 \cdot 78 \text{ d.}/10{,}000 \text{ Cal.}$$

The cost of buying energy in the form of coal is about 4d. per 10,000 Calories.

A glance down the list of foods shows that lard is about the cheapest of foods in terms of calorific value, and we have seen that it is twelve times as expensive as coal. Thus, even if we assume that the human body is as efficient as a good steam turbine in converting chemical energy into mechanical energy, we can see that, looked at from a purely mechanical point of view, muscle power cannot be an economical source of work. If the reader will work out the costs of the ordinary items of diet such as bread and butter, potatoes and meat, as sources of energy and compare them with the cost of electricity as a source of energy, it should become apparent that it is worth considering whether it is cheaper to sit restfully in a launderette, knitting and watching the electricity cope with the washing, or to put in the same amount of work at the wash-tub and then have to pay for this work at the prices charged for the food needed to satisfy the extra appetite the hard work at the wash-tub has given.

This, of course, is not the whole story. We do not eat food solely for its calorific value. The protein content is just as important. A minimum daily diet for healthy condition of tissues should contain a minimum of 80 grammes of proteins. Calorific requirements for men are roughly, for sedentary occupations, 3200 Calories, for moderately hard work, 3800 Calories, and for heavy work, 4500 Calories per day. For women the corresponding calorific requirements are less by as much as 700 Calories a day. These figures are necessarily approximate and are subject to wide variations for different living conditions. The *Encyclopaedia Britannica* gives the Calorific requirement of lumbermen in Sweden as 8000–9000 per day.

In this chapter examples of compound units have been selected from only a few fields of general interest. It is hoped that readers will explore other topics and bring many interesting relationships to light for themselves.

Since completing this chapter, the author's attention has been drawn to the Bill which came before the British Parliament in 1960 which stated that

"The yard or the metre shall be the unit of measurement of length and the pound or the kilogram shall be the unit of measurement of mass by reference to which any measurement involving a measurement of length or mass shall be made in the United Kingdom: and

(*a*) the yard shall be 0·9144 metre exactly;

(*b*) the pound shall be 0·45359237 kilogram exactly."

These definitions have come into use throughout the British Commonwealth, and the Federal Register in July 1959 made them effective in the U.S.A. for virtually all purposes.

International conferences now are establishing far greater uniformity and the International Organization for Standardization agrees that in addition to the units of force called dyne (dyn), newton (N) and poundal (pdl) which correspond to g cm s^{-2} kg m s^{-2} and lb ft s^{-2} respectively, there exist "technical" units of force called kilogram-force (kgf), pound-force (lbf) etc. which are the forces on bodies of mass 1 kg, 1 lb, etc. when these have standard acceleration defined exactly to be $g_n = 980·665$ cm s^{-2}.

The symbol lbf therefore replaces the symbol Lb in the preceding pages.

7

Algebra

MAN LONG ago acquired the ability to think about things and to make plans without actually being in the presence of the objects of his thoughts. To a large extent this has become possible because he has learnt to make use of a system of signs, symbols and signals which "represent" things to him. The simplest forms of representation include a large element in common with the thing they represent, such as models, pictures or imitative movements, and these grew into the primitive picture writings which contained such obvious characters as the ⟨image⟩ from the Egyptian hieroglyphics mentioned in Chapter 4 (page 41). On a par with picture writing are the onomatopoeic sounds such as "cuckoo" or "bubble". Once the idea of writing and of sounds to represent things was established, the "representation" of things developed naturally until today the symbol and the thing represented have no common element. The visual pattern which looks like *boy* has nothing in common with what the eye sees when we are actually looking at a boy, and there is nothing in the sound we make at the sight of the word "boy" which could remind us directly of any of the multifarious sounds which emanate from a boy.

The development of signs, symbols and signals has enabled mankind to evolve a complex society in which there can be detailed communication between different people and in which thinking has progressed remarkably as man has learnt to use his symbolism and signs to control and discipline and extend his trains of thought. Words and a grammar are essential for a language. Words vary from those which are specific, such as "Billy Bunter", which refers to one individual; "boy", which refers to a whole class whose members share a number of well-defined characteristics; "people", which refers to a much wider class sharing less well-defined characteristics, to words such as "thing" or "entity", which are devoid of specific meanings. Lest it be argued that "thing" refers to a class of objects which have some material existence, it should be pointed out that in common usage the word "thing" could well be used in a sentence such as "The thing that worries me is loneliness", wherein the word "thing" refers to an unsubstantial idea. It might, equally aptly, be used to refer to a "thing" such as the Eiffel Tower. The French, also, have a word, *machin*, as indefinite in its meaning as "thing".

Language consists of words used in accordance with a generally accepted convention which is codified into a grammar. For instance, "John sees James" and "James sees John" have different and quite distinct meanings and one does not imply the other; if John happens to be peeping through a keyhole, one sentence may be true and the other false.

A language that is unambiguous and simple is a prerequisite of systematic thought. The requirements are words and a grammar. Since there is a limit to the amount a person can carry in his mind at one time, any reduction in the space taken up by the expression of an idea is a gain in the effective span of comprehension. An "eyeful" is an inelegant but expressive word and it is useful in describing a quantity that can be taken in at a glance. For reasoning purposes a system of expressing in an "eyeful" the contents of a paragraph may be a contribution to clarity of thought. There is no reason why anything so devoid of meaning as "thing" should take up the space occupied by five letters or have to be translated into a quite different French word, with six letters. A single letter would serve just as well, and in either language x has no meaning that would detract from its generality.

There are many aids to assimilation: underlining, heavy type, illustration and diagrams. A pamphlet such as the *Highway Code* makes use of all these devices. The *Highway Code*, however, is specific and its intentions are limited; a study of the *Highway Code* would give no insight into railway signalling or procedure in traffic lanes at sea and international rules relating to navigation. It is, by its nature, limited in its usefulness. It is important to realize that there are very many modes of thought having a very wide application, and in practice we very rarely begin to think about a completely new problem that is not similar in some ways to related problems we have met before and found means of solving. Orderly thought involves relationships between ideas, some of which may be completely abstract, others of a general nature but not of universal application, and still others specifically related to particular objects. When describing very general laws it is of great advantage to be able to express them in abstract symbols which evoke no mental pictures. If this can be achieved, then no generality is lost in the expression of the thought. The more abstract the formulation and expression of a law, the wider its application; the more concrete the expression, the more restricted will be the field of usefulness.

Examples and analogies are sometimes unwisely used since they may introduce trains of thought which restrict the universality of general laws. However, in spite of this, the point may be illustrated by saying that a statement such as

$$\text{"If } x < y \text{ and } y < z \text{ then } x < z\text{"}$$

applies to sunspots, love, sentences, baldness, the number of vertebrae in eels, the consistency of jellies or the sizes of fig leaves, hurricanes or committees. The form of the statement itself is unbiased towards any particular context.

It is because of its abstract form that algebra is so extremely useful, for any statement that can be made about x, whatever x may be, is a statement which may, in the first place, be made about anything. Algebra may, therefore, be thought of as the most succinct form of language. As a form of language, it consists of grammatical sentences, implying that it must, at least, have nouns, verbs and a codified convention governing the expression of these items in sentences of unambiguous construction.

The Grammar of Algebra

It is essential to formulate every statement in algebra as a complete and "grammatical" sentence. The word "grammatical" was put in inverted commas because the grammar of algebra is a modification of the grammar of English and its rules are the rules of algebra.

VERBS

The verbs are

$=$ which is read "is equal to",
$>$ which is read "is greater than",
$<$ which is read "is less than".

These are occasionally supplemented by

$\equiv$ which is read "is identical with",

and in the algebra of classes by

$\in$ which is read "is a member of".

ALGEBRAIC EXPRESSIONS

A single letter such as x, or a number of letters connected by signs such as $+$ or $-$ etc., is an algebraic expression. Such an expression may be the subject or the object of the verb. Examples of algebraic expressions are x, $ax+b$, $(ax+b)(cy-d)$, etc.

Rules of Combination

In any systematic thinking, where more than one entity is concerned, combinations of "things" (by which, remember, we mean both concrete "things" and unsubstantial attributes) play an important role. It seems to be quite a general law that there are two distinct ways of combining things, and the various conventions of recording thought take account of these two modes of combination. In grammar, for example, there is the distinction between the simple conjunction *and*, and the disjunctions *or* and *but*. In arithmetic there is the distinction between *addition* and *multiplication*, in chemistry between *mixtures* and *compounds*, in biology between *sexual* and *asexual* reproduction.

PRODUCTS

A general convention for recording the product of two things is simple juxtaposition: ax means the product of a and x, Englishman means a person who is English and a man, FeS means the compound of iron (Fe) and sulphur (S). When clarity or the possibility of ambiguity requires some modification of this convention, a full-stop or a sign $\times$ or a conjunction "and" or the logical symbol $\cap$ may be placed between the two symbols or words. (24 means twenty-four, so we must write 2.4 or 2×4).

ax may be written $a.x$ or $a \times x$. FeS (iron sulphide).
"Englishman" may be expressed as "English and male" or English $\cap$ male.

SUMS

The sum of two quantities is denoted by the two words or symbols with a "$+$" between them; grammatically they enter into a sentence connected by "and", "or", "but", or some such word according to the context.

$a+x$, English or Welsh, Fe$+$S (the mixture of iron and sulphur).

The distinction between these two types of combination is obvious if we think of male and female, English and Welsh. The attributes English and male may be true of a single person, whereas English people are made up of male persons and female persons but no person shares both male and female attributes. Iron sulphide is a homogeneous substance, whereas a mixture of iron filings and flowers of sulphur, Fe + S, is composed of particles of iron and particles of sulphur.

The sentence, or equation,

$$(m+f)\,(e+w+s) = me+fe+mw+fw+ms+fs$$

could be read as indicating that either of the attributes, male or female, could be combined with any of the nationalities English, Welsh or Scots, giving the separate categories of Englishmen, Englishwomen, Welshmen, Welshwomen, Scotsmen or Scotswomen.

We could, equally, substitute numbers for the letters, say $m = 3, f = 5, e = 7, w = 11, s = 2$, giving the equation

$$(3+5)\,(7+11+2) = 3.7+5.7+3.11+5.11+3.2+5.2$$
$$8 \cdot 20 \quad = 21+35+33+55+6+10$$

The combination of qualities could be represented with the m or f separation vertically and the e or w or s horizontally.

m	me	mw	ms
f	fe	fw	fs
	e	w	s

BRACKETS
Brackets are used to indicate that the quantities inside the brackets are combined in such a way that so long as they remain together within brackets they must be treated as constituting a single entity. In the example above $(m+f)$ all the British males plus all the British females when united in this way may be thought of as the British people.

Rules of Algebra
The rules of algebra are simply formal expressions of everyday experience and common sense.

COMMUTATIVE LAWS

$a.b = b.a$ $(2 \times 3 = 3 \times 2)$
(A person who is male and English could, equally, be described as being English and male.)

$a+b = b+a$ $(2+3 = 3+2)$
(The English and Welsh together make up the same population as the Welsh and English.)
(A mixture of iron and sulphur is the same as a mixture of sulphur and iron.)

ASSOCIATIVE LAW

$$(a+b)+c=a+(b+c) \quad . \quad . \quad . \quad . \quad . \quad . \quad . \quad . \quad . \quad (1)$$

This being true we can agree to write either expression in the form $a+b+c$ without ambiguity. A numerical example of this is:

$$(2+3)+7=2+(3+7)=2+3+7$$

that is, $5 \quad +7=2+ \quad 10 \quad =2+3+7=12.$

The associative law is concerned with grouping. The statement (1), above, could be illustrated by the following statement in words, which gives a particular instance of the law:

The English and the Welsh, together with the Scots, make up the same set of people as the English together with the Welsh and the Scots. Thus, we arrive at the same population in both cases, and this population may be described as "the English and the Welsh and the Scots".

DISTRIBUTIVE LAW

$$m(e+w+s)=me+mw+ms$$

This may be illustrated numerically by

$$4(2+3+7)=4.2+4.3+4.7$$

that is, $4.12 \quad = \quad 8+12 \quad +28=48$

A verbal illustration could be:

English, Welsh and Scottish men constitute the same set of people as Englishmen, Welshmen and Scotsmen.

DIFFERENCES AND QUOTIENTS

The rules so far described have referred only to sums and products. Subtracting may be regarded as the reverse process of adding, and the reversibility of the process of multiplication gives rise to division, that is, to quotients.

For example: $(b+f)(d+c)=bd+bc+fd+fc$ is a statement which may be read as "b plus f into d plus c is equal to bd plus bc plus fd plus fc".

No particular meanings have been given to any of the letters, and the statement is true according to the associative and distributive laws of algebra.

If the term fc is subtracted from both sides of the equation, since two equal quantities, on the two sides of the equation, have been treated in the same way, the statement will remain true. Thus,

$$(b+f)(d+c)-fc=bd+bc+fd$$

is true, being equivalent to the original statement. Numerically, we may substitute whatever numbers we please, say $b=5, f=7, d=9, c=2$, then

$$(5+7)(9+2)-7.2=5.9+5.2+7.9$$

that is, $12.11 \quad - 14 = 45 + 10 + 63$

$132 \quad - 14 = \quad 118$

Verbally, we could regard this as a symbolic expression of any classification of entities which could be described in terms of two distinct types of attribute. For instance, if b means British, f means foreign, d means dessert and c means cooking, then the statement

$$(b+f)(d+c)-fc=bd+bc+fd$$

could mean that a greengrocer who started off with British and foreign apples and sold out his foreign cookers would have left British dessert apples, British cooking apples and foreign dessert apples.

$$w=m.h$$

is a general statement. If both sides of the equation are divided by h, the statement

$$\frac{w}{h}=m$$

is equivalent to the original statement, expressing precisely the same relationship between the three entities w, m and h.

Numerically, since $\qquad\qquad 35=7.5$

then $\qquad\qquad\qquad\qquad \frac{35}{5}=7.$

The statement could indicate that the amount of work, w, required to complete a task is measured by the number of men, m, working, multiplied by the number of hours, h, during which they are at work. The second form of the statement simply says that the amount of work to be done divided by the time available for doing it will give the number of men required. Thus, if $w=35$ man.hours and $h=5$ hours the statement $\frac{w}{h}=m$ becomes

$$\frac{35\text{ man.hours}}{5\text{ hours}}=m$$

giving the result that 7 men will be required. Note that when the 5 is cancelled and the hours are "cancelled", the answer "7.man" means seven times a man or seven men.

The symbols $\cup$ and $\cap$, used in logic and in the algebra of sets, are important where sets overlap. For example, some governors of a school are members of the local council and some governors are not council members and some council members are not school governors. If the governors are represented by a small circle and councillors with a large circle (Fig. 7.1):

(i) On speech day the prefects may be told that "if a person is a governor or a councillor he is to be shown on to the platform, governor $\cup$ councillor (Fig. 7.2).

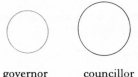

governor   councillor

Fig. 7.1

governor $\cup$ councillor

Fig. 7.2

Thus, all the people who are represented by the small and large circles will be on the platform.

(ii) At a meeting of the local council, the only spokesmen for the school are people who are both governors and councillors, governor ∩ councillor (Fig. 7.3).

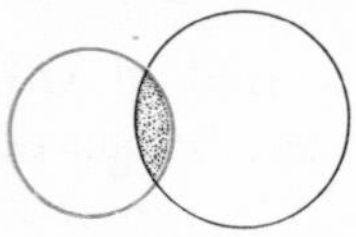

governor ∩ councillor

Fig. 7.3

Thus, the people who are spokesmen are only those who are represented in both the circles.

A great deal of fun can be obtained with this algebra. Those complicated problems about Mr. Baker, Mr. Smith, etc., who were, but not respectively, a baker and a smith, etc., when the smith went to London with Mr. Butcher, etc., come out simply by using Boolean algebra. An understanding of these ideas is fundamental to the comprehension of books such as Godfrey Thomson's *Factorial Analysis of Human Abilities*.

Zero and Unity

For the purposes of algebra, *zero*, whose symbol is 0, is defined by the equations

$$a.0 = 0, \qquad 0.a = 0$$
$$a + 0 = a, \qquad 0 + a = a$$

for all values of *a*.

Unity, whose symbol is 1, is such that

$$a.1 = a, \qquad 1.a = a$$

for all values of *a*.

The simple idea of unity is not likely to cause children much difficulty. Further discussion here might well introduce complications without meeting the difficulties involved and leave confusion where at present there is none. It might, however, be mentioned that since G. Frege published his *Grundgesetze der Arithmetik* in 1893, followed by G. Péano's *Formulaire de Mathématiques* in 1901, much has been written on the subject, and it is discussed at great length in Whitehead and Russell's monumental *Principia Mathematica* (1910). It continues to interest one school of mathematicians and logicians.

Other Conventions

There are many conventions in algebra which serve either to economize in writing or to simplify expressions. Examples of such conventions are:

(i) INDICES. $a.a.a$ is written a^3.

$a.a.a.a.a.a.a$ is written a^7 (said as *a* to the seventh).

$a.a.a \ldots \ldots \ldots a$ to "*r*" factors is written a^r (said: *a* to the power *r*).

(ii) LOGARITHMS.* If $x = a^r$ then this equation expresses a relationship between the three quantities x, a and r. It is often convenient to re-arrange this relationship so that r is expressed in terms of the x and the a.

$$r = \log_a x \quad \text{(``}r\text{'' is equal to log } x \text{ to the base ``}a\text{'')}$$

is an alternative way of writing the relationship

$$x = a^r.$$

(iii) FACTORIAL. The product $1.2.3.4.5$ is written $5!$ and called "factorial five". Similarly $1.2.3.4.5.6.7.8$ is "factorial eight" or $8!$

(iv) SUMMATION. A series of quantities which follow some law and are added together may be written

$$S = a_1 + a_2 + a_3 + a_4 + \ldots + a_n$$

and the summation is indicated by using the Greek capital sigma, thus

$$\sum_{r=1}^{n} a_r \text{ means } a_1 + a_2 + a_3 + \ldots + a_n$$

and is read as "the sum of terms such as a_r from $r = 1$ to $r = n$".

Thus, $1^3 + 2^3 + 3^3 + 4^3 + 5^3 + 6^3 + 7^3 + 8^3 + 9^3$ would be written $\sum_{r=1}^{9} r^3$. (Read as sigma, r, from 1 to 9, of r cubed.)

Equations

Since the object of algebra is to write down relationships in their simplest possible forms, omitting all frills and irrelevancies, the information in an algebraic equation is more easily manipulated than the same information expressed at length in words.

When algebra is to be used there are three stages in the solution of a problem:

(i) Extracting the given information from the actual situation and expressing it in algebraic form.

(ii) Manipulation of the algebraic equations to give an algebraic solution of the problem.

(iii) Translating the algebraic solution back into the original context of the problem.

Some considerable practice is required before sufficient competence in the second of these three stages has been acquired to enable problems of much intrinsic interest to be solved. Similar comments could, of course, be made about most subjects; it is some years before a pupil acquires the vocabulary and language sense to say, convincingly, anything really worthwhile in French. One of the difficulties in teaching algebra is to find, at each appropriate stage, problems which pupils want to solve because they would like to know the answer. In its early stages algebra is sometimes dragged in so that its use is not unlike the use of a sledge-hammer to crack a nut; sometimes the examples are "over-clever" and bordering on the facetious; all too often the practice is just imposed as a dull routine. A good teacher can ring the changes on types of question. At the level of the very simplest of equations there are routine questions such as

"If $7x + 27 = 69$, what is the value of x?"

---

* *See* Chapter 9.

This involves only the stage (ii) referred to on the previous page, the manipulation of algebraic quantities, but it is an essential first step.

$$7x + 27 = 69. \quad \cdots \cdots \cdots \quad (1)$$

To find the value of x we wish to have x on one side of the equation and numbers on the other side and this may be achieved by subtracting 27 from both sides of the equation, giving

$$7x = 42. \quad \cdots \cdots \cdots \quad (2)$$

Having obtained a value for $7x$ it is clear that if both sides of the equation are now divided by 7, we shall obtain

$$x = 6 \quad \cdots \cdots \cdots \quad (3)$$

which is the required answer.

There is an opportunity here to comment that at every stage *both sides of the equation were treated in the same way*. When anything was added to one side, an equal quantity was added to the other side; when one side was divided by seven, the other side was also divided by seven. The other point to be noticed is that from $7x + 27$ to x, the stages were first to deal with the term 27, which required an operation (subtracting 27) involving only pure numbers, and then to deal with the $7x$ term (by dividing by 7), which modified the term in x.

This simple equation might be introduced, not as a formal solution of an algebraic equation, but clothed in words while yet being concerned only with number, un-associated with any suggestion of a concrete context:

I thought of a number, multiplied it by five, then added 17, *then subtracted the number I had first thought of and the result was* 61. *What was the number I had thought of?*

In this case there is a rudimentary stage (i) which consists of saying "Let n be the number I first thought of" and then writing

$$5n + 17 - n = 61. \quad \cdots \cdots \cdots \quad (4)$$

Subtracting 17 *from both sides of the equation*, we obtain

$$5n - n = 44. \quad \cdots \cdots \cdots \quad (5)$$

Collecting terms together on the left-hand side of the equation (note that in doing so we are not altering its value, so that there is no compensating operation to be performed on the other side), we obtain

$$4n = 44 \quad \cdots \cdots \cdots \quad (6)$$

and dividing *both sides of the equation* by 4,

$$n = 11$$

which is the required answer. It is as well that you should go back to the original question and check that if 11 is the number I first thought of the procedure set out will give, finally, 61.

A simple equation could then be illustrated in a context which is quite real, although rather trivial. For instance:

An interior-sprung mattress on a double bed is 4 *ft* 6 *in. wide and* 6 *in. deep. How much of a sheet* 90-*in. wide is available on each side of the bed for tucking in under the mattress?*

Here stage (i) can really be introduced, and a diagram at this stage would not be out of place.

Stage (i). Let the amount tucked in each side be of length x inches (Fig. 7.4); then,

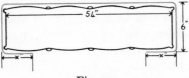

Fig. 7.4

working in inches throughout,

$$x + 6 + 54 + 6 + x = 90. \quad . \quad . \quad . \quad . \quad . \quad . \quad . \quad (7)$$

Stage (ii). Collecting terms on the left-hand side, we obtain

$$2x + 66 = 90. \quad . \quad . \quad . \quad . \quad . \quad . \quad . \quad (8)$$

Subtracting 66 from both sides of the equation gives

$$2x = 24 \quad . \quad . \quad . \quad . \quad . \quad . \quad . \quad (9)$$

and dividing *both sides of the equation* by 2,

$$x = 12.$$

Stage (iii). The answer given by algebra is 12 in. Now we do not measure with a ruler to see that when we make beds there is *exactly* the same amount of sheet tucked in on each side and we should try to give our answer in an appropriate form. A reasonable answer would be: "A 90-in. sheet will leave a margin of about a foot each side for tucking under the mattress."

Simple equations of this type can arise only from very simple problems but it is necessary to get some experience with them. In doing so, great stress must be laid, particularly on the fact that some operations, such as sorting out or re-arranging terms on one side of the equation, do not alter the value of that side of the equation and so require no compensating operation to be performed on the other side, but that any addition, subtraction, multiplication or division affecting one side of the equation must be balanced by a corresponding treatment of the other side.

Sets

Whether in ordinary conversation or in a scientific description or in such diverse fields as art, music, gardening or washing-up, we are constantly dealing with complex objects, ideas or processes which have quite a variety of aspects or properties, and we are constantly sorting and re-sorting and shuffling in terms first of one property and then of another. Using everyday language, let us look at the sentence: *I enjoy music such as Beethoven's Fifth Symphony.*

"*I*". There is a classification implied here. Instead of "I" any of the phrases "Many people", "All my family", "Most musicians" would make sense if used instead of "I", but "Armchairs", "Vaccination scars", or "Foul smells" would make nonsense if made the subject of this sentence instead of "I". By implication, therefore, we have framed our sentence in such a way that its subject can be a member only of the set of all non-deaf human beings, and the actual subject of the sentence, "I", is one member of this set.

"*enjoy*" implies also classification into the set of things enjoyed as distinct from the complementary set of things not enjoyed.

"*music*". Although there might well be differences of opinion as to what ought to be included in the set described by the word "music" and what in the set described as "not music", each person could assign anything into one or other of these complementary sets.

"*Beethoven's*". Having defined music to our own satisfaction we may then divide it into sub-sets by means of naming the composers. We should have Beethoven's music, Handel's music, Scarlatti's music, Schubert's music, Irving Berlin's music and so on.

"*Symphony*". Having previously defined music we may divide it into sub-sets in another way, according to the form, using such categories as "Symphony", "Concerto", "Ballad", "Opera", "Oratorio", "Calypso".

Having narrowed our understanding of what the sentence is about to one person enjoying Beethoven's symphony, the word "*Fifth*" serves to select one of the very limited set of things common to the two sets "Beethoven's music" and "symphony".

Obviously gardeners are always doing the same sort of thing: "weeds", "not weeds"; "roses", "not roses"; "standards", "bushes", "climbers", etc. Washers-up think in terms of "clean", "dirty", "greasy", "non-greasy", "china", "cutlery", "plastic" and so on.

There is a special notation used for describing this sorting and combining of data classified in this sort of way. If m_1, m_2, m_3, . . . are all the pieces of music ever written we say that $\{m_1, m_2, m_3, \ldots\}$ is the set M and this statement is written

$$\{m_1, m_2, m_3, \ldots\} = M \quad \ldots \ldots \ldots \quad (10)$$

which means that $m_1 \in M$, $m_2 \in M$, $m_3 \in M$, and is read as "m_1 is a member of set M, m_2 is a member of set M, etc." The set M contains music written by Beethoven, Schubert, Handel, Ravel, etc.

We write B for the sub-set of M which consists of all the pieces of music written by Beethoven, and we write

$$B \subset M \quad \ldots \ldots \ldots \ldots \quad (11)$$

which is read as "B is contained in M".

The set M also contains music described as symphonies, concertos, oratorios, etc. We write S for the set of all symphonies. The set of all symphonies, S is a sub-set of all music and so

$$S \subset M \quad \ldots \ldots \ldots \ldots \quad (12)$$

which is read as "The set S is contained in the set M".

A Beethoven symphony, m, belongs to both set B and to set S, and this statement is written

$$m \in B \cap S \quad \ldots \ldots \ldots \ldots \quad (13)$$

which is read as

"m belongs to the set B and to the set S" or, more concisely,
"m belongs to the *intersection* of sets B and S".

As on page 91, this may be represented diagrammatically if we let $\bullet_1 \bullet_2 \bullet_3 \ldots$ stand for the pieces of music written by Beethoven and we put all these inside one circle (Fig. 7.5)

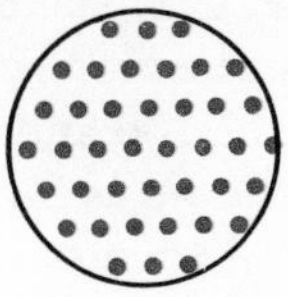

The sub-set B.

Fig. 7.5

and we let $\square_1 \square_2 \square_3, \ldots$ represent all symphonies ever written, and we put these inside another circle (Fig. 7.6).

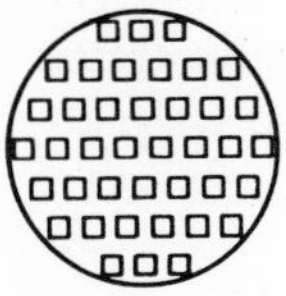

The sub-set S.

Fig. 7.6

Then the *intersection* of these two sub-sets is what is contained in both circles and is represented by ▣ in the diagram for $B \cap S$ (Fig. 7.7).

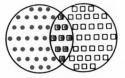

The intersection of sub-sets B and S.

Fig. 7.7

All Beethoven's music and all symphonies together constitute the *union* of the two sub-sets B and S, and we can write

$$\{ \ \blacksquare_1\blacksquare_2\blacksquare_3 \ldots \square_1\square_2\square_3, \ldots \bullet_1\bullet_2\bullet_3 \ldots \ \} = B \cup S$$

which we read as

> "all the members marked ▣ and all the members marked □ and all the members marked ● are members of the union of sub-sets B and S".

Function

$$\{x_1, x_2, x_3, \ldots\} = A \text{ and } \{y_1, y_2, y_3, \ldots\} = B \text{ are two sets.}$$

This means that some things which we will label x_1 and x_2 and x_3 and so on are all defined in some sort of way which ensures that they belong to a well-defined set of things which we call A. Another set of things which we label with the symbols y_1 and y_2 and y_3 and so on are all defined in another sort of way, which we shall say defines the set B. There may be some sort of connexion between the x's and the y's so that each x is associated with a particular y.

For instance, the x's may all be towns in England and the y's may all be distances measured in miles from St. Paul's Cathedral in London; thus, to each x there corresponds a particular y. In this instance, if x_1 stands for Axminster, the corresponding y will be 146, and if x_2 stands for Bath, the corresponding y will be 105, and if x_3 stands for Chester, the corresponding y will be 180 and so on.

A relationship such as this defines the y's as functions of the x's and we write $y = f(x)$ which is read "y is a function of x", and we now can say that $x \in A$ and $f(x) \in B$.

Sometimes there is a very simple relationship between the x's and the y's. For instance, the main line distance from Liverpool to London is 194 miles. If x is the distance in miles from Liverpool of a place, p, and y is the distance in miles of p from London, then for the set of places, p, which is on the main line from Liverpool to London, the relationship between the x's and the y's is given by $y = 194 - x$.

A relationship such as this, when illustrated graphically will give rise to a simple curve, in this instance a straight line, if we plot equal numbers against equal lengths on both axes (Fig. 7.8):

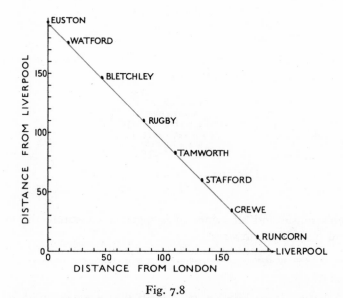

Fig. 7.8

Sometimes there is no simple algebraic or arithmetical relation between the x's and the y's but there is, nevertheless, a well-defined means of knowing precisely the y which corresponds to a particular x. Such relationships are common, for example, in statistical work. For instance, if x is the mark obtained for mathematics by a person in an examination and y is the mark obtained in English by the same person, then for each person in the set of those who took both subjects there will be an x and a y precisely defined. If, in cases such as this, we again plot values of x and values of y against rectangular axes, we obtain a set of points which will not, in general, lie on any well-defined curve, but will be scattered over the diagram. Such a "scatter diagram" is of great value in statistics; it may look something like Fig. 7.9.

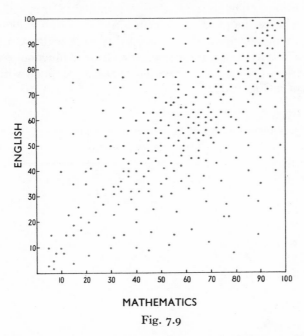

MATHEMATICS

Fig. 7.9

Quite a lot of information can be obtained from such a diagram. For example, in the diagram above, it is clear that the dots are most dense along the diagonal. This means that more people have roughly similar marks in both subjects than have very different marks. The comparative emptiness of the bottom right-hand corner shows that comparatively few people with good marks in mathematics have very poor marks in English.

A scatter diagram compiled from two sets of scores which were quite unrelated, for example, the weight of a person in pounds and the numbers on his medical registration form, would be expected to give a scatter diagram in which there was no apparent pattern. On the other hand, a scatter diagram in which the points lie on, or very nearly on, a well-defined curve, would indicate an algebraic relationship between the quantities concerned. Many advances in both the physical and the biological sciences have followed the observation of the existence of such patterns. Among many hundreds of possible examples one might mention the "Russell diagram", in astronomy, which led to an extension of the range over which distances of stars could be measured, and the work of Mendel, who compared heights of peas of one generation with heights of peas of the next generation, and from the pattern of relationship between the two sets of observations developed the laws of heredity.

Because examples of functional relationship arise in a simple form such as $y = 2x + 3$ or $y = 4x^2$, many people will have had plenty of experience of solving equations and drawing graphs illustrating these relationships. They form an extremely important group of functions, and one can achieve little in mathematics or science without the facility which comes from having practised many exercises on functions of this type. It is worthy of comment, however, that important and familiar though they are, they form but a small sub-set of all the possible functional relationships.

Some functional relationships can be defined very precisely in simple mathematical terms, but the definition cannot be reduced to a "formula". For instance, in the middle of the eighteenth century the great mathematician Euler, who explored many of the properties of prime numbers, found that he needed to work with a function now known as "Euler's function". If n is a positive integer, then Euler's function (ϕn) is the number of positive integers less than n which have no factor in common with n and are not themselves factors of n (Fig. 7.10).

Number, n	Numbers $< n$ not factors of n and having no factor in common with n	Euler's function $\phi(n)$
1	—	0
2	1	1
3	1, 2	2
4	1, 3	2
5	1, 2, 3, 4	4
6	1, 5	2
7	1, 2, 3, 4, 5, 6	6
8	1, 3, 5, 7	4
9	1, 2, 4, 5, 7, 8	6
10	1, 3, 7, 9	4
11	1, 2, 3, 4, 5, 6, 7, 8, 9, 10	10
12	1, 5, 7, 11	4
13	1, 2, 3, 4, 5, 6, 7, 8, 9, 10, 11, 12	12
14	1, 3, 5, 9, 11, 13	6
15	1, 2, 4, 7, 8, 11, 13, 14	8
16	1, 3, 5, 7, 9, 11, 13, 15	8
17	1, 2, 3, 4, 5, 6, 7, 8, 9, 10, 11, 12, 13, 14, 15, 16	16
18	1, 5, 7, 11, 13, 17	6
19	1, 2, 3, 4, . . . 15, 16, 17, 18	18
20	1, 3, 7, 9, 11, 13, 17, 19	8

Fig. 7.10

A function such as $\phi(n)$ is exactly defined and its value may be calculated without ambiguity for each value of n. A number of facts may be mentioned:

(i) No algebraic formula can be found to give $\phi(n)$ in terms of n.

(ii) When the n's are arranged in order 1, 2, 3, 4, 5, . . . then the corresponding values of $\phi(n)$ 1, 2, 2, 4, 2, 6, 4, . . . are not in order.

(iii) Although to each value of n there corresponds only one value of $\phi(n)$ the reverse is not the case, for instance $\phi(n) = 4$ corresponds to $n = 5$, $n = 8$, $n = 10$, $n = 12$, similarly for $\phi(n) = 2$ and for $\phi(n) = 6$, etc.

(iv) $20 = 4 \times 5$, $\phi(20) = \phi(4) \times \phi(5)$; $15 = 3 \times 5$, $\phi(15) = \phi(3) \times \phi(5)$ and, in general, if n can be expressed as the product of two factors p and q which have no common factor, then $\phi(pq) = \phi(p) \times \phi(q)$.

(v) The diagram illustrating the relation between n and $\phi(n)$ has no pattern except that its peaks, corresponding to the prime numbers, lie on a straight line which can be given the equation $y = x - 1$, where $y = \phi(x)$ when x is a prime number (Fig. 7.11).

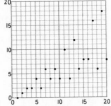

Fig. 7.11

Diagram illustrating Euler's function $\phi(n)$ plotted vertically
against values of n plotted horizontally.

If there is a functional relationship such as $y = 4x^2 + 7$ it is a simple matter to say what value of y will be associated with any particular value of x. Similarly, for a precisely defined relationship such as Euler's function, even when there is no corresponding simple algebraic equation, a knowledge of x enables $\phi(x)$ to be calculated. For a relationship such as that between English and mathematics marks there is no way of telling exactly what mark in one subject will be associated with a particular mark in another, but if there is a pattern in the scatter diagram it is possible to estimate the chances that one variable lies within a given range of "the most likely value". This much information may be very useful and is discussed in Chapter 14. It does, however, happen that there are occasions when complete unpredictability of any relationship is desirable. For instance, Premium Bonds are sold with serial numbers on them. At some later date certain numbers will be associated with certain prizes, but, at the time they are bought the future association must be quite unpredictable. ERNIE was built at Blackpool to produce electronically a completely random set of numbers so that the relationship between Bond and Prize is an absolutely unstructured, random association. The association of each of the elements of one set with an element of another set is called "mapping". In algebra the word is not used specifically to describe the process of drawing things on charts or plans, as in geography, although this is an example of mapping in which a particular name of a town or other physical feature is associated with a particular position on a piece of paper.

$$\{a_1, a_2, a_3, \ldots\} = A \quad \text{and} \quad \{b_1, b_2, b_3, \ldots\} = B$$

are two sets. If from the set A one element a_n is selected and this is associated with a particular element of the set B by some systematic process, that is, when A is mapped into B, then we can also say that set B is a function of set A, which can be written $f(A) \to B$ if we are referring to the sets as such, or $f(a) = b$ if we are referring to elements in the sets.

One-to-one correspondence

In a public examination it is quite usual for each candidate to be given a number so that the identity of examinees is unknown to the examiners. In such an arrangement, to one number there corresponds one and only one candidate and, on the other hand, to one candidate there corresponds one and only one number.

When one is travelling from one country to another, baggage has to be examined in customs sheds, and the usual method of grouping baggage together in the sheds is that each item of baggage is labelled with a large letter which is the initial letter of the owner's surname. Thus, Mr. Smith's luggage is labelled only with the letter S. On the other hand, luggage labelled with the letter S may belong to Mr. Smith or Mr. Sutherland or Mr. Sandford, etc. Thus, each owner is associated with one letter but one letter is associated with several owners.

These two instances illustrate the principal types of correspondence met with in elementary algebra, in which one of the variables is determined uniquely in terms of the other variable.

There are, of course, many examples of relationships which do not fall into this category. As an example, we may imagine that of all the buses belonging to Westhampton Corporation twelve are available for use on route "R", and of all the Westhampton Corporation bus drivers twenty drivers are available to drive on route "R". If this is all the information we have, then all we can say is that each driver may drive one of twelve different buses and that each bus may be driven by one of twenty different men.

Other examples might be considered of which the following is one. If E is the set of all British Railways engines and N is the set of all positive integers less than 100,000, since each engine is given a number, *every member of set E is associated with one member of set N*. Such mapping is a mapping of E on to N.

On the other hand, each type of engine is given a number in which the thousands indicate the type of engine, and the hundreds, tens and units indicate the engine number in that particular type. Thus, if, say, only 480 engines of type 22,000 were built, there would be no engine numbers between 22,480 and 22,999. In this instance only some numbers of set N are associated with members of set E. This is a *mapping of a sub-set of N on to E*.

EXAMPLES

Wood Screws. The sizes of screws are indicated by numbers. The size of a screw indicates the diameter of its shank. The table below gives the mapping of diameters on to sizes:

Diameter of shank of screw in thousandths of an inch	66	80	94	108	122	136	150	164	178	192	206
Standard size of screw	1	2	3	4	5	6	7	8	9	10	11

This mapping may be illustrated on a graph (Fig. 7.12).

A glance at the table will show that the size number of each consecutive screw increases by one, and that the diameter of each consecutive screw-shank increases by 14-thousandths of an inch, hence, on the graph, each consecutive point is located one unit farther along the horizontal axis and fourteen units farther up the vertical axis than the previous one. As one would expect from the fact that there is a uniform increase of shank diameter

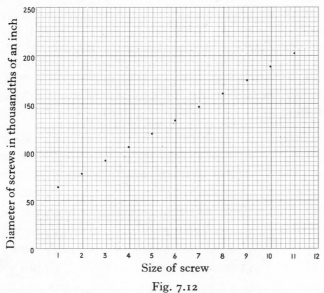

Fig. 7.12

with each consecutive screw-number, the points on the graph lie in a straight line slanting upwards.

In the table it will be seen that if 1 is subtracted from the standard size-number for the screw, 14 is subtracted from the number of thousandths of an inch in the top row of the table. If we continued this process one place farther to the left we should have "screw-size 0" corresponding to diameter 52 "thous". Then we see at once that $66 = 52 + 14 \times 1$, $80 = 52 + 14 \times 2$, $94 = 52 + 14 \times 3$ and so on.

This rule for finding the diameter of a screw, given its size-number, can be summarized in the formula

$$d = 52 + 14 . N$$

where d is the diameter in thousandths of an inch and N is the screw-number.

Since the same amount is added each time we move from one point to the next point of the table, we have only to multiply this common increment, 14, by the number of places, N, we have moved from the beginning of the table to find the number to be added to the zero position, 52.

This procedure describes the way we obtained a set of points lying on a straight line when we drew the graph; it also describes how we obtained the equation

$$d = 52 + 14 . N$$

which corresponds to the straight line.

This is quite general. Any equation such as $y = 52 + 14 . x$ or $y = 27 + 9 . x$ or $y = 4 + 2 . x$ corresponds to a straight line sloping up to the right. Obviously if the numbers corresponding to y (the vertical axis) were becoming small as the numbers corresponding to x (the horizontal axis) were becoming bigger, the line would slope down to the right.

In general: *any equation such as $y = mx + c$ corresponds to a straight line.* This slopes up to the right if m is a positive number and down to the right if m is a "negative" number. c is the value of y when $x = 0$.

Knitting needles. Wool manufacturers supply gauges which may be used to test the sizes of knitting needles. I had one of these gauges, and a set of rods whose diameters increased exactly in sixty-fourths of an inch. I wished to discover the relation between the size-number of a knitting needle and its diameter and to draw up a table similar to the wood-screw table, which was taken from an engineers' pocket book. The procedure adopted was first to take the largest hole of the gauge, size 7, and to insert feeler rods, one by one in decreasing order of size, until one of them just went through the hole.

Hole no. 7 . . . $\frac{12}{64}$ would not go in . . . . $\frac{11}{64}$ went in easily

Hole no. 8 . . . $\frac{11}{64}$ would not go in . . . . $\frac{10}{64}$ went in easily

Hole no. 9 . . . $\frac{10}{64}$ would not go in . . . . $\frac{9}{64}$ went in fairly easily

Hole no. 10 . . $\frac{9}{64}$ would not go in . . . . $\frac{8}{64}$ went in fairly easily

Hole no. 11 . . $\frac{8}{64}$ would not go in . . . . $\frac{7}{64}$ went in very easily

Hole no. 12 . . $\frac{7}{64}$ would not go in : . . . $\frac{6}{64}$ went in very easily

Hole no. 13 . . $\frac{6}{64}$ would not quite go in . .. $\frac{5}{64}$ went in very easily

Hole no. 14 . . $\frac{6}{64}$ would not go in . . . . $\frac{5}{64}$ just went in.

It is this kind of information that is obtained in engineering workshops when feeler gauges are used. It puts a limit to each size. We obtain two sets of points on a graph, and the actual value of the size lies between them (Fig. 7.13).

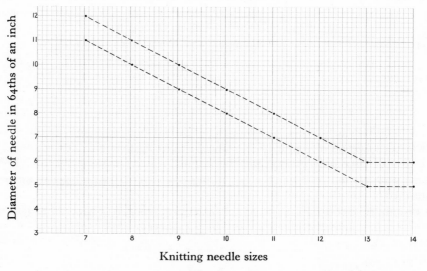

Fig. 7.13

An examination of the limits shows that a straight line just will not go in the space between the limiting rows of points, and so the relation between the knitting-needle size and diameter of needle is not a simple *linear* relation, as for wood screws, of the form

$$y = mx + c$$

but is a little more complicated.

The best relationship we can obtain is to draw as smooth a curve as possible between the two bounding lines and to use this as a means of obtaining the diameter when we know the standard size-number. This is a one-to-one correspondence and we have a simple curve. The diagram below shows this curve drawn in as well as we can from the available information (Fig. 7.14).

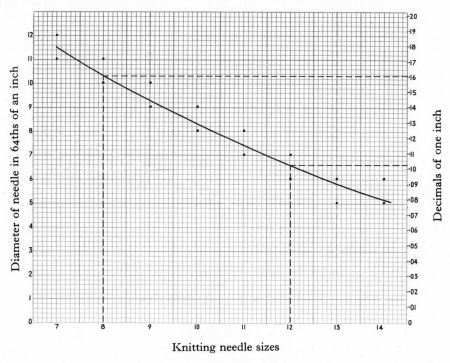

Fig. 7.14

It is clear from the table drawn up for this curve that sixty-fourths of an inch are not suitable units for measuring knitting-needle diameters. When a vulgar fraction is unsuitable it is usually convenient to try to express the values as accurately as possible in decimal fractions. To do this a scale has been drawn on the right of the graph, starting with the simple fraction $\frac{8}{64} = \frac{1}{8} = 0·125$. Then 0·1 is four-fifths of this. It is easy to measure from 0 to 8 on the left-hand side, take 4/5 of this, and to measure this distance up the right-hand side, call it 0·10, and then divide it into tenths and so calibrate the right-hand scale.

When this has been completed, it is possible to read across from the points on the curve to the right-hand margin and draw up a table of knitting-needle diameters in decimals of an inch. A smooth curve has been drawn to satisfy the conditions and, to the scale of this drawing, it would be possible to give diameters to three decimal places of an inch, but it must be remembered that it is possible to draw a number of smooth curves lying between the bounding points and that there is no means of discriminating between them from the data available. The table, therefore, gives values only to the nearest two-hundredths of an inch, which is the most accurate estimate that can be made from the information obtainable from the needle gauge and the apparatus available for measuring it.

Size of knitting needle	7	8	9	10	11	12	13	14
Diameter in inches	0·18	0·16	0·145	0·13	0·115	0·105	0·09	0·08

(On Fig. 7.14 the dotted lines are drawn in to show how 0·16 is obtained for size 8 and 0·105 for size 12.)

This is about all we can do with the information available. We note that the curve is not a straight line, therefore the algebraic relation is not linear; since diameters decrease as size-numbers increase, the curve slopes down to the right, a negative slope.

Standard wire gauges. Another type of measure, very similar to the standard sizes of screws and knitting needles, is that which relates diameters of wires and the standard sizes associated with them. Such information is given very fully in any engineers' pocket book. Diameters are usually measured in thousandths of an inch, and the following table gives the mapping of diameters on to sizes:

Imperial standard wire gauge

Number of gauge	1	2	3	4	5	6	7	8	9	10	11	12
Diameter of wire in "thous"	300	276	252	232	212	192	176	160	144	128	116	104

Before we go any further we see that the diameters we estimated for knitting needles agree so closely (for the same range of size numbers) with the diameter of corresponding wire sizes that we may assume that the knitting needle sizes are simply the standard wire sizes.

It is difficult, at a glance, to see just how the numbers are behaving. This being so, we might first look at the differences and, if they show no clear pattern, then draw a graph and see what that looks like.

Number of gauge	1	2	3	4	5	6	7	8	9	10	11	12
Diameter in "thous"	300	276	252	232	212	192	176	160	144	128	116	104
Differences		24	24	20	20	20	16	16	16	16	12	12

The differences are decreasing but there are not enough terms to see just how the pattern of differences will continue. An engineers' pocket book gives

Gauge	12	13	14	15	16	17	18	19	20	21	22	23	24	25	26	27
Diameter	104	92	80	72	64	56	48	40	36	32	28	24	22	20	18	16·4
Differences		12	12	8	8	8	8	8	4	4	4	4	2	2	2	1·6

Successive differences are   24, 24,
                                            20, 20, 20,
                                            16, 16, 16, 16,
                                            12, 12, 12, 12,
                                            8, 8, 8, 8, 8,
                                            4, 4, 4, 4,
                                            2, 2, 2,
                                            1·6,   etc.

When a graph is drawn showing diameters against gauge numbers it looks at first glance like a smooth curve but it is, in fact, made up of a series of straight lines. There is no simple and obvious formula connecting gauge number with diameter, and the nature of the relationship can best be appreciated by looking at it on a graph (Fig. 7.15).

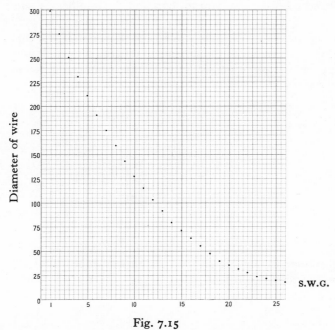

Fig. 7.15

Graph showing relation between *standard gauge number* of a wire
and its *diameter* in thousandths of an inch.

From the shape of this graph one deduces a systematic relation between gauge number and diameter, but it is not easy to find a simple algebraic equation which links the two sets of numbers. Before we can find such an equation, it would be useful to look at a few number sequences built up from known rules and to see the shapes of the curves which correspond to them.

The next chapters deal with a few well-known number sequences, their equations, the curves which illustrate them, and a few of the many practical situations in which a knowledge of some of these curves opens new fields of interest.

8

Number Sequences and their Graphs

Linear Sequences and Straight Lines

The simplest possible way of building up a number sequence is to begin with a number, add another number to it and then continue adding that same number. Thus, if we begin with, say 7, add 3 and continue adding 3, we build up the sequence

$$7, \quad 10, \quad 13, \quad 16, \quad 19, \quad 22, \ldots$$

It is not at all easy to take in the nature of a whole string of numbers at a glance and it is, for some purposes, a great help to represent the numbers in some convenient way. For example, they may be represented by piles of pennies. The piles get steadily taller and taller, rising uniformly like the steps of a staircase. If the piles had represented numbers in a sequence in which the terms had differed by 5 instead of 3 the piles would have sloped up more steeply, so, in general, the common difference determines the steepness of the slope.

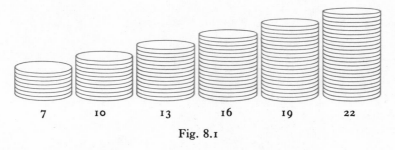

| 7 | 10 | 13 | 16 | 19 | 22 |

Fig. 8.1

An algebraic equation which gives rise to this sequence of numbers can be found if we write them out in order, calling them the set y, and then simply number them off 1, 2, 3, 4, . . . calling these the set x.

$$y = 7 \quad 10 \quad 13 \quad 16 \quad 19 \quad 22 \ldots$$
$$x = 1 \quad 2 \quad 3 \quad 4 \quad 5 \quad 6 \ldots$$

The y's are now mapped on to the x's, giving the very simple order relation between them that when the x's increase one at a time the y's increase three at a time.

If both sequences are continued one further term to the left then $y = 4$ would correspond to $x = 0$.

The numbers in sequences x and y can be paired off so that

$$x = 0 \quad : \quad 1 \quad : \quad 2 \quad : \quad 3 \quad : \quad 4 \quad : \quad 5 \quad : \ldots$$
$$y = 4 \quad : \quad 3 \times 1 + 4 \quad : \quad 3 \times 2 + 4 \quad : \quad 3 \times 3 + 4 \quad : \quad 3 \times 4 + 4 \quad : \quad 3 \times 5 + 4 \quad : \ldots$$

giving, in each case, the pattern $y = 3x + 4$.

108

When we wish to represent graphically some algebraic expression, we do not draw in imaginary pennies; instead we indicate, by some convenient mark, a point whose distance above the x-axis is y. The two graphs below illustrate two sequences, one with a common difference of 3 and the other with a common difference of 5.

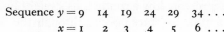

Sequence y = 7   10   13   16   19 . . .   Sequence y = 9   14   19   24   29   34 . . .
      x = 1   2   3   4   5 . . .   x = 1   2   3   4   5   6 . . .

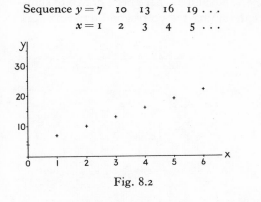
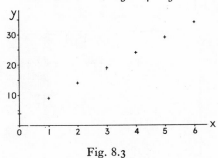

Fig. 8.2   Fig. 8.3

Equation $y = 3x + 4$ Equation $y = 5x + 4$
Slope throughout is $\frac{3}{1}$ Slope throughout is $\frac{5}{1}$

The *slope* of a curve at any point is the rate of increase of y relative to x. In the first sequence, y increases by 3 as x increases by 1 and the slope is $\frac{3}{1}$. In the second sequence illustrated, y increases by 5 as x increases by 1 and the slope is $\frac{5}{1}$.

The slope of a graph is measured by the "tan" of the angle it makes with the direction of the x-axis. The ordinary trigonometrical meaning of the "tan" of an angle is explained in the diagram:

If *PQR* (Fig. 8.4) is a right-angled triangle with the right-angle at R, and if θ is the size of the angle P, then

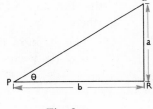

$$\tan \theta = \frac{QR}{PR}$$

$$= \frac{\text{length of side opposite } \theta}{\text{length of side joining } \theta \text{ to the rt } \angle}$$

$$= \frac{a}{b}.$$

Fig. 8.4

There is one simple convention which needs to be explained. When we draw graphs for the purpose of looking to see what sort of shape we are dealing with, or for the purpose of comparing the relative sizes of things, for setting out the x's horizontally and the y's vertically we choose scales which give us graphs of convenient size to look at. When we are analysing graphs and we talk about the "slope", we use the expression to describe the tan of the angle the curve would make with the x-axis *if equal scales were chosen for x and for y*.

The sequence of numbers 7, 10, 13, 16, 19, . . . consists of a set of separate whole numbers, which are represented by separate crosses in Fig. 8.2. The equation $y = 3x + 4$

not only gives $y = 7$ when $x = 1$, $y = 10$ when $x = 2$, and all the numbers of the sequence, but, also, it gives a value for y whatever value is substituted for x. For instance, if $x = 1.6$, $y = 3 \times 1.6 + 4 = 4.8 + 4 = 8.8$. Thus, whereas the sequence is correctly represented as in Fig. 8.2 by a set of separate points, the equation $y = 3x + 4$ is correctly represented by a continuous straight line. Figs. 8.5, 8.6 and 8.7 have been drawn to show continuous lines passing through the points representing the corresponding sequences of whole numbers.

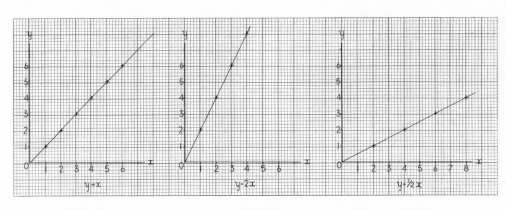

Fig. 8.5   Fig. 8.6   Fig. 8.7

If the equation $y = 3x + 4$ is represented by a graph (Fig. 8.2) the 3 tells us that the slope of the line is 3; the 4 tells us that the line crosses the y-axis where $y = 4$.

If the equation $y = 5x + 4$ is represented by a graph (Fig. 8.3) the 5 tells us that the slope of the line is 5; the 4 tells us that the line crosses the y-axis where $y = 4$.

The graph of the equation $y = mx + c$ is a straight line of slope m which crosses the y-axis where $y = c$.

LINES REPRESENTED BY THE EQUATION $y = mx + c$

$$y = x$$
$$y = 2x$$
$$y = \tfrac{1}{2}x$$
$$y = 2x + 3$$
$$y = 2x - 4$$
$$y = \tfrac{1}{2}x + 3$$
$$y = -2x + 1$$

are all equations of the form

$$y = mx + c$$

where m and c may take any numerical value, positive, negative or zero. They are all represented by straight-line graphs whose precise properties depend upon the values assigned to the m and the c.

THE CASE WHERE $c = 0$

When $c = 0$ the equation takes the form

$$y = mx.$$

Whatever the value of m, it is clear that when $x = 0$, y is also 0. Each line will, therefore, pass through the "origin", where both x and y are zero. Equations with large values of m will be represented by lines sloping steeply up to the right.

The three figures illustrate three lines passing through the origin. The first line, representing the equation $y = x$, has a slope 1 (Fig. 8.5). From the definition of tan θ it will be seen that if, in Fig. 8.4 on page 109, $QR = PR$, then the triangle PQR will be an isosceles right-angled triangle and θ will be 45°. The slope of the line in Fig. 8.5 is 45°.

EQUATIONS OF THE FORM $y = 2x + c$

The lines which represent the three equations (Fig. 8.8)

$$y = 2x$$
$$y = 2x + 3$$
$$y = 2x - 4$$

will all have the same slope, 2. Corresponding to the values 1, 2, 3, 4, . . . for x we obtain the three sequences:

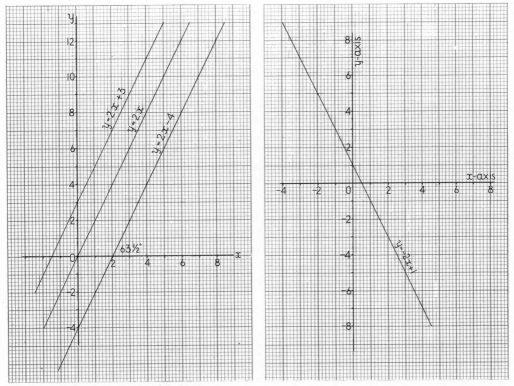

Fig. 8.8   Fig. 8.9

$$
\begin{array}{lcccccc}
x = & 1 & 2 & 3 & 4 & 5 & 6 \ldots \\
2x = & 2 & 4 & 6 & 8 & 10 & 12 \ldots \\
2x + 3 = & 5 & 7 & 9 & 11 & 13 & 15 \ldots \\
2x - 4 = -2 & & 0 & 2 & 4 & 6 & 8 \ldots
\end{array}
$$

From these sequences it will be seen that each term is 2 greater than the one which precedes it, so the three lines slope up to the right at an angle whose tan is 2. This is an angle of $63\frac{1}{2}°$. They are, therefore, parallel lines, and at every point the line $y = 2x + 3$ is 3 units above the line $y = 2x$ and the line $2x - 4$ is 4 units below the line $y = 2x$.

The line $y = 2x$ passes through the origin, where $x = 0$ and $y = 0$.

The line $y = 2x + 3$ crosses the y-axis where $y = 3$.

The line $y = 2x - 4$ crosses the y-axis where $y = -4$.

THE CASE WHEN m IS NEGATIVE

If x and y are connected by an equation such as

$$y = -2x + 1$$

an increase in x will correspond to a decrease in y. The sequence of values of y which correspond to $x = 1$, $x = 2$, $x = 3$, . . . will all be negative numbers and it is convenient to extend the sequences to the left to include values of y corresponding to $x = 0$, $x = -1$, $x = -2$, . . .

$$
\begin{array}{lccccccccc}
x = & -4 & -3 & -2 & -1 & 0 & 1 & 2 & 3 & 4 \ldots \\
y = & 9 & 7 & 5 & 3 & +1 & -1 & -3 & -5 & -7 \ldots
\end{array}
$$

These points have been plotted in Fig. 8.9 and the straight line drawn through them to represent the equation $y = -2x + 1$. Fig. 8.9 has been printed next to the figure which illustrates lines whose slope is $+2$ so that the reader can compare the two figures. When a line has a slope of -2 it slopes up to the left, making an obtuse angle with the positive direction of the x-axis.

The line crosses the y-axis where $y = +1$, illustrating again that the line representing the equation $y = mx + c$ cuts the y-axis where $y = c$.

EXAMPLES

Of all the possible types of relationship between two quantities, the one that can be expressed by a linear equation and a straight line graph is the most usual. A few examples are given to illustrate some of the contexts in which it may be met.

1. *A salary agreement has been negotiated for an initial salary of £600 per annum with an annual increment of £25 per annum for 15 years. Draw a graph to illustrate this and use it to find the salary after 12 years' service.*

Since the increase is the same each year, the points representing the annual incomes will all lie on a straight line. The quickest way to draw this line is to put in one point at the beginning of employment when $x = 0$ and $y = 600$ (*see* Fig. 8.10) and another point after 10 years when the increments will have amounted to $10 \times £25$ or £250, giving an £850 salary. The point will then be where $x = 10$ and $y = 850$. A vertical through $x = 12$ cuts the line at the level where $y = 900$, giving £900 as the salary after 12 years.

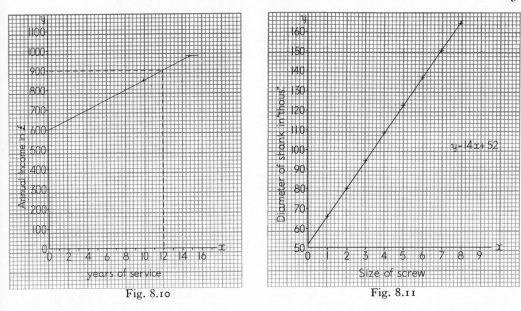

Fig. 8.10   Fig. 8.11

2. *The relation between the size of a standard wood screw and the diameter of its shank is given by the table*:

Size of screw	1	2	3	4	5	6	7	8	9	...
Diameter of shank in thousandths of an inch	66	80	94	108	122	136	150	164	178	...

Plot these numbers on a graph and find the algebraic equation to the line which passes through these points.

It is easily verified from the table that diameters increase by 14 "thous" for each increase in screw size. The points shown in Fig. 8.11 all lie on a straight line which cuts the y-axis where $y = 52$. The slope of the line is 14, since y increases by 14 when x increases by 1. The equation to the line is, therefore, $y = 14x + 52$.

Any simple change in the units used for measuring a quantity will give a relationship between the two sets of numbers expressing the size of the quantity in the two different units. One such change of units is from degrees Fahrenheit (°F) to degrees Centigrade (°C) for temperature.

3. *Given that the relation between temperature measured in °C and °F is linear, that melting point of ice is 0°C and 32°F and that boiling point of water is 100°C and 212°F, draw a graph to represent the relationship between °C and °F and use it to give the temperature in °F which is the same as the temperature 45°C.*

Since one, and only one, line can be drawn to pass through two points, the point M ($x = 0$, $y = 32$) corresponding to the melting point of ice, and the point B ($x = 100$, $y = 212$) corresponding to the boiling point of water, are sufficient to determine the *straight line* representing the relationship which we are told is *linear*. We draw in the axes, mark the points M and B, join them by a straight line, mark the point T on this line vertically above 45°C and find the value of y which is level with T. This gives a temperature of 113°F (Fig. 8.12).

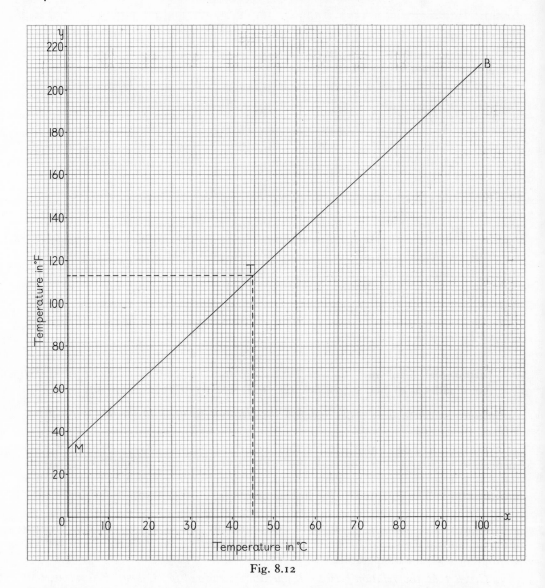

Fig. 8.12

To find the equation to this line we note that when x increases by 100 from 0 to 100, y increases by 180 from 32 to 212. An increase of 1 in x will correspond, therefore, to an increase of 1·8 in y. The slope of the line is thus 1·8 and it cuts the y-axis where $y = 32$. Hence, the equation is

$$y = 1 \cdot 8x + 32.$$

The relation between temperatures is

$$f = 1 \cdot 8c + 32$$

where f is the temperature measured in °F and c is the temperature measured in °C.

Arithmetic Progressions

We have illustrated, in a variety of ways, that a number sequence in which the difference between adjacent terms is constant throughout gives a straight line graph. When the terms of such a sequence are added together they form an *arithmetic progression*.

It is sometimes useful to know the sum of such a series, for instance, we may wish to know the sum, S, of the series

$$S = 7 + 10 + 13 + 16 + 19 + 22 + 25 + 28.$$

We can, of course, simply add the terms together in the ordinary way and this is not particularly arduous in the example given. There is, however, a way of simplifying the work which is very useful both when there are many terms in the series or when the terms are awkward, as they are if they contain fractions. The method is to write out the series as it stands, then to write it out again in the reverse order and then add these two series together term by term. Using the series already quoted, we have

$$S = 7 + 10 + 13 + 16 + 19 + 22 + 25 + 28$$
$$S = 28 + 25 + 22 + 19 + 16 + 13 + 10 + 7$$
$$2S = 35 + 35 + 35 + 35 + 35 + 35 + 35 + 35$$
$$= 35 \times 8$$
$$= 280$$

giving
$$S = 140.$$

This procedure may be carried out with any arithmetic progression, and the general rule is simple.

The sum of n terms of an arithmetic progression is half the sum of the first and last terms multiplied by the number of terms.

This rule is a direct analogue of the rule for finding the area of a trapezium, which is described on page 197. The area of a trapezium is *half the sum of the parallel sides times the distance between them.* Since the terms of an arithmetic progression all lie on a straight line, the first term, a, and the last term, l, and the number of terms, n, will be represented graphically as in Fig. 8.13. The area under the straight line will be $\frac{1}{2}(a+l) \times n$. The sum of the arithmetic progression containing n terms

$$S = a + (a+d) + (a+2d) + \ldots + l$$

is
$$S = \frac{1}{2}(a+l) \times n.$$

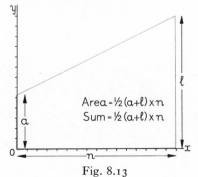

Area = ½(a+ℓ)×n
Sum = ½(a+ℓ)×n

Fig. 8.13

In any arithmetic sequence or series, the difference between any term and the one which precedes it is the same throughout. The difference which is the d in the series $S = a + (a+d) + (a+2d) + \ldots$ is called the *common difference*.

EXERCISES

1. Below are several number sequences which are *linear*. For each sequence:
    (i) Draw a graph illustrating the sequence.
    (ii) State the slope of the line and the point where it crosses the y-axis.
    (iii) Write down the equation to the straight line drawn on the graph paper which passes through the points plotted from the sequence.
    (iv) Find the sum of the series for the number of terms stated in each case.

    (a)   5, 8, 11, 14, 17, 20, 23
    (b)   31, 29, 27, . . .   11, 9
    (c)   13, $12\frac{1}{2}$, 12, $11\frac{1}{2}$, 11, . . .   to 18 terms
    (d)   12, 31, 50, 69, . . .   to 10 terms.

2. At the beginning of 1959 a two-year-trained teacher received a salary of £525 in her first year of teaching, with the expectation of being paid £550 in her second year, £575 in her third year and so on. Calculate the total salary she would expect to have received by the end of her sixth year of teaching.

    A teacher pays 6 per cent of salary received into superannuation contributions. Should she leave to marry at the end of six years, calculate how much she would expect to receive in the way of repayment of superannuation contributions (omitting interest accrued).

3. Prove that $1 + 2 + 3 + 4 + 5 + \ldots + n = \dfrac{n(n+1)}{2}$.

4. Prove that $1 + 3 + 5 + 7 + 9 + \ldots$ to n terms $= n^2$.

5. If a clock strikes *one* at one o'clock, *two* at two o'clock, etc., but does not strike at the half hours, how many times will the bell be struck in the course of twenty-four hours?

9

Logs, Pianos and Spirals

Sequences of powers: the exponential curve and logarithms

The sequences discussed in Chapter 8 were built up by successive additions. In this chapter we shall discuss *geometrical progressions*, which are sequences built up by successive multiplications by a number which characterizes each particular sequence and is called the *common ratio*. Examples are:

$$2; \quad 4; \quad 8; \quad 16; \quad 32; \quad 64; \quad 128; \quad 256; \quad 512; \quad 1024; \ldots \text{ common ratio} = 2.$$

$$3; \quad 9; \quad 27; \quad 81; \quad 243; \quad 729; \quad 2187; \quad 6561; \quad 19683; \ldots \text{ common ratio} = 3.$$

$$7; \quad 49; \quad 343; \quad 2401; \quad 16,807; \quad 117,649; \quad 823,543; \ldots \text{ common ratio} = 7.$$

$$10; \quad 100; \quad 1,000; \quad 10,000; \quad 100,000; \quad 1,000,000; \ldots \text{ common ratio} = 10.$$

The common ratio is obtained by dividing any term of the sequence by the term which precedes it. A glance at the examples shows how quickly the terms of the sequences grow when the common ratio is greater than one. A common ratio not very much greater than 1 gives a sequence whose terms do not increase so quickly. The sequence whose common ratio is $1\frac{1}{3}$ or $1\cdot33333\ldots$ is:

$$1\cdot333; \quad 1\cdot778; \quad 2\cdot370; \quad 3\cdot160; \quad 4\cdot214; \quad 5\cdot618; \quad 7\cdot491; \quad 9\cdot988; \quad 13\cdot32\ldots$$

and we can go as far as the sixteenth term before reaching a hundred.

When the common ratio lies between 0 and 1, the terms of the sequences decrease. Examples are

$$0\cdot667; \quad 0\cdot444; \quad 0\cdot296; \quad 0\cdot197; \quad 0\cdot132; \quad 0\cdot088; \quad 0\cdot058; \quad 0\cdot039\ldots \text{ common ratio } \tfrac{2}{3}$$

$$0\cdot5; \quad 0\cdot25; \quad 0\cdot125; \quad 0\cdot063; \quad 0\cdot031; \quad 0\cdot016; \quad 0\cdot008; \quad 0\cdot004\ldots \text{ common ratio } \tfrac{1}{2}$$

THE IDEA OF A LOGARITHM

The sequences we have been looking at possess many interesting properties. To begin with, it is probably easiest to work with the sequence containing the simplest numbers, the sequence whose common ratio is 2. In studying the sequence we shall be calling 2 the "first term", 4 the "second term", 8 the "third term" and so on. It will, therefore, be convenient to write down the terms of the sequence and then simply number them off 1, 2, 3 . . .

Sequence N	2	4	8	16	32	64	128	256	512	1024	. . .
Sequence L	1	2	3	4	5	6	7	8	9	10	. . .

when sequence N is the sequence of numbers we are studying and sequence L is the simple numbering of the terms.

We might notice here that if we continued sequence N one term farther to the left, by dividing by 2, we should have a term 1 in sequence N and the corresponding term in sequence L would be 0.

Below are set out some simple multiplications and divisions of numbers belonging to the sequence N. To the right of each multiplication or division are placed the corresponding numbers from sequence L (Fig. 9.1).

Numbers from sequence N multiplied	Corresponding numbers from sequence L	Numbers from sequence N divided	Corresponding numbers from sequence L
64 × 8 —— 512	6 +3 —— 9	512 ÷ 64 —— 8	9 − 6 —— 3
16 × 32 —— 512	4 +5 —— 9	1024 ÷ 128 —— 8	10 − 7 —— 3
32 × 8 —— 256	5 +3 —— 8	128 ÷ 16 —— 8	7 − 4 —— 3

Fig. 9.1

In every case the *product* of two terms of sequence N corresponds to the *sum* obtained by adding corresponding terms of sequence L.

Similarly, if terms of the geometric sequence N are divided, the corresponding terms of sequence L are subtracted.

This remarkable property, that terms of a geometrical sequence N mapped on to the terms of an arithmetical sequence L when *multiplied* by one set of numbers correspond to *addition* of the other set, was observed as early as 1594 by John Napier, the Scotsman already mentioned in Chapter 1 in connexion with Napier's rods. He developed the theory of logarithms and published a book about the wonderful properties of logarithms in 1614. (It was written in Latin and called *Mirifici Logarithmorum Canonis Descriptio*.) Since 1614, logarithms have come into general use and very simple tables have been produced. It will help in the understanding of logarithms if we define a few terms in general use today.

From the table showing sequence N and sequence L, it will be seen that $N = 32$ corresponds to $L = 5$, the common ratio of sequence N being 2. The relationship between 32, 5 and 2 may be written in two distinct ways:

$$32 = 2^5$$
$$\text{or} \quad 5 = \log_2 32.$$

$32 = 2^5$, read as "thirty-two is equal to two to the power five", simply means $32 = 2 \times 2 \times 2 \times 2 \times 2$, there being *five* factors, each factor being *two*.

$5 = \log_2 32$, read as "five is equal to the logarithm of thirty-two to the base two", means the same thing, namely, that "five is the number of factors, each equal to the base, 2, which must be multiplied together to give the number, 32".

In the expression 2^5, the five is called the *power* of 2. It is also called the *index*, indicating the power to which 2 has been raised, or the *exponent*, showing the power to which 2 has been raised.

We can illustrate the use of these words by looking at another sequence.

Sequence N 1   6   36   216   1296   7776   46656 . . . common ratio 6.
Sequence L 0   1   2   3   4   5   6   . . .

Either of the forms

$$1296 = 6^4 \quad \text{or} \quad 4 = \log_6 1296$$

describes the relationship between the number 1296, the base 6 and the index 4. This sequence with a common ratio 6 may be used to illustrate the properties of logarithms in a similar way to the sequence whose common ratio was 2. From the table:

	Numbers multiplied	*Logarithms added*
$\log_6 36\ =2$	36	2
$\log_6 216\ =3$	$\times\ \underline{216}$	$+\ \underline{3}$
$\log_6 7776 = 5$	$\underline{7776}$	$\underline{5}$

As they stand, these sequences are not very useful. One so rarely wishes to multiply 36 by 216 that the fact that this comparatively hard operation can be replaced by the simple addition $2 + 3 = 5$ is of little value. Our number system is based on 10 and it is logarithms to the base 10 which are of such great practical value. At first sight the sequence

Sequence N 1   10   100   1000   10,000   100,000   . . . common ratio $= 10$
Sequence L 0   1   2   3   4   5   . . .

does not look very promising because multiplications such as 100×1000 present no difficulties; it is the numbers between 10 and 100 or between 100 and 1000 which provide the difficult multiplications. We are, in fact, interested in all numbers and not simply those which happen to be terms in one of these simple geometrical sequences.

This difficulty can be overcome in a way which will be easy to follow once we have looked at some of the properties of the graphical representations of these sequences.

To represent the sequence 1, 2, 4, 8, 16, 32, 64, 128 . . .

(*a*) Mark off equally spaced points up the vertical left-hand margin of some graph paper.

(*b*) Mark off equally spaced points along the horizontal margin along the bottom and label these points 0, 1, 2, 3, 4, 5, 6, 7.

(*c*) Place a cross, $\times$, at a height 1 above the point marked 0

,, ,, ,, $\times$,, ,, ,, 2 ,, ,, ,, ,, 1
,, ,, ,, $\times$,, ,, ,, 4 ,, ,, ,, ,, 2
,, ,, ,, $\times$,, ,, ,, 8 ,, ,, ,, ,, 3
,, ,, ,, $\times$,, ,, ,, 16 ,, ,, ,, ,, 4

and so on.

The pattern of crosses is quite clearly seen, sweeping gracefully up to the right (Fig. 9.2). The step (*b*) stated vaguely "equally spaced points". The detailed appearance of the representation will depend upon this spacing. A second set of crosses has been drawn

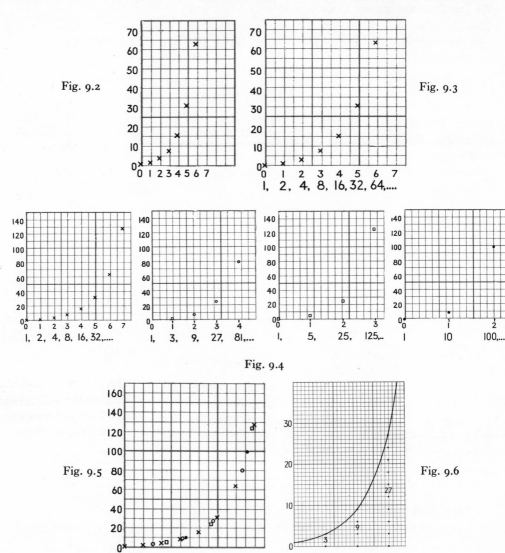

Fig. 9.2

Fig. 9.3

1, 2, 4, 8, 16, 32, 64,....

1, 2, 4, 8, 16, 32,....

1, 3, 9, 27, 81,...

1, 5, 25, 125,..

1 10 100,...

Fig. 9.4

Fig. 9.5

Fig. 9.6

with the same vertical spacing but with a bigger horizontal spacing, giving a representation which does not sweep up so steeply (Fig. 9.3).

We have, therefore, this degree of freedom of choice in drawing out our representations of any of the sequences of numbers. By carefully choosing the horizontal spacing we can draw out representations for a number of sequences so that when they are superimposed the points obtained from the various sequences of numbers all lie on a smooth curve. Above, there are drawn out representations for the sequences with common ratios

2, 3, 5 and 10 (Fig. 9.4). The result of superimposing these on one another is shown also (Fig. 9.5).

Even with the small scale diagram illustrating this process, it should be obvious that the various sets of points do lie on a single smooth curve. This is a most important curve. It arises from geometrical sequences but it would be rather misleading to call it a "geometrical curve"; the terms power-curve and index-curve would also suggest other meanings of the terms "power" or "index". The name *exponential curve*, by which it is usually known, avoids other interpretations and adequately describes the curve. The curve illustrated was built up from points arising from a number of geometrical sequences. An alternative way of describing this property is: that *any* geometrical sequence may be used to provide the set of points through which the smooth curve can be drawn, and that by altering the horizontal spacing along the bottom axis the numbers belonging to another geometrical sequence can be read off the graph. This will become clear if a curve is carefully drawn. Using graph paper, mark numbers in ink up the left-hand margin, making one small square represent one unit (10 units to the inch). Along the bottom mark off the half-inches in pencil. Mark a point opposite 2 above the first half-inch; mark a point opposite 4 above the second half-inch; 8 opposite the third half-inch; and then 16 and 32. Join these points in pencil with a smooth curve and when you are satisfied that it is a smooth curve passing accurately through the points, ink it over. This curve has been built up from the sequence with common ratio 2. Rub out any pencil marks and you will have a curve which shows no evidence of the fact that it was built up from the 1, 2, 4, 8, 16, 32 . . . sequence. If along the bottom margin equally spaced points 0·8 in. apart are marked off, it will be found that the curve is 3, 9, 27 units above these points on the horizontal axis (Fig. 9.6). This should demonstrate that any convenient geometrical sequence may be used for drawing the exponential curve, and when drawn, the curve can be used to illustrate the properties of any other geometrical sequence.

This valuable property enables us to obtain a continuous set of logarithms. The drawing of a continuous curve between a number of separate points is the geometrical counterpart of filling in numbers between the widely separated 1, 10, 100, 1000, . . . of the sequence with common ratio 10.

An accurate, smooth curve can most easily be drawn when the points which it must pass through are as close together as possible. The particular sequence which happens to be extremely convenient is that whose common ratio is $1\frac{1}{3}$.

Sequence N	1·33	1·78	2·37	3·16	4·21	5·62	7·49	9·99	13·32	. . .
Sequence L	1	2	3	4	5	6	7	8	9	. . .

It will be seen that the eighth term happens to be so nearly equal to 10 that, to any ordinary scale, the difference would be less than the thickness of the curve. We are going to draw the exponential curve accurately from the figures of this sequence, and it will be most convenient if the 9·99 point could come exactly ten squares to the right of the left-hand margin. Since $8 \times 1\frac{1}{4} = 10$, to draw the curve we shall choose a scale such that the horizontal distances between the points which represent the terms of the sequence are $1\frac{1}{4}$ cm.

Using a scale of 1 cm to 1 unit vertically, the first four points plotted will look like Fig. 9.7. Working in pencil, mark in all the points up to the ninth. Join them with a smooth curve which passes accurately through them all. Now ink in the curve and the numbers

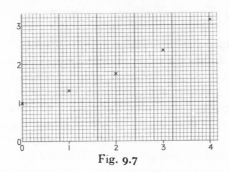

Fig. 9.7

up the left-hand margin, and there is an accurate exponential curve which passes through a point opposite 10 in the left-hand margin and ten squares to the right of this margin. Our aim is to fill in numbers between the terms of the sequence

Sequence N	1	10	100	. . .
Sequence L	0	1	2	. . .

so we write 0 at the extreme left of the horizontal axis, and 1 under the point 10 cm to the right of this.

The interval 0 to 1 may now be divided into ten equal parts, and at 1-cm intervals we may mark in the points 0·1, 0·2, 0·3, etc. These are numbers between 0 and 1 in sequence L. We are, however, more interested in inserting numbers between 1 and 10 in sequence N.

From Fig. 9.8 we see that the point of the curve opposite 2 is above 0·3, the point opposite 3 is above 0·48, the point opposite 4 is above 0·60 and so on. In this way we can draw up a table interpolating the corresponding numbers in sequences N and L. The number in the first sequence N has a logarithm to the base 10 given by the number in the second sequence L.

Sequence N	1	2	3	4	5	6	7	8	9	10	11	12	13	. . .
Sequence L	0	0·30	0·48	0·60	0·70	0·78	0·85	0·90	0·95	1·0	1·04	1·08	1·11	. . .

These are the numbers printed in the ordinary tables of logarithms. From a graph we have been able to find them to two places of decimals only. Most logarithm tables give them to four places and from logarithm tables we can give the logarithms more accurately:

Number:	1	2	3	4	5	6	7	8	9	10
Logarithm:	0·0000	0·3010	0·4771	0·6021	0·6990	0·7781	0·8451	0·9031	0·9542	1·0000

We have taken liberties with the mathematics, and it is outside the scope of this book to justify our procedure. We have defined a logarithm for certain fixed numbers, 10, 100, 1000 and so on, and we have assumed that a continuous function exists which defines $\mathrm{Log}_{10}N$ for all values of N. Readers who wish to pursue this further should consult a standard algebra text-book for a definition of a logarithm as a continuous function.

So far we have inserted numbers between 1 and 10. We may continue this interpolation very simply. Since multiplying numbers corresponds to adding logarithms we may give, as an illustration,

	Number	Logarithm
$\log_{10}6 = 0{\cdot}778$	6	0·778
$\log_{10}10 = 1{\cdot}000$	× 10	+ 1·000
$\log_{10}60 = 1{\cdot}778$	60	1·778

For numbers of various sizes, the table at the top of page 125 may help in placing decimal points and the whole number part of logarithms.

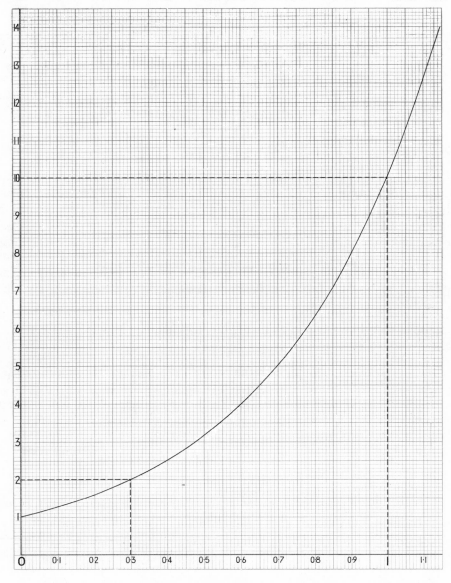

Fig. 9.8

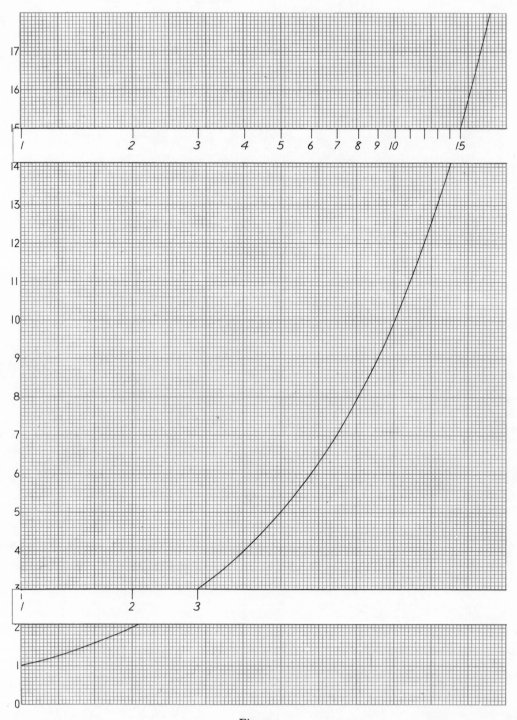

Fig. 9.9

Number	Logarithm
I - 0
4·5	0·6532
10 - I
45·0	1·6532
100 - - - - - - - - - - - - - - - - - - 2
450·0	2·6532
1000 - - - - - - - - - - - - - - - - 3
4500·0	3·6532
10,000 - - - - - - - - - - - - - - 4

If a number is between 10 and 100 its logarithm is between 1 and 2 and so on.

EXERCISES

1. Verify from tables that $\log_{10}5\cdot6 = 0\cdot7482$. Write down $\log_{10}56$ and $\log_{10}560$.
2. $\log_{10}32 = 1\cdot5051$. Check this from tables. Since $32 = 2 \times 2 \times 2 \times 2 \times 2$,
$$\log_{10}32 = \log 2 + \log 2 + \log 2 + \log 2 + \log 2 = 5 \times \log 2.$$

$$\therefore \quad \log 2 = \tfrac{1}{5} \log 32 = \tfrac{1\cdot5051}{5}$$
$$= 0\cdot3010.$$

This can be verified from tables.

In a similar way use tables to find $\log_{10}81$. Using the fact that $81 = 3^4$, calculate $\log_{10}3$ and verify from tables.

The Slide Rule

Fig. 9.9 consists of exactly the same curve as that constructed in Fig. 9.8, and on the left the y-axis is numbered vertically in the same way but the figures along the bottom have been omitted. Our purpose is to mark, along a horizontal strip of paper, the same numbers which appear on the vertical scale, but so spaced that the distances between them are equal to the distances from the y-axis to the curve.

Having drawn in the curve very carefully, take a strip of paper and place a mark on its upper edge and label this with a "1". Always keep this mark exactly on the y-axis. Slide the strip up until the top edge coincides with the figure 2 on the y-axis and, keeping the top edge of the strip along the line of the squared paper, mark the edge where it cuts the curve and label this mark with a 2. Then move the strip up until the top edge is level with the 3 on the y-axis, mark the point where it cuts the curve, label this with a 3, and so on. You will then have a strip which will look like that drawn in Fig. 9.10.

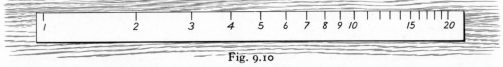

Fig. 9.10

The actual spacing of the numbers along this strip expresses in another form the relationship which determines the shape of the graph. The curve is that of $y = C^x$, or its equivalent $x = \log_C y$, so the horizontal or x spacings will be proportional to the logarithms of the y's. The strip will, therefore, be numbered in such a way that the *lengths* measured along the strip are proportional to the *logarithms* of the numbers.

We have already seen that when numbers are multiplied the logarithm of their product is equal to the sum of their logarithms. Two lengths can be added simply by putting them end to end and adding the total length (Fig. 9.11):

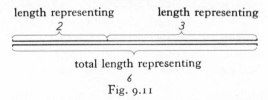

length representing
2

length representing
3

total length representing
6

Fig. 9.11

This is the principle of the *slide rule*. The scale drawn out on the strip of paper in the way just described is repeated on a similar strip. One strip may then slide along the edge of the other strip, giving a simple mechanical way of *adding* the logarithms and so of multiplying the numbers (Figs. 9.12 and 9.13).

Fig. 9.12
The two strips alongside each other.

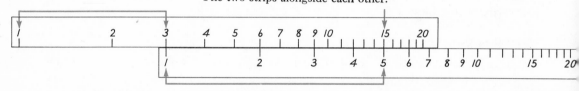

Fig. 9.13
The two strips arranged to show the multiplication $3 \times 5 = 15$.

The strips are aligned to illustrate $3 \times 5 = 15$, but a more careful look at them will show that the whole of the table of threes is illustrated. Each number on the lower scale is against a number three times as big on the upper slide. Thus, when the slide is set as in the diagram with the lower 1 against the upper 3, any multiplication (or division) by three can be performed. A home-made slide rule, such as this, serves well enough to illustrate the principle by which it works but is not accurate enough for practical use.

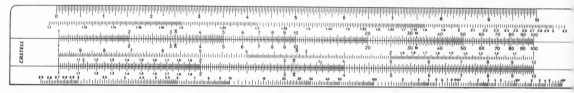

Fig. 9.14
A slide rule (half size).

The manufactured slide rule, the inseparable companion of many engineers, made as a practical working calculator, consists of an ivory or plastic slide, freely moving in a well-fitting groove, and engraved very accurately for working to be carried to three significant figures. Fig. 9.14 illustrates a commercial slide rule and it indicates both the scale to which a slide rule is made and the accuracy of the engraving. A good engineer's slide rule, made to stand a great deal of wear and give accurate results, is expensive, but there are on the market plastic slide rules which are cheap and serve the purpose of learning how to use one and pass on the information to boys and girls who, long before they reach the stage of owning a first-grade instrument of their own, want to know what a slide rule is and how it works.

How the sequence grows

The sequences we are examining in this chapter were defined as sequences of numbers built up by successive multiplications. They may also be examined from the point of view of the number to be added to each term to give the next term and they may be represented, as in Fig. 9.15, by points built up by a sequence of steps. These sequences will be found to show the property that the amount added each time (increment) is proportional to the term to which it is added.

Fig. 9.15 illustrates the following:

$$\text{Sequence,} \quad y = 1 \quad 2 \quad 4 \quad 8 \quad 16 \quad 32 \quad \ldots$$
$$\text{Increment,} \quad \Delta y = \quad 1 \quad 2 \quad 4 \quad 8 \quad 16 \quad \quad \ldots$$

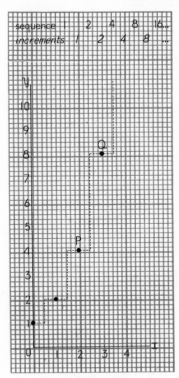

Fig. 9.15

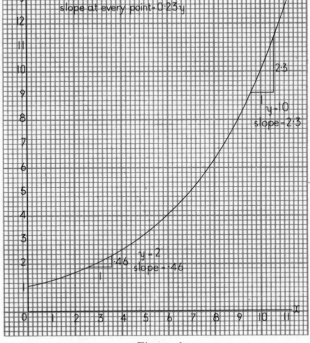

Fig. 9.16

For this sequence each increment is equal to the term to which it is added, and in Fig. 9.15 the point Q is as much above the point P as P is above the x-axis.

Other examples are:

$$\text{Sequence,} \quad y = 1 \quad 3 \quad 9 \quad 27 \quad 81 \quad \ldots$$
$$\text{Increment,} \; \Delta y = \quad 2 \quad 6 \quad 18 \quad 54 \qquad \ldots$$

for which the increment is equal to twice the term to which it is added, and

$$\text{Sequence,} \quad y = 1 \qquad 1\cdot333 \qquad 1\cdot778 \qquad 2\cdot370 \qquad 3\cdot160 \quad \ldots$$
$$\text{Increment,} \; \Delta y = 0\cdot333 \qquad 0\cdot444 \qquad 0\cdot592 \qquad 0\cdot790 \qquad \ldots$$

for which the increment is one third of the term to which it is added.

The idea of slope was introduced in Chapter 8 on page 109, but there the points representing the sequences all lay on straight lines whose slopes were the same at all points. The sequences we are now discussing are represented by points lying on curves which become progressively steeper. Fig. 9.16 illustrates such a curve, of the family $y = a^x$.* If at any point a tangent is drawn to the curve and the slope of this tangent is measured, it will be found that the slope is equal to $0\cdot23\,y$, where y is the ordinate of the point of contact of the tangent. In the diagram the slopes are shown at the points where $y = 2$ and $y = 10$. Every curve of the family $y = a^x$, which passes through points representing the terms of one of the geometric sequences is such that as the terms increase so the curve becomes steeper.

A knock-out tournament

A simple example of a sequence of this type is the number of teams in the various rounds of any knock-out competition. Fig. 9.17 is a list of teams which, one year, might be playing in the last five rounds of the Football Association Cup. The list fits into a pattern, and the reader will see that the curve drawn through the tops of the columns has the same form as the curves in Figs. 9.8, 9.9 and 9.16. It is reversed, since the longest list has been placed to the left of the diagram.

Starting from the right of the diagram, the number of teams in each of the columns is 2, 4, 8, 16, 32, which is the sequence used for building up several of the curves we have been discussing in this chapter. Fig. 9.18 is the same figure as Fig. 9.17, slightly embellished with a few decorations along the bottom. It represents the outline of the top of a grand piano. The wave-length of a musical note is exactly twice the wave-length of the note which is precisely one octave higher. Middle C has twice the wave-length of upper C, and lower C has twice the wave-length of middle C. The ordinary piano has a range of several octaves; so, starting from the treble end, the wave-lengths of the various C notes over the range of the piano will be in the same proportion as the numbers of the sequence 1, 2, 4, 8, 16, 32. . . . Any musical instrument in which the length either of a wire or of a column of air varies with the wave-length will, in one way or another, reflect the shape of an exponential curve. One example is the shape of a grand piano, and another is the shape of sets of organ pipes. The decorated organ screens in our churches

---

* The value of a chosen for the curve of Fig. 9.16 is $a = 1\cdot2589$ for which $\log_{10}a = 0\cdot1$. This value for a gives $y = 10$ when $x = 10$ so that the curve $y = a^x$ passes through the point ($x = 10$, $y = 10$). $\log_e a = 0\cdot23026$.

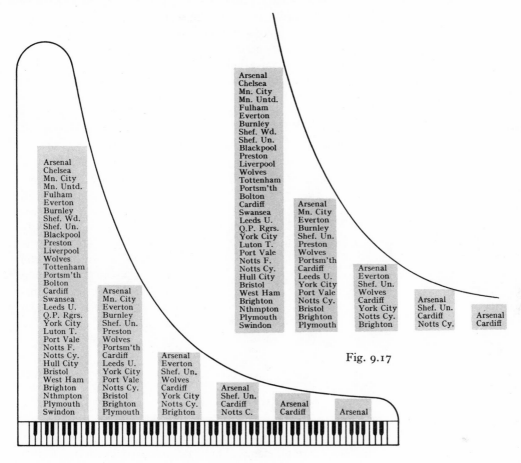

Fig. 9.17

Fig. 9.18

must be designed to meet both architectural and musical requirements, which impose a precise geometrical pattern on the arrangement of pipes. Many beautiful effects have been produced in our churches and cathedrals by blending the graceful exponential curves we have been examining with the arcs of circles in the arches. The architect's problem is illustrated in Fig. 9.19.

Fig. 9.19
The profile of organ pipes is an exponential curve.

The wave-length of a musical note is always double the wave-length of the note which is one octave higher in pitch. In the ordinary chromatic scale the octave is divided into twelve notes: C, D, E, F, G, A, B, which are white notes on a keyboard instrument, and C♯, D♯, F♯, G♯, A♯, which are the black notes. In an evenly tempered scale the wave-length of each note is 1·0595 times* the wave-length of the note which is one semitone higher in the scale. The wave-length of B is 1·0595 times that of upper C and the wave-length of A♯ is 1·0595 times that of B. Thus the wave-length of A♯ is (1·0595)², or 1·1225 times that of upper C (C′). A has 1·0595 times the wave-length of A♯, that is, (1·0595)³ times the wave-length of C′. If successive powers of 1·0595 are worked out to four places of decimals, they give the following table of wave-lengths in terms of that of C′:

Wave-length of B   is 1·0595 × wave-length of C′

„   „   „ A♯ is 1·1225 ×   „   „   „ C′

„   „   „ A   is 1·1892 ×   „   „   „ C′

„   „   „ G♯ is 1·2599 ×   „   „   „ C′

„   „   „ G   is 1·3348 ×   „   „   „ C′

„   „   „ F♯ is 1·4141 ×   „   „   „ C′

„   „   „ F   is 1·4983 ×   „   „   „ C′

„   „   „ E   is 1·5874 ×   „   „   „ C′

„   „   „ D♯ is 1·6818 ×   „   „   „ C′

„   „   „ D   is 1·7819 ×   „   „   „ C′

„   „   „ C♯ is 1·8878 ×   „   „   „ C′

„   „   „ C   is 2·0000 ×   „   „   „ C′

In Fig. 9.22 lengths for the notes on a guitar are drawn according to this rule and their positions on the exponential graph are indicated. The lengths of string required to produce the various notes are not left to the judgment of a guitar player: ridges or frets are provided which accurately fix the length of the part of the string that is free to vibrate. A violinist is left to judge the position of the finger of the left hand that determines the exact pitch of the note being played; this, of course gives far greater flexibility but demands a far higher standard of musical ability and training.

The wave-lengths set out in the table above give a sequence of semitones which differ from one another by exactly equal intervals. A tune transcribed from one key to another would not be altered in any way other than the absolute pitch in which it was played. There is, however, a traditional scale which differs slightly from the perfectly exponential scale. It is known as the "diatonic scale" and the frequencies of notes are in the proportion of eight simple whole numbers. These are set out in the table which follows, together with their decimal equivalents when the sequence is adjusted to give the wave-length of C′ as unity. The corresponding exponential values are set out for comparison.

---

* A change of twelve semitones is the same as an octave. Thus the wave-length of C is $(1·0595)^{12}$ × the wave-length of C . The number 1·0595 was found by calculating the twelfth root of 2. Since $\log_{10} 2 = 0·30103$, $\frac{1}{12} \log_{10} 2 = 0·02509 = \log_{10} 1·0595$.

C	D	E	F	G	A	B	C′	
$\frac{1}{24}$	$\frac{1}{27}$	$\frac{1}{30}$	$\frac{1}{32}$	$\frac{1}{36}$	$\frac{1}{40}$	$\frac{1}{45}$	$\frac{1}{48}$	} Diatonic scale
2·000	1·778	1·600	1·500	1·333	1·200	1·067	1·000	Diatonic scale
2·000	1·782	1·587	1·498	1·335	1·189	1·060	1·000	Exponential scale

These differences are sufficient to make a change in key produce a slight alteration in the intervals which could be detected by a trained musician. They would make it impossible for two instruments to play together if tuned according to the different scales.

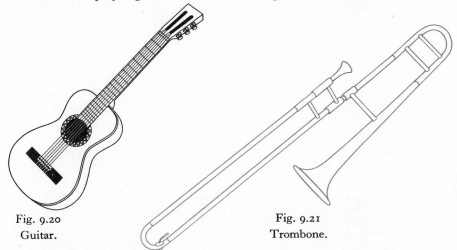

Fig. 9.20
Guitar.

Fig. 9.21
Trombone.

From the drawing of a guitar (Fig. 9.20) it will be seen that the distance between the frets for two lower notes is greater than the distance between the frets for two higher notes. These distances increase in the same way as the exponential curves already drawn several times in this chapter. Although there are no frets to guide him, the violinist has to learn so to space his fingers that he feels in his finger-tips the exponential sequence of numbers. Similarly, a trombone player (Fig. 9.21) must pull his slide in and out in movements which are in accordance with the same sequences. Thus the movement in and out of a trombone player's slide has something in common with the slide rule which is pushed backwards and forwards by an engineer in that both sets of graded movements depend upon the relation between numbers and their logarithms.

Fig. 9.22 shows the relation between the lengths of the strings corresponding to the various notes of the scale and illustrates their conformity with the curve used in Fig. 9.9 for giving the spacings for a slide rule.

Fechner's Law

In the middle of the nineteenth century a German psychologist, G. T. Fechner, enunciated a law which states that the response to any stimulus is proportional to the logarithm of the stimulus. This law applies to all five senses but its implications are most readily understood when related to light and sound. Physically, the measure of the intensity of a light falling on a photometer, or on one of those light meters or exposure meters familiar to photographers, is a measure of light energy. Physiologically, observed brightness of a light is the interpretation of the strength of signals which reach the brain through the

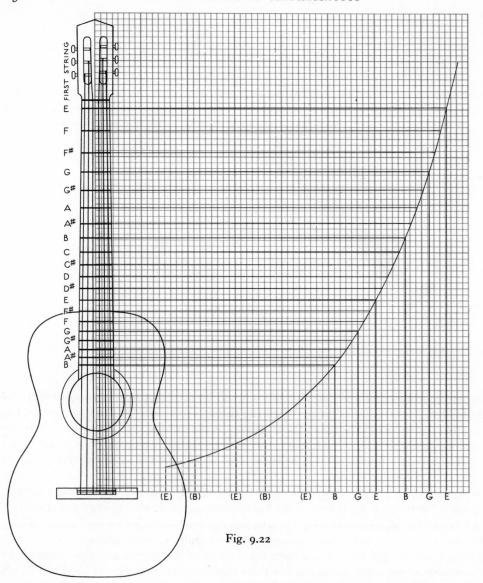

Fig. 9.22

optic nerve when light energy falls on cells in the retina of the eye and excites them to electro-chemical activity. Light energy emitted by an electric light bulb can be measured directly but it is more difficult to assign a numerical value to our judgment of brightness. A brief description of a simple experiment may help to explain how actual brightness and our judgment of brightness may be compared.

A, B, C, D, E, F are six electric light bulbs joined in parallel to a supply of electricity so that the current flowing through each bulb may be controlled independently by turning the knob of a variable resistance. The subject is asked to regulate the currents until he judges that B is the same amount brighter than A as C is brighter than B. He then adjusts D until he judges that D is as much brighter than C as C is brighter than B and so on. Each lamp is compared with the lamps on either side of it until the subject is satisfied that the brightness of the lamps increases from A to F in equal stages. The currents passing through the various lamps are measured and the output of energy of each lamp recorded. If the results are now plotted (Fig. 9.23) with observed brightness (response) along the x-axis (horizontal axis) and actual brightness or light-energy (the stimulus) along the vertical y-axis, the lamps A, B, C, . . . will be placed at equal distances along the x-axis to correspond to the judged equal increases in brightness, and the corresponding vertical distances will be proportional to the recorded light energies. The curve obtained is typical of the exponential curves for which values along the x-axis are proportional to the logarithms of values on the x-axis. If the experiment is carried out on a number of people the curve which best fits the various points on the graph will be found to have the shape of that drawn in Fig. 9.23.

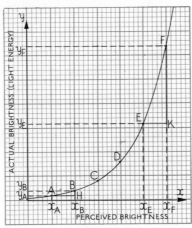

Fig. 9.23
Response.

The slope of the curve in Fig. 9.23 increases as the intensity of the light increases. Between A and B, where the light is dimmest, the curve does not slope up very steeply and a very small change in intensity of light from y_A to y_B is perceived as a change represented by the length $x_A\,x_B$ along the x-axis. Between E and F, when the light is much brighter, the large increase in intensity represented by $y_E\,y_F$ produces the response $x_E\,x_F$ which is equal to the response $x_A\,x_B$. Thus, when the illumination is small our eyes are able to distinguish between very small changes in brightness, and we can, in fact, pick out quite a lot of things in starlight when out of doors during a moonless night. On the other hand, when light is intensely bright, it takes a great deal of difference in brightness for our eyes to respond, so that our eyes are very much less sensitive in very bright sunlight. The slope of the curve between A and B, which is measured by the ratio BH/AH, is small, and between E and F the slope of the curve, FK/EK, is large. This slope represents the sensitivity of the eye, the eye being very sensitive when the slope is small and far less sensitive when the slope is large. This change in slope explains how it is that so delicate an organ as the eye can function effectively in very dim light and yet is robust enough to withstand the very severe glare of bright sunlight. Readers interested in photography will find many interesting relationships between visual estimates of brightness and the appropriate shutter speeds and sizes of aperture.

The relation between amount of noise and perception of noise is just the same as the corresponding relations for light, and a curve of the same shape as Fig. 9.23 would be obtained if intensity of sound were plotted vertically against estimated loudness of sound plotted horizontally. When the curve has least slope the ear is at its most sensitive and when it has a steep slope the ear is less sensitive. The ear can distinguish between minute sounds when all is still and quiet and yet is robust enough to withstand the violence of the noise of an explosion. Telephone and radio engineers who are responsible for amplifying sound to increase its audibility have to devise their apparatus so that they multiply the energy in order to add to the audibility.

Sensitivity to touch is less easily described. Here we shall do no more than point out that we are sensitive to subtle differences in the feel of various cloths and yet able to withstand violent blows in boxing and survive quite severe accidents. It is not difficult to agree, in general, that when we touch things gently we can be very discriminating and that our sensitivity decreases as pressure or violence increases, but it is very much more difficult to devise experiments which enable such relationships to be expressed in precise terms.

Fechner's law is not an exact description of the stimulus/response relationship. Many other factors such as fatigue, attention and interest intervene. It is, however, a good working rule that is extremely useful in helping us to understand this aspect of the mechanism of our own bodily functioning.

Astronomical magnitudes

We have inherited from ancient times a system of classifying stars according to their apparent brightness, as they appear to the naked eye. The brightest stars are called first magnitude stars, those not quite so bright are called second magnitude stars and so on. Today this system is retained but it has been made more precise by giving the number 1 to the magnitude of the *brightest* first magnitude star, the number 2 to the magnitude of the brightest second magnitude star, and grading the stars in between so that if there were a star exactly half way between the brightness of stars of magnitudes 1 and 2 it would be assigned the magnitude 1·5.

Today the actual brightness of stars can be measured accurately and it is found that the magnitude classification conforms to one based on the logarithm of the actual brightness. A star of magnitude 1 is 100 times as bright as a star of magnitude 6. Thus a change of 5 magnitudes corresponds to a change of 100 times the brightness, so that a change of one magnitude corresponds to a change in brightness corresponding to a multiplication by the fifth root of 100, which is 2·512.

If a star of magnitude 1 is taken as the basis of calculation and its brightness is also called 1, then a star of magnitude 2 will have a brightness of $\dfrac{1}{2\cdot512}$, a star of magnitude 3 will have a brightness of $\dfrac{1}{(2\cdot512)^2}$ and so on. The formula connecting magnitude and brightness is

$$\text{magnitude} = 1 - \log_{2.512}(\text{brightness}).$$

The actual brightness, the relative reactions of our eyes to the brightness, and the magnitude of a few heavenly bodies are given in the table below. This is set out in such a way that the numbers indicate the brightness of the heavenly bodies but the spacing of the table indicates the relative impact of their brightness as the impression reaches the brain through the optic nerve, and although the moon is only about one millionth as bright as the sun, its position in the scale of apparent brightness is roughly half way between that of a first magnitude star and the sun.

	Actual brightness	Relative reaction of eyes	Magnitude
SUN	109,650,000,000	27·6	−26·6
MOON (Full)	190,550	13·2	−12·2
VENUS (Max.)	129	5·3	− 4·3
JUPITER (Max.)	20	3·25	− 2·25
SIRIUS	10·8	2·6	− 1·6
VEGA	2·2	0·86	+ 0·14
RIGEL	1·84	0·66	+ 0·34

The Malthusian Curve

In the realm of economic history, the problems of growing populations and their increasing needs in terms of food and raw materials have troubled economists for many years. A statement of the nature of these problems was made by Thomas Malthus (1766–1834) who in 1798 published his famous essay on the principle of population as it affects the future improvement of society. In this essay he put forward the view that population always increases to the limits of the means of subsistence and is prevented from increasing beyond these limits by war, famine, pestilence and the influence of misery. When these checks are not limiting its growth, population increases geometrically and subsistence arithmetically. From this theory Malthus drew the important practical conclusion in the England of his day that the existing Poor Law system, with its indiscriminate bounties and doles, was utterly to be condemned as tending to aggravate the very evils that it was supposed to remedy. This simple statement of the Malthusian law is an example of the relationships discussed in this chapter. If the numbers 2, 4, 8, 16, 32 in geometrical progression are marked off vertically and the numbers 1, 2, 3, 4, 5, which are in arithmetic progression, are marked off horizontally, we arrive at the graph shown in Fig. 9.24 which illustrates the law of Malthusian development.

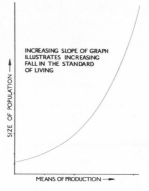

Fig. 9.24

Since population is measured vertically and the ability of this population to provide means of subsistence for itself is measured horizontally, it will be seen from the graph that the increasing slope of the curve indicates the increasing poverty of the nation. Malthus's pessimistic prophecies were in fact modified by increasing emigration from this country, the new sources of wealth which sprang from the industrial revolution and the new sources of food which we were able to obtain by development of the Colonial territories. Great Britain has not, therefore, suffered as Malthus prophesied. Nevertheless, today, if we look at the rapidly increasing populations in countries such as Egypt and India and we bear in mind that there are no outlets for their populations in hitherto undiscovered territories, it seems likely that increasing shortages of food, such as those predicted by Malthus, are not far away from these countries. A study of the exponential curve, in relation to population trends in Asia, may help one to understand something of the difficulties facing men such as Pandit Nehru and President Nasser and the government of Indonesia.

The Concept of Time

While on the subject of history, it is interesting to think about the nature of our concept of time. If we ask an ordinary person who is not a history specialist to write down all the facts about British history he can recall for successive periods of 450 years beginning at the year A.D. 150, he might only be able to mention three or four names for the period from A.D. 150 to 600. For the period 600 to 1050 he is likely to know considerably more, and names like those of Canute, King Alfred and Ethelred are more familiar. The period from 1050 to 1500 through the Norman conquest, the Plantagenets, the Wars of the Roses to the discovery of America contains a great deal of history which is quite well known, and the period from 1500 to 1950 is likely to be so well known that many pages could be written by almost everybody about people and events of the last 450 years. This general description suggests that the amount of information we have about past eras increases rapidly as we approach nearer to our own day and that the graphs we have been drawing in this chapter might possibly give a fair representation of our increasing knowledge. This is not an easy theory to check, in the context of the history of the last

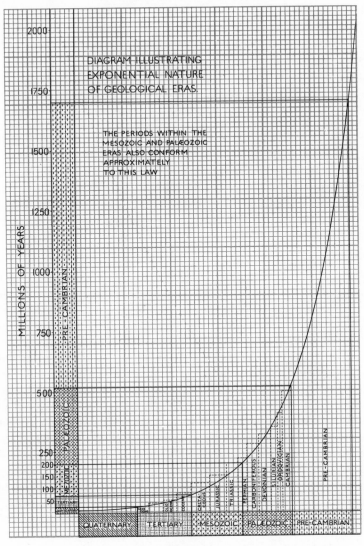

Fig. 9.25

1800 years, for although the Norman conquest in the middle of the eleventh century and the Reformation at the end of the fifteenth century are the beginnings of new chapters in English history, these are by no means the only significant dates since the departure of the Romans. If, however, we consider much longer periods of time and look at the geologists' time scale we find that the main periods of geological time have been assigned dates. Fig. 9.25 illustrates the lengths of these geological periods, the dates being taken from a standard text-book in geology. It is remarkable how closely they correspond with the theoretical exponential curve which is superimposed. This is fairly convincing evidence that our concept of time is such that our impression of time past is proportional to the logarithm of the actual time which has elapsed since an event.

Our concept of large numbers

When we think of big numbers such as 4,000,000,000 or 400,000,000,000 we are inclined to judge the size of the number by its length when set out in figures. Thus 40,000,000,000 looks only a little bigger than 4,000,000,000 and does not give the impression of being ten times as big. In fact, the casual reader of a popular newspaper might hardly notice the difference in appearance between an annual budget of £40,000,000,000 and one of £4,000,000,000. The reason for this is simply that the length of a number is proportional to its logarithm and not to the number itself and we are, therefore, always tempted to judge sizes of large numbers by their logarithms. This is a tendency which educated people must resist if they are to preserve any balanced judgment on such important matters as national economic problems. It is difficult to do this if we look only at the figures themselves, and it helps very considerably to draw diagrams to scale when we are attempting to understand exactly what the figures mean. For example, if 1 cm is drawn to represent £100,000,000, then a line 10 cm long would have to be drawn to represent £1,000,000,000. Contrast the visual impression given by the two lines (Fig. 9.26)

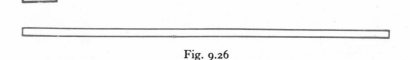

Fig. 9.26

compared with the numbers

£100,000,000

£1,000,000,000.

The two lines give the correct impression of the relative size of the two numbers.

A similar problem exists when children are looking at decimals. In the chapter on decimals some space was given to an appreciation of these sizes. It is worth noting, however, at this stage, that in the recurring decimal 0·333333 . . . if the figures are drawn so that their heights are proportional to the size of the numbers they represent, the line joining the tops of the figures is precisely the exponential curve relating numbers (vertically) to their logarithms (horizontally) which we have been discussing in this chapter (Fig. 9.27).

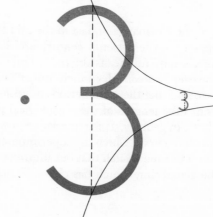

Fig. 9.27

Inflation

During the twelve years from 1945 to 1957 the value of the pound sterling decreased in terms of its purchasing power. Since prices at the end of a year had increased by some proportion of their level at the beginning of that year, the trend of inflation was that of a geometrical rather than an arithmetical progression. The difficulty of representing such a trend to the general public by the press was discussed in an article in *The Times* of November 15th, 1957. The spacing of the vertical scale in proportion to its logarithm was described, and subsequent articles have been illustrated in this way. Fig. 9.28 is reproduced from *The Times* of April 1st, 1960.

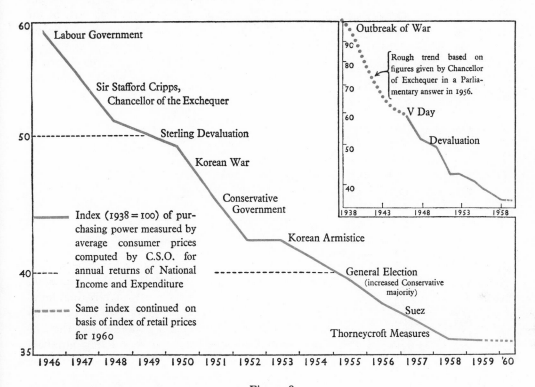

Fig. 9.28

The equiangular spiral

So far in this chapter we have drawn a number of graphs, representing successive terms of geometrical sequences such as 2, 4, 8, 16, 32 . . . or 1, 10, 100, 1000, . . . etc., by sets of equally spaced vertical lines. If, instead of drawing these parallel vertical lines, we first draw radial lines passing through a single point like the spokes of a wheel, and then we mark off the appropriate distances along these spokes, we obtain a most interesting curve.

CONSTRUCTION

1. Mark a point *O* on a sheet of paper. Through *O* draw a straight line *Ox*. With a protractor mark off points round the circumference of the protractor at 15° intervals and

join these points to O to give 24 radial lines, Oa, Ob, Oc, Od, . . . etc., at angles of 15° to one another.

2. When we were discussing musical scales we calculated a suitable table with a common ratio of 1·0595, which doubled the value every twelfth term. So let us take this sequence and now mark off lengths to give point A on Oa so that $OA = 1·00$ in.

B on Ob so that $OB = 1·06$ in

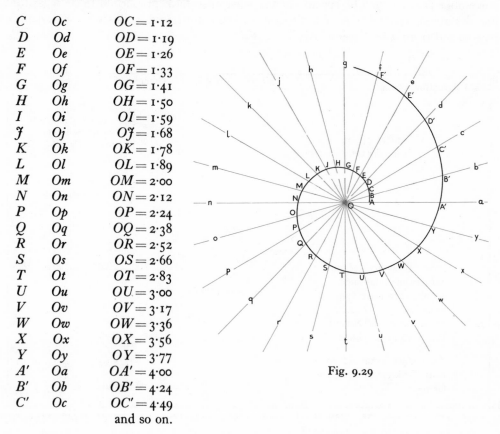

C	Oc	$OC = 1·12$
D	Od	$OD = 1·19$
E	Oe	$OE = 1·26$
F	Of	$OF = 1·33$
G	Og	$OG = 1·41$
H	Oh	$OH = 1·50$
I	Oi	$OI = 1·59$
J	Oj	$OJ = 1·68$
K	Ok	$OK = 1·78$
L	Ol	$OL = 1·89$
M	Om	$OM = 2·00$
N	On	$ON = 2·12$
P	Op	$OP = 2·24$
Q	Oq	$OQ = 2·38$
R	Or	$OR = 2·52$
S	Os	$OS = 2·66$
T	Ot	$OT = 2·83$
U	Ou	$OU = 3·00$
V	Ov	$OV = 3·17$
W	Ow	$OW = 3·36$
X	Ox	$OX = 3·56$
Y	Oy	$OY = 3·77$
A'	Oa	$OA' = 4·00$
B'	Ob	$OB' = 4·24$
C'	Oc	$OC' = 4·49$

and so on.

Fig. 9.29

Join the points A, B, C, D, . . . with a smooth curve (Fig. 9.29).

3. If the lengths along each of the radii are measured, it will be found that $OC' = 4 \times OC$, $OD' = 4 \times OD$, $OE' = 4 \times OE$ and so on. If this process is continued round once more to give points B'', C'', D''. . . . then $OB'' = 4 \times OB' = 16 \times OB$, $OC'' = 4 \times OC' = 16 \times OC$, etc.

4. If Z is any point whatever on the curve, and a ruler is laid along the curve so that it is tangential to it, touching it at Z, a tangent can be drawn whose point of contact is Z. If the angle between this tangent and the radius OZ is measured, it will be found that this angle is always the same, wherever Z may be on the curve. For the spiral just constructed (Fig. 9.29), this angle is about $77\frac{1}{2}°$. The name "equiangular spiral" is given to this curve because it makes equal angles with all the radii. It is also called a "logarithmic

spiral" because the angles between the radii and the initial direction, *Oa*, are proportional to the logarithms of the distances of points of the curve from the centre, *O*.

Logarithmic spirals occur in a variety of ways in nature. Each radius represents a growth from the previous radius, and if a shell goes on growing so that there is a constant percentage increase in size, then the resulting complete shell will be in the form of an equiangular or logarithmic spiral. This is beautifully illustrated by the nautilus. Fig. 9.30 is an exact drawing of an actual nautilus shell from the Natural History Museum, Fig. 9.31 is a tracing of its outline, and Fig. 9.32 is a mathematically constructed equiangular spiral. The reader is invited to trace the equiangular spiral and to see for himself how very nearly the natural shell conforms to the shape of a perfect spiral. In nature we expect to find individual deviations from exact mathematical rules, and this is so with shells. An individual shell is rarely a perfect equiangular spiral but it is surprising to find how closely many families of shells conform to this shape.

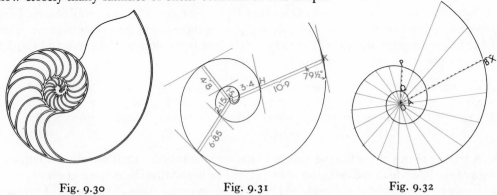

Fig. 9.30   Fig. 9.31   Fig. 9.32

FITTING AN EQUIANGULAR SPIRAL TO A NAUTILUS SHELL

The shell of a nautilus is a very accurate equiangular spiral. It is not very difficult to construct mathematically a spiral curve which fits an outline of a shell. Fig. 9.30 is the drawing of a nautilus shell based on an actual shell in the Natural History Museum at South Kensington. Fig. 9.31 is a tracing of the outline of Fig. 9.30. A ruler was placed on this tracing at the point *K* and was moved until it was judged to be tangential to the curve at *K*, and the tangent at *K* was drawn. By the usual method of placing the edge of a set-square along the tangent at *K* and then sliding the set-square along a straight-edge so that the edge of the set-square remained parallel to the tangent at *K*, the point *H* was found where the tangent was parallel to the tangent at *K*. The line *KH* was drawn and produced. This procedure was repeated at two other places. The three lines joining the points of contact of parallel tangents passed almost exactly through a single point. This point was taken as the centre of the spiral. The distances from the centre to the points of contact of the tangents were measured. The figures on the diagram are the lengths in centimetres on the original diagram, reduced in scale in this reproduction. From the centre to *K* was 10·9 cm and from the centre to *H* was 3·4 cm. $\frac{10\cdot9}{3\cdot4} = 3\cdot20$. Thus, in growing round a complete turn, the radius of the spiral had increased 3·20-fold. The other ratios, $\frac{4\cdot8}{1\cdot5} = 3\cdot20$ and $\frac{6\cdot85}{2\cdot15} = 3\cdot19$, are so very nearly the same that to within an error no greater than corresponds to the thickness of the lines in the diagram, the curve is an equiangular spiral whose radius increases by a factor of 3·20 per revolution.

From tables of logarithms we obtain $\log_{10} 3\cdot20 = 0\cdot5051$ or $3\cdot20 = 10^{0\cdot5051}$. Thus, when we turn through a complete revolution, or 360°, the growth in the radius is ten to the power 0·5051. When we turn through an angle $A°$, the growth factor will be ten to the power $\dfrac{A}{360} \times 0\cdot5051$ or $10^{0\cdot0014\,A}$. This information has been obtained by analysing Fig. 9.31.

From the equation $r = 10^{0\cdot0014\,A}$ (r in cm; A in degrees) we can construct Fig. 9.32. Begin by drawing a line OX, O being the centre of the spiral and OX the direction from which angles are measured.

If through O we now draw a line OQ so that angle $XOQ = 60°$, then the length OQ will be $10^{0\cdot0014 \times 60} = 10^{0\cdot084} = 1\cdot214$ and the point Q is plotted in by drawing angle $XOQ = 60°$ and measuring from O so that $OQ = 1\cdot21$ cm. Fig. 9.32 was obtained by repeating this procedure at 20° intervals and joining these points by a smooth curve. The table below gives the lengths of the radii for the first few points on the curve and for the first few points on the second circuit of the spiral.

A (in degrees) =	0	20	40	60	80	...	360	380	400	420	...
$0\cdot0014 \times A$ =	0	0·028	0·056	0·084	0·112	...	0·504	0·532	0·560	0·588	...
$r = 10^{0\cdot0014\,A}$ =	1	1·067	1·14	1·21	1·29	...	3·19	3·40	3·63	3·87	...
	(A)			(Q)			(B)			(P)	

A tracing of this curve fits the outline of the original nautilus shell to within the thickness of the line which indicates the curve. It will be found that the tangent at every point to the curve is inclined at the angle $79\frac{1}{2}°$ to the radius vector through the point of contact and thus provides another example of the property which gives the curve the name "equiangular spiral".

Readers whose mathematical knowledge extends to the quantity "e" and the *radian* as the unit of circular measure will be able to relate the equation

$$r = 10^{0\cdot0014\,A} \qquad (A \text{ in degrees})$$

to the angle $79\frac{1}{2}°$ which is characteristic of this particular spiral. Since $10 = e^{2\cdot3026}$ and the angle $A°$ is equal to the angle θ radians where $A = 57\cdot30\,\theta$, the equation to the spiral may be written

$$r = e^{2\cdot3026 \times 0\cdot0014 \times 57\cdot3 \times \theta}$$

that is $$r = e^{0\cdot185\theta} \qquad (\theta \text{ in radians})$$

0·185 is cot $79\frac{1}{2}°$ and so the equation to the spiral takes the form

$$r = e^{\theta \cdot \cot K}$$

where K is the characteristic angle of the spiral (in this case $79\frac{1}{2}°$).

It is of some interest to note that if K is a right-angle, $\cot 90° = 0$ and the equation reduces to

$$r = e^0 = 1.$$

Thus the circle turns up as the member of the family of equiangular spirals which cuts all the radii at right angles and has a constant radius.

Spiders' webs also conform fairly closely to the equiangular spiral shape; their transverse threads are parallel to one another and all are equally inclined to the main radial threads.

A somewhat unexpected place to come across equiangular spirals is in the arrangement of the tiny florets in the heads of flowers of the *Compositae* family; flowers such as the daisy, helenium, sunflower and aster have centres in which the dozens of tiny florets are crowded together in an arrangement which, on analysis, proves to be made up of two families of intersecting equiangular spirals. Fig. 9.33 is a photograph of the head of a pyrethrum, and Fig. 9.34 (*b*) is a constructed figure based on the intersection of two sets of equiangular spirals. Fig. 9.34 (*a*) indicates how Fig. 9.34 (*b*) was constructed.

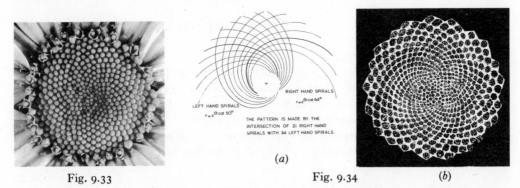

(*a*)

Fig. 9.33   Fig. 9.34   (*b*)

The connexion between geometrical progressions and musical scales has already been mentioned. Their relationship with our ability to hear is rather more complex. In our ears is an enormous number of tiny sensitive receptors which pick up sounds and transmit nervous impulses to the brain, where they are interpreted as the sound we hear. These receptors are hair-like processes graded in length to receive the whole range of resonant frequencies and they are arranged in a compact form in the spiral cochlea in our inner ears. We can see an interesting chain of ideas beginning with sets of numbers in geometrical sequences; strings and columns of air whose lengths are proportional to these numbers form the basis of our musical instruments; these same numbers measured along successive radii define equiangular spirals; the receptors in our ears fit into spiral cochlea. The form of the geometrical number sequence is, therefore, the link between the conventional musical scales which have been developed over the centuries and the particular structure of the organ which receives these sounds and passes them on to the brain.

One final reference to the spiral may be included here. It is on a vastly different scale from the cochlea in our ears. On the earth itself a "rhumb-line" is the path we travel if we keep on going in the same direction. If we start anywhere on the earth's surface, other than at the north pole, and we move in the direction N 60° E and continue in this direction, we shall cut each meridian at the same angle, 60°. As we get nearer and nearer to the north pole we shall find that we spiral round it, getting a little nearer each circuit. On a polar map, our course will be an equiangular spiral, centre the pole, cutting each meridian at 60°. The points at which a particular meridian is crossed on successive circuits will be successively nearer and nearer to the pole, the actual lengths forming a geometrical progression.

The exponential and logarithmic relationship between sets of numbers is one of the fundamental elements in the pattern of the universe. In this chapter a few examples have been given, but they could be multiplied a thousandfold, for there are few aspects of the natural world which do not provide some illustration of this relationship.

Common Ratio less than unity

In sequences such as

$$\frac{1}{2}, \frac{1}{4}, \frac{1}{8}, \frac{1}{16}, \frac{1}{32}, \frac{1}{64} \ldots$$

or

$$1, 0\cdot9, 0\cdot81, 0\cdot729, 0\cdot656 \ldots$$

each term is obtained from its predecessor by multiplying by the same factor, which is less than 1, and the terms of the sequences diminish in size quite quickly; but however many terms are taken, they never vanish altogether.

Radioactive decay provides an example of sequences like these. During the course of a year a proportion of the atoms of a given piece of radioactive material disintegrate, emitting rays and leaving a disintegration product of less atomic weight. For any radioactive element the proportion of atoms which disintegrate per year is constant. If, for example, one tenth disintegrates each year, nine tenths will remain unchanged. For such an element the amount remaining unchanged at the end of successive years would be given by the table

Time in years	0	1	2	3	4	5	6	7 ...
Mass unchanged	1	0·9	0·81	0·729	0·656	0·590	0·531	0·478 ...

After 6 years a little more than half, and after 7 years a little less than half of the original material remains unchanged by the radioactive decay, so that half of it will have decayed during the period of about $6\frac{1}{2}$ years. This period is called the *half-life* of the radioactive substance. Because the sequence of numbers representing the remaining portion of the original material never becomes exactly zero, the "whole-life" cannot be calculated and the "half-life" is used to describe the time of decay. For radium, 1/2280 disintegrates each year, so we have to multiply the fraction 2279/2280 by itself until the answer is 0·5 in order to find its half-life. For radium the half-life is 1580 years and for uranium it is 4,600,000,000 years. Strontium is an element which resembles calcium in some of its chemical properties and, like calcium, when some strontium is included in our diet, it finds its way into the bone. Several isotopes of strontium exist, two being radioactive, strontium 89 with a half-life of 53 days and strontium 90 with a half-life of 19·9 years. These are produced in thermo-nuclear explosions and are deposited in the fall-out which follows the test explosions of "hydrogen bombs". They are deposited on pasture land, ingested by cows, and ultimately some enters the human body and traces become incorporated in the bone structure. It takes up to 20 years for the constituents of bones to be replaced, so any strontium 90 which enters the bones remains an internal source of radioactivity over this long period of time, whereas the radioactivity of strontium 89 falls off much more quickly and other radioactive materials pass through the body and are excreted in a fairly short time. Strontium 90 is one of the most worrying constituents of "fall-out" because of this particular combination of half-life and chemical properties.

From the point of view of pure mathematics, the sum of terms of a geometrical progression whose common ratio is less than unity is of particular interest, because it provides such a simple example of the idea of a "sum to infinity".

If we take a piece of ribbon two inches long, we can cut from it a piece of length 1 in. and have 1 in. over. This latter can be cut to give a piece of length $\frac{1}{2}$ in. and leave $\frac{1}{2}$ in. over. This remainder can be cut to give a piece of length $\frac{1}{4}$ in. and leave $\frac{1}{4}$ in. over. We can then say that $1 + \frac{1}{2} + \frac{1}{4} = 2 - \frac{1}{4}$. If this process is carried on a little further we should have

$$1 + \frac{1}{2} + \frac{1}{4} + \frac{1}{8} + \frac{1}{16} + \frac{1}{32} + \frac{1}{64} + \frac{1}{128} = 2 - \frac{1}{128}.$$

From this it will be seen that if we go on and on adding terms which are always half their predecessors we shall get nearer and nearer to the number 2 but shall never quite reach 2. If the process is continued indefinitely we shall reach a sum which is only infinitesimally less than 2. The sum of the series

$$1 + \frac{1}{2} + \frac{1}{4} + \frac{1}{8} + \frac{1}{16} + \dots \text{ to infinity}$$

is said to be 2 since if we take an infinite number of terms the sum will be equal to 2 minus a quantity which ultimately approaches zero.

We may take a similar example to illustrate the series $1 + \frac{1}{4} + \frac{1}{16} + \dots$ Suppose three boys have four sweets between them; each boy takes one sweet and there is one sweet over. This sweet is divided into quarters; each boy takes one of the quarters and there is $\frac{1}{4}$ over. This remaining quarter is divided into four parts; each of the three boys takes one of these parts and there is one part over which is $\frac{1}{16}$ of the original sweet. This piece is divided into four parts; each boy takes one of these parts and there is one part over, which is $\frac{1}{64}$ of the original sweet. This process is continued, and after some time it is obvious that a negligible part will be left over and that each boy will have one third of the original four sweets or $\frac{4}{3}$ of a sweet. If we add together the amounts each boy receives and equate this to $\frac{4}{3}$ we obtain

$$1 + \frac{1}{4} + \frac{1}{16} + \frac{1}{64} + \dots = \frac{4}{3}.$$

Similar arguments can be used to find the sum to infinity of the series $1 + \frac{1}{3} + \frac{1}{9} + \frac{1}{27} + \dots$ or $1 + \frac{1}{7} + \frac{1}{49} + \frac{1}{343} + \dots$

If a series is written in the general form, the sum to infinity, S, will be given by

$$S = 1 + r + r^2 + r^3 + r^4 + \dots \quad (r < 1).$$

Multiplying by r, $\qquad rS = r + r^2 + r^3 + r^4 + \dots$

and subtracting, gives $\qquad (1 - r)S = 1 \quad \text{or} \quad S = \dfrac{1}{1 - r}.$

Thus, when $r = \frac{1}{4}$, $\qquad S = \dfrac{1}{1 - \frac{1}{4}} = \dfrac{1}{\frac{3}{4}} = \dfrac{4}{3}.$

If we take as an approximate example a plant which grows 8 inches in one week, two-thirds of 8 in. or 5·333 in. during the next week, two-thirds of 5·333 or 3·555 in. the following week, and so on, its height will be the sum of the series

$$S = 8\left(1 + \frac{2}{3} + \frac{4}{9} + \frac{8}{27} + \dots\right).$$

The sum to infinity of this series is $S = 8\,\dfrac{1}{1 - \frac{2}{3}} = 8 \times 3 = 24$ in. If the reader will add together the terms of the actual series, he will find that after eight weeks the height of the plant will be 23·16 in. and after ten weeks it will be 23·79 in., so the first eight or so terms contribute the greater part of the sum of an infinite number of terms.

Interest in the idea of a sum to infinity has a very long history. Zeno, living in the fifth century B.C., posed the problem of Achilles and the tortoise. In simple language this paradox is that Achilles gives a tortoise 1000 yards start and Achilles runs ten times as fast as the tortoise. When Achilles reaches the point where the tortoise started he will have run 1000 yards and the tortoise will then be 100 yards ahead. When Achilles reaches this point, 100 yards beyond the tortoise's starting point, the tortoise will have run another 10 yards and will then be 10 yards ahead; when Achilles reaches this point the tortoise will be 1 yard ahead. Thus although Achilles gets nearer and nearer to the tortoise he will never quite catch him up, since however many terms of this series are taken there will be a very small distance for Achilles to catch up. The argument is patently fallacious somewhere. The explanation of the paradox is that the argument refers to decreasing *distances* whereas the word "never" in the concluding sentence, by implication, refers to time. If the time taken for each of the elements in the argument is calculated, these times will be found to be in geometrical progression and they will have a sum to infinity which is a finite quantity. In other words the sum to infinity of the series of distances is attained in a finite time, and Achilles does catch the tortoise in a finite time.

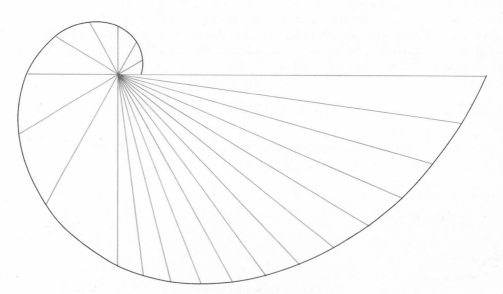

EQUIANGULAR SPIRAL

This spiral was drawn so that its radii are equal to the lengths illustrating the successive frets in the diagram on page 132 arranged in order at $7\frac{1}{2}°$ intervals. One octave is arrayed in a right angle.

10

Squares, Parabolas and Telescopes

The sequence of the squares of numbers and the parabola

The sequence of numbers 1, 4, 9, 16, 25, 36, 49, . . . which is obtained simply by writing out 1 × 1, 2 × 2, 3 × 3, 4 × 4, . . . etc., has many interesting and important properties.

As we did for the linear sequences, we call the sequence of squares the y sequence and we number these terms off, in order, and call the numbers the x sequence, so that a mapping of the squares on to the natural numbers gives

$$y = 1, 4, 9, 16, 25, 36, 49, 64, 81, \ldots$$
$$x = 1, 2, 3, 4, 5, 6, 7, 8, 9, \ldots$$

and in each case we can see that the *equation* relating each y to the corresponding x is

$$y = x^2.$$

If points are drawn successively 1, 4, 9, 16, 25, . . . etc., above evenly spaced-out points on a base line, we obtain a curve which slopes gracefully up to the right, sloping up more and more steeply as we move along the curve (Fig. 10.1).

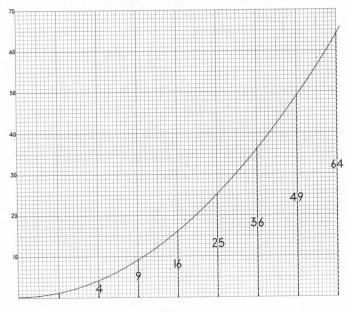

Fig. 10.1
Parabola.

It will be remembered (page 37) that minus a minus quantity is positive and so

$$-2 \times (-2) = +4.$$

If, therefore, the x and y sequences are continued to the left, we obtain:

$$y = \quad 64 \quad 49 \quad 36 \quad 25 \quad 16 \quad 9 \quad 4 \quad 1 \quad 0 \quad 1 \quad 4 \quad 9 \quad 16 \quad 25 \quad 36 \quad 49 \quad 64$$
$$x = -8 \quad -7 \quad -6 \quad -5 \quad -4 \quad -3 \quad -2 \quad -1 \quad 0 \quad +1 \quad +2 \quad +3 \quad +4 \quad +5 \quad +6 \quad +7 \quad +8$$

When the whole of this sequence is drawn we obtain a parabola which is a symmetrical curve, looking like Fig. 10.2.

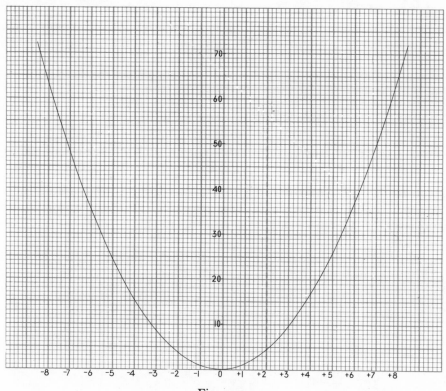

Fig. 10.2

Parabola.

If we draw proper algebraic curves, using the same scale on each of the axes, we see that the effect of a coefficient in front of the x^2 in the table is to alter the scale to which the parabola is drawn.

Equation $y = \frac{1}{4} x^2$: *sequences*

$y =$		25	16	9	4	1	0	1	4	9	16	25
$x =$		−10	−8	−6	−4	−2	0	2	4	6	8	10

Equation $y = \frac{1}{9} x^2$: *sequences*

$y =$		25	16	9	4	1	0	1	4	9	16	25
$x =$		−15	−12	−9	−6	−3	0	3	6	9	12	15

Equation $y = \frac{1}{16} x^2$: *sequences*

$y =$		25	16	9	4	1	0	1	4	9	16	25
$x =$		−20	−16	−12	−8	−4	0	4	8	12	16	20

and when they are drawn to the same scale, these graphs are as shown in Fig. 10.5.

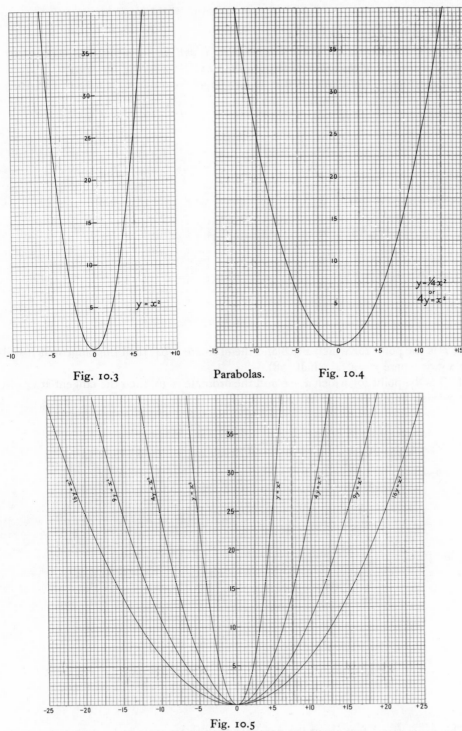

Fig. 10.3   Parabolas.   Fig. 10.4

Fig. 10.5
Four parabolas drawn to same scale.

TANGENTS TO THE PARABOLA

If a tangent is drawn at any point to a parabola, it will cut the x-axis half way between the origin and the foot of the ordinate through the point of contact of the tangent.

The meaning of the terms used in this statement should be clear from Fig. 10.6.

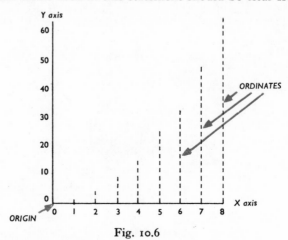

Fig. 10.6

If P is the point for which $x = 8$ and the ordinate is 64, then the tangent at P will cut the x-axis where $x = 4$ ($4 =$ half $\times$ 8).

If Q is the point for which $x = 6$ and the ordinate is 36, then the tangent at Q will cut the x-axis where $x = 3$ ($3 =$ half $\times$ 6).

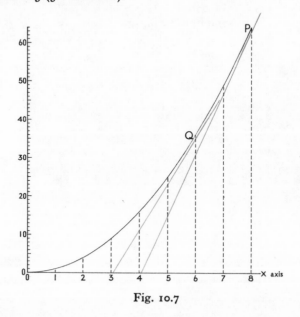

Fig. 10.7

This geometrical fact about the parabola enables tangents to be drawn to a parabola very accurately (Fig. 10.7).

Parabolas are used as the shapes for mirrors in headlamps of motor cars and for reflectors which bring radiation to a focus. The largest parabola made is the reflector of the Jodrell Bank Radio Telescope, which was brought into use just in time to plot the course of the Russian satellite launched on October 4th, 1957.

REFLECTION

When a ray of light (or radiation of any wavelength) hits a reflecting surface, the reflected ray makes the same angle with the surface as the incident ray (Fig. 10.8).

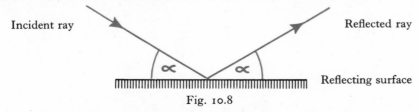

Incident ray   Reflected ray

∝   ∝   Reflecting surface

Fig. 10.8

When the reflecting surface is curved, the reflected ray and the incident ray are equally inclined to the tangent to the surface at the point at which the light is reflected (Fig. 10.9).

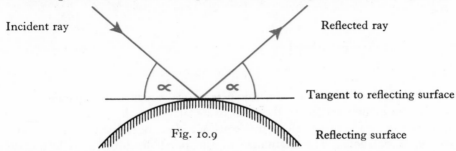

Incident ray   Reflected ray

∝   ∝   Tangent to reflecting surface

Fig. 10.9   Reflecting surface

If the reader will take pencil, ruler and graph paper and follow through carefully the construction described below, all the geometrical properties of reflection by parabolic surfaces will be drawn to scale.

FOCUSING PROPERTIES OF A PARABOLIC MIRROR

Begin by drawing a parabola from the information given on page 148. This will give a curve which is symmetrical about the y-axis. By joining the points on the curve to the appropriate points on the x-axis, as in Fig. 10.7, construct the tangents accurately. Now suppose that the parabola is the mirror of a telescope pointing vertically upwards and that rays of light, represented by the red lines in Fig. 10.10, are entering the telescope vertically from above. Select one ray and follow its course. The ray labelled R at the top of the figure meets the parabola at the point P. TPT' is the tangent to the parabola at P. Through P draw a line PK so that the angle $TPK =$ angle RPT'. Then PK will be the line representing the reflected ray. Let F be the point where the reflected ray cuts the y-axis.

In this way a point F is obtained on the y-axis, which is the axis of symmetry of the parabola. If this construction is now followed through carefully for other rays, they will all be found to pass through the single point F, lying on the y-axis. This is the focus of

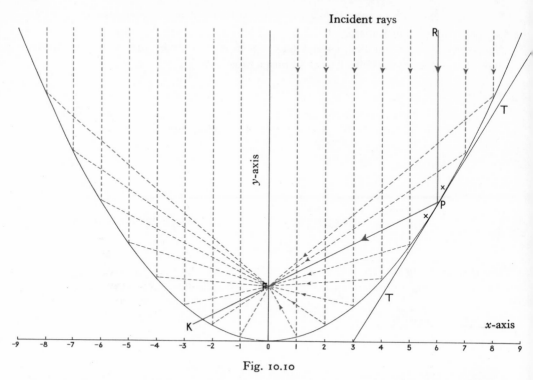

Fig. 10.10

the parabola and it is because of this geometrical property that parabolic surfaces are used for headlamp reflectors, the bulb being placed at the focus. In electric fires, the long bar element is placed along the focus of a sheet of reflecting material whose cross-section is parabolic. The usefulness of the parabolic form in reflecting telescopes, including the very large radio telescope at Jodrell Bank, needs no further explanation. It is of interest to observe that "focus" is the Latin word for "fireplace" or "hearth", where the family gather together.

DIRECTRIX OF A PARABOLA

In Fig. 10.11 incident and reflected rays have been drawn in carefully, the reflected rays all passing through F. If now the lengths P_1F, P_2F, P_3F, ... etc., are measured and the lines R_1P_1, R_2P_2, R_3P_3, ... are produced to D_1, D_2, D_3, ... etc., so that

$$P_1D_1 = P_1F$$
$$P_2D_2 = P_2F$$
$$P_3D_3 = P_3F$$
$$\text{etc.} = \text{etc.}$$

then the points D_1, D_2, D_3, ... etc., will all lie on a straight line parallel to the x-axis and the same distance below this axis as F is above it.

It is obvious that the distances R_0D_0, R_1D_1, R_2D_2, R_3D_3, ... RD, ... are all equal. Now $RD = RP + PD = RP + PF$ (since $PD = RF$), so that all the lengths $R_1P_1 + P_1F$,

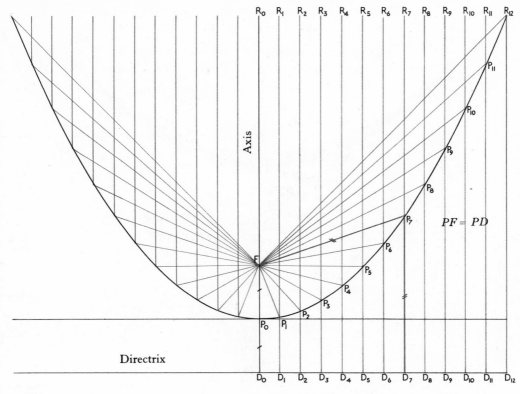

Fig. 10.11

$R_2P_2 + P_2F$, $R_3P_3 + P_3F$, . . . are equal to one another. Thus, the distances from the various points R to the single focus F are all equal. Those familiar with physics will realize this means that rays of light emanating from a distant source of light such as the sun or a star and brought to a focus by a parabolic mirror will all travel precisely the same distances and so will arrive at the focus in phase with one another, no interference phenomena occurring at F as a consequence of phase differences due to differences in the lengths of path.

From a geometrical point of view, the directrix is a line such that if D is any point on this directrix and DT, DT' are tangents to the parabola, then TDT' is a right angle and the line joining the points of contact of these tangents passes through F.

THE JODRELL BANK TELESCOPE

The giant radio telescope built for the University of Manchester is shaped like a giant circular dish, accurately parabolic in cross-section. It is 250 ft in diameter and the actual aerial, at the focus of the parabola, is at the top of a 62-ft mast rising from the centre of the dish. The reflecting surface is made of accurately bent steel plates and weighs about 800 tons. It is supported by two towers 185 ft in height. The reflector is driven by powerful motors which can swing the reflectors round the compass in 18 minutes, and about a horizontal axis it can loop the loop in about 15 minutes. The diagram on page 154 gives an idea of the shape, to a scale of 1 in. to 60 ft approximately.

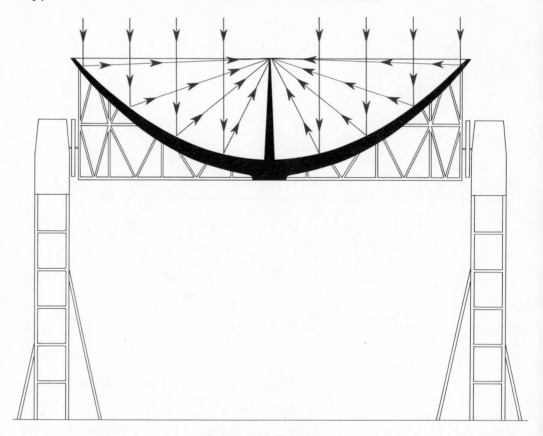

Jodrell Bank Telescope.

Falling Bodies

In 1589, at the age of twenty-five, Galileo was appointed Professor of Mathematics at Pisa. What young man, still energetic enough to climb the leaning tower, could resist dropping things over the side?

During the next three years, from a series of experiments on falling bodies, carried out from the leaning tower, he established the first principles of dynamics. He moved, in 1592, to Padua, where he stayed until 1610, and in 1612 he published his *Treatise on Mechanics*, in the course of which he deduced the relations between velocity, space and time. Galileo proved that the path of a projectile is a parabola and that the distance a body falls is proportional to the square of the time that has elapsed since the instant at which it was dropped.

In this instance the squares of the times are proportional to the distances the body has fallen *downwards*, and so, as we measure the distances downwards proportional to these squares, we obtain a parabola which is the other way up from those we have drawn so far.

A body projected horizontally from the top of a cliff will move along a parabolic path as in Fig. 10.12

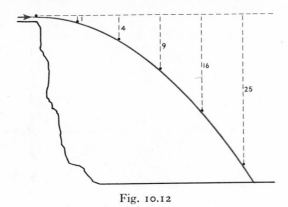

Fig. 10.12

and a ball thrown into the air will move along a path as in Fig. 10.13.

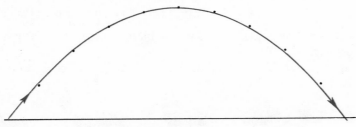

Fig. 10.13

If the same scale is kept for the y-axis (the vertical axis) but different scales are chosen for the x-axis or, in less formal words, if we begin with the sequence of squares 0, 1, 4, 9, 16, 25, . . . and draw a series of graphs, plotting the vertical columns farther apart in some graphs than in others, we obtain a series of parabolas of different sizes (Fig. 10.14). The parabolas in Fig. 10.5 will provide the required set of curves if they are turned upside down.

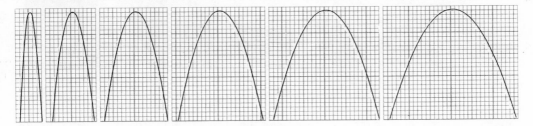

Fig. 10.14

By cutting these out in card and drawing round them, a variety of parabolic outlines is available. Fig. 10.15 represents a fountain from which water is issuing in many directions. Each jet will describe a parabolic path, and the outline of all these parabolas is itself a parabola whose focus is at the opening of the fountain (*see* over).

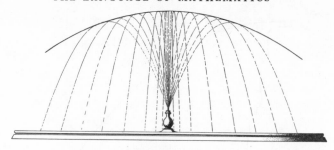

Fig. 10.15

Natural numbers, their squares and cubes

A glance at the three sets of numbers

$n =$	1	2	3	4	5	6	7	8	9	10	11	12
$n^2 =$	1	4	9	16	25	36	49	64	81	100	121	144
$n^3 =$	1	8	27	64	125	216	343	512	729	1000	1331	1728

shows that as numbers increase, their squares increase more rapidly and their cubes very much more rapidly.

If we *look* at these numbers by building their squares and cubes out of inch-cube building bricks (Fig. 10.16)

Fig. 10.16

we can see something of the relative sizes of the numbers involved, but a better idea of the relative increases may be obtained if we begin with *one inch*, *one square inch* and *one cubic inch*, and then consider *one foot*, *one square foot* and *one cubic foot*. The increases are 12 times, 144 times and 1728 times respectively.

The *foot* of 12 inches is a well-known, easily recognized length. The 144 bricks obtained from the square foot, if set out in a row, would just about stretch the length of the wall of a typical room of a dwelling-house; the 1728 bricks obtained from cutting up the cubic foot, if put in a row along the edge of the floor of a typical room, would go round the room about three times.

Some such visual approach to the interpretation of these numbers helps our judgments in a variety of contexts.

Judgment in reading about areas and distances depends upon the readiness with which a distance of 10 miles is associated with an area of 100 square miles. For instance, if towns with secondary schools in them are 10 miles apart, each school serves an area of 100 square miles. At first reading, 10 miles does not sound a very great distance, but 100 square miles sounds like an enormous tract of country.

When foot and mouth disease has been confirmed on a farm it does not sound so drastic if all movement is restricted over an area "within 10 miles of the infected area" as when all movement of animals is restricted in an "area of 314 square miles", yet this is the area of a circle of radius 10 miles.

SCALE MODELS

An appreciation of these relative growths of the series of numbers, their squares and their cubes helps an understanding of problems associated with models and with the effects of size on living creatures. A model aeroplane constructed exactly to a scale which is a tenth of the length of the full-sized machine will have a hundredth of the wing surface and a thousandth of the volume. Since the "lift" depends upon wing surface and the weight upon volume, the relationships between lift and weight will be quite different in the model from those in the full-sized machine. The interpretation of data obtained from models, whether of aircraft in wind tunnels or ships in water tanks, or of engines or even of component parts, is extremely complicated, and results so obtained can be very misleading until a careful analysis has been performed. A very simple example of this is the dressing of a small doll. If a full-scale flared skirt were to be made for a person 5 ft 6 in. in height, out of material heavy enough for the skirt to hang gracefully, and then, exactly to one-twelfth of the scale, an exact replica of the skirt were to be made to fit a doll $5\frac{1}{2}$ in. in height, the material would probably stand out in a stiff-looking cone-shape and would fail to drape gracefully. The reason for this is that, although the skirt is made to scale, the various relations between areas and lengths, between weight and fibre stiffnesses can be very different, some changing in the ratio of 12 to 1 and some in the ratio of 144 to 1, and the balance between weight and stiffness, area and length, is not retained in the model.

SIZES OF ANIMALS

Biologically these contrasting ratios have led to a variety of evolutionary developments. A mouse and an elephant are extremes in size of mammals living on dry land and sharing a common environment. When food is eaten by a mammal it is first chewed up mechanically in the mouth; it passes into the stomach, where digestive juices act upon it chemically, and then into the intestine, where it is absorbed through the semi-permeable membrane and carried through the blood stream to the cells throughout the body. (Here we need not consider functions of the liver and various other modifications of this simple picture of digestion.)

Food provides the building material for the development of the body cells, the energy expended during the contraction of muscles, and the heat, generated within the body, which maintains animal temperatures at a uniform level, virtually independent of the surrounding atmosphere.

The number of body cells to be maintained depends upon the volume of the animal; the loss of heat to the surrounding atmosphere occurs through the surface of the skin of the mammal and so depends upon its surface area; the absorption of food through the walls of the intestine depends partly upon the length of the intestine and partly upon the speed of passage through it of foods of various types.

If we imagine an animal, about 3 ft in length, which is exactly like a mouse enlarged by a factor of ten, then a simple enlargement would increase the body volume a thousand-fold (10 × 10 × 10) and so the weight and the number of cells to be nourished and the volume of blood would be increased a thousand times. The surface area of the skin, and so the energy lost in the form of heat, would be increased a hundredfold (10 × 10), so also would be the surface area of the inside walls of the lungs which supply the blood stream with oxygen and remove the carbon dioxide from the blood. The area of cross-section of bones, and so their strength, would also be increased a hundred times. The length of the veins and arteries would be increased tenfold; so would the length of the intestine.

Some of the problems involved in this increase of size by ten times the linear measurements are:

There would be

(i) 1000 times the volume of blood circulating through only 10 times the length of artery and vein channels. What would be the effect of this on the speed of circulation?

(ii) 1000 times as much blood, 1000 times as many cells to supply and 1000 times the volume of muscle to supply with oxygen, but only 100 times the surface area of lungs through which the oxygen could enter the blood stream and carbon dioxide be removed. This points to rapid oxygen starvation and carbon dioxide poisoning.

(iii) 1000 times the heat produced in the muscular and other activities of the body but only 100 times the surface area of skin for cooling purposes. This would cause a breakdown in the heat-balance and a rapid rise in body temperature.

(iv) 1000 times the weight of the animal but only 100 times increase in the strength of the skeleton. The animal might collapse under its own weight.

(v) 1000 times the number of cells to be nourished and 1000 times the weight to be maintained and energy to be provided, but only 10 times the length of intestine through which food can pass in the process of absorption.

As larger animals have evolved from the primitive mammals of the Mesozoic era which were, on the average, no bigger than a rat or a mouse,* modifications in structure become apparent. The most obvious of these is the long "small intestine", which in man is coiled in the abdominal cavity and has a total length of some 20 ft. Some smaller animals have intestines which are short and almost straight, but in mammals bigger

---

* See *Man and the Vertebrates* by A. S. Romer (Pelican), Vol. II, also Vol. I, pp. 127 and 128.

than man there is even more coiling, and a cow, which is both larger than a man and herbivorous, has almost 100 ft of small intestine. Variations in the ratio of diameter to lengths of arteries and differences in rate of heart-beat solve the problems of variations in the proportions of volume of blood to length of circulatory systems. A complex network of capillaries and folding of the lung walls provide enough margin of adaptability for maintaining adequate oxygen supplies for the blood stream under different conditions of size.

Point (iii) above, surface area and volume in relation to heat loss in warm-blooded animals, has not been so effectively solved in the evolutionary processes. Tiny animals such as the tree shrew, which is only $1\frac{1}{2}$ in. in length, have to eat continuously for about 22 hours out of the 24 to absorb enough energy to keep up their body temperature. Small mammals cannot survive in very cold climates, and the principal bird inhabitants of the polar region, the penguins, are large birds. To some extent fur coverings have helped, and it is in the frozen, bitter conditions of the Canadian north that men hunt for fur-bearing animals whose furs serve to reduce the effective area of heat-losing surface skin. Point (iv) above is illustrated by the absence of graceful ankles in large mammals such as the elephant and by the mechanically strong arched form of the backbone of the prehistoric giant reptiles. It is comforting to think that the horrid giants of fairy stories had to lead sedentary lives, for their bones would have broken under their own weight had they stood up.

This very superficial discussion about squares and cubes in relation to biological structures touches only the fringe of what is a very complex study, full of interest and surprises. Trees and smaller plants also present problems of a somewhat similar nature.

11

Geometry: the Understanding of Space

ALTHOUGH ESTIMATES vary, it is generally agreed that most, possibly as much as 70 per cent, of the knowledge and information which form the basis of our understanding is received through the eyes. Of the remainder, some is heard and some vital information comes to us through the sense of touch. It is not easy to separate the visual and aural contributions to the reception of information quite as tidily as the allocation of precise percentages would suggest, because a most potent form of instruction is the spoken explanation of material visually presented. It is not very important for us, in this context, however, to know what percentages are allocated to eyes and ears provided we realize the outstanding importance of visually presented information. Geographers must use maps and plans, the drawing office is at the heart of engineering development, the glossy magazines are profusely illustrated, not only with glamorous photographs, but with diagrams and plans of houses, dress patterns, family budgets and sequences of exercises to be performed to improve the figure.

If visually presented information is to be accurately received, training is necessary both for those who prepare the illustrations and for those who look at them. The need for this training is well understood by all who aspire to success with drawing, painting or modelling, and appreciation of the visual arts needs much knowledge and understanding. The appropriate use of maps involves specialist knowledge, but all these skills ultimately depend upon an understanding of the fundamental properties of space and shapes, that is, of basic geometry.

Geometry is concerned partly with the properties of space in which bodies are situated, in which they move and in which events happen, and partly with the shapes and configurations of objects in space. It is a property of space that the sum of the lengths of two sides of a triangle is greater than the third side, and for this reason it is not possible to construct any triangular object for which this is not true.

The design of an aircraft wing, for example, is a geometrical problem. The designer can be given certain specifications which arise from mechanical requirements, dependent upon such matters as weight of aircraft, power developed by engines, and information about air flow derived from wind-tunnel experiments, and the designer has to produce a shape which meets these specifications as closely as possible and one which is geometrically consistent with the properties of space. The proper study of pure geometry is the building up of the body of knowledge about space. This is an abstract study, and in the earlier stages of reading and learning geometry it is not easy to envisage empty space, in which no objects are situated, as possessing properties. We do, therefore, have to pose situations which involve geometrical problems, and it is often possible to discuss these later and eliminate from them the non-geometrical data and extract geometrical facts from them. This point may be illustrated by an example.

EXAMPLE

A farmer has 64 yards of fencing. How can he place his fencing in a flat field so that a horse may have an area of 192 square yards (192 yd²) in which to graze?

The answer is that the farmer may make a wide variety of shapes for his field including a rectangular shape 8 yd by 24 yd.

Fig. 11.1 (*a*)

Similarly, if he wishes to enclose an area of 240 square yards, he may arrange his fencing as a rectangle 20 yd by 12 yd.

Fig. 11.1 (*b*)

Or an area of 256 square yards by making a square enclosure 16 yd by 16 yd.

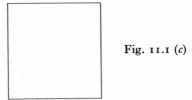

Fig. 11.1 (*c*)

The farmer could go on enclosing larger and larger areas until he encloses an area of 326 yd², by making a circular enclosure

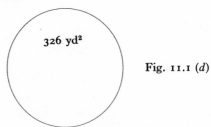

326 yd²

Fig. 11.1 (*d*)

of circumference 64 yd, *but he cannot enclose an area greater than 326 square yards no matter how he arranges his fences.*

Discussion. Clearly the areas and lengths involved in this example are quite independent of whether there is a horse or goat or a mowing machine in the field. They will not be affected by whether grass is growing in the field, or a crop of lettuces is being protected from rabbits by the fencing. The problem would be the same whether the area was grazing land or a concrete school playground, or whether there was a fence or just a painted line round part of a playground. It does matter whether or not the field was flat, since a fence round a hillock would enclose a greater surface than a fence around a flat field (Fig. 11.2 (*a*) and (*b*)).

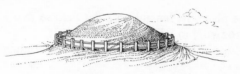
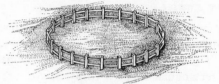

Fig. 11.2 (a)   Fig. 11.2 (b)

It is also clear that one might take aerial photographs of the fields from various heights

Fig. 11.3

and if the square field encloses a greater area than a rectangular field alongside it, this fact would be true of photographs taken from 1000 ft or 2000 ft where the length of the bounding line might appear to be 6·4 cm on one photograph or 3·2 cm on the other.

Circles and Spheres

The geometrical fact illustrated by the above example is that: *a plane area bounded by a closed curve of fixed length is greatest when the curve is a circle.* This is a statement with no superfluous information.

The corresponding geometrical fact in solid geometry is: *a volume bounded by a closed surface of given area is greatest when the surface is a sphere.*

This same geometrical fact could be stated in the form: *the surface area of a closed surface bounding a given volume is least when its shape is spherical.*

APPLICATIONS

These are plain geometrical facts and all of us, including engineers, draughtsmen, housewives, architects, painters and designers have to submit to them. Instances of the applications of these facts are many and diverse.

Retention or loss of heat. The heat lost by a body is lost through its surface, so the smaller the surface area the less heat is lost. For this reason, the most efficient shape for teapots and jugs is as near spherical as is compatible with the requirements of standing in a stable position and effective pouring (Fig. 11.4).

Fig. 11.4
Efficient shapes for heat-retaining teapots and jugs.

Sometimes we wish to lose heat as quickly as possible, as in the cooling fins of refrigerators or motor cycle engines. The cooling fins in refrigerators are made in long, flat rectangular shapes, giving the greatest possible surface area for volume of contents (Fig. 11.5).

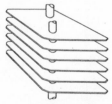

Fig. 11.5
Cooling fins in a refrigerator.

Containers. As air is blown into a soap bubble, the bubble takes on a spherical shape enclosing the greatest amount of air for the minimum stretching of its surface. When sugar or dried fruits are put into a paper bag, which starts off folded in a more or less rectangular shape, the bag quickly adjusts itself to its contents and assumes a more or less cylindrical shape (Fig. 11.6).

Fig. 11.6

In the design of containers other factors, such as packing, storage, fitting together and ease of carrying, play an important part. The reader might like, however, to make a comparison between several bottles and complete the table which follows. To the three which are illustrated the reader could well add others based on well-defined geometrical shapes (Fig. 11.7).

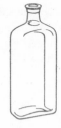

Milk bottle
(cylindrical).

Ink bottle
(nearly spherical).

Medicine bottle
(roughly rectangular).

Fig. 11.7

	Quart milk bottle	Medicine bottle	Ink bottle	
(a) Weight of water that bottle will hold				
(b) Weight of glass of empty bottle				
(c) Ratio of $\dfrac{\text{wt. of content}}{\text{wt. of container}}$				
(d) Approximate shape				

The Study of Geometry

The example of the length of fencing available limiting the area it can enclose is an obvious illustration of the fact that the nature of space is such that relationships exist between various geometrical entities. Geometry is the study of these relationships. Professor Choquet of the University of Paris points out* that the sort of geometry which is built up depends upon the instruments used. He does not speak of modelling clay, but young children spend some time playing with this medium and it seems appropriate in this chapter to begin with this material.

Modelling clay geometry

Information obtained from pressing clay into sundry shapes is topological. It is not concerned with the lengths between points or the sizes of angles, nor is it concerned with straight lines and planes and lines passing through points. For example, some geometrical entity might be described as a "lump with a hole through it" if it had any of these shapes (Fig. 11.8):

Fig. 11.8

Such shapes can be modified one from another without losing the fundamental property that makes them all belong to the same family.

If a finger is poked through to form a second hole, a distinctly different set of objects is formed, like these (Fig. 11.9):

Fig. 11.9

* *L'enseignement des mathématiques* (1955, Delachaux & Niestlé), Chapter V.

Another set might be interlocking, like these (Fig. 11.10):

Fig. 11.10

At present, children play with modelling clay when they are in primary schools, and the experiences of working with such material are rarely systematized by following up this sort of work at later stages. Because of this, many simple but precise statements that can be made about bodies such as those illustrated in Figs. 11.8, 11.9 and 11.10 are unknown to many people who have some knowledge of formal geometry.

SOME TOPOLOGICAL IDEAS

Genus. If a ring of red clay is pressed into the surface of a simple lump of green modelling clay, it is possible to put on the surface of the clay two points between which an ant could not crawl without crossing the closed red curve somewhere. This is described as a surface of *genus* 0. It is illustrated in Fig. 11.11, on which two such points are marked.

Fig. 11.11   Fig. 11.12 (*a*)   Fig. 11.12 (*b*)   Fig. 11.13

A lump of modelling clay with a hole through it can, however, have a closed red curve drawn on it without the curve separating any pair of points. In Figs. 11.12 (*a*) and 11.12 (*b*) two such curves are illustrated, and for both these cases no two points can be found which are separated from one another by the closed curve. Such a surface in which *one* closed curve can be drawn without breaking the continuity of the surface is a surface of genus 1.

A surface on which *two* closed curves can be drawn and yet leave the surface so that it is possible to move on the surface from *any* point to *any* other point without crossing over either closed curve is a surface of genus 2. Such a surface is illustrated in Fig. 11.13.

EXAMPLES

(i) The human body is a surface of genus 0. Wherever there is a point of skin infection, it is possible to isolate this to prevent the spreading of infection to other parts. No closed curve could be drawn on the skin without isolating one part of the skin from that on the rest of the body.

(ii) *The Wooden Horse*, one of the great escape stories of the last war, may be described in the form: The Germans selected a part of Germany where the surface was of genus 0 and constructed an electrified fence, isolating a part of the surface from the rest of Germany, and placed prisoners within the enclosure. By constructing a tunnel, the prisoners converted the surface to one of genus 1 and moved from one part of the surface to the other without passing through the fence.

Colouring maps. In colouring maps it is usual to use different colours to indicate any two countries having a common boundary. It has been found that no arrangement of boundaries has ever made necessary the use of more than four colours, but four colours are certainly necessary, as the simple Fig. 11.14 shows. 1 has a frontier with 2, 3 and 4, and so 1 could not be coloured in the same way as 2 or 3 or 4. Similarly 2 has common frontiers with 3, 4 and 1, and so 2 could not be coloured like 3 or 4 or 1, etc.

In whatever way one tries to make regions double back on themselves or to map them on any surface of genus 0, any change of shape which brings frontiers of two similarly coloured areas alongside each other isolates another area and enables an appropriate colour change to be made without involving the introduction of a fifth colour (Figs. 11.14 and 11.15). This theorem has not yet been proved by any rigid process of reasoning and it remains a conjecture that no pattern that requires five colours will ever be found.

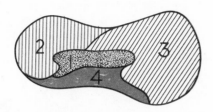

Fig. 11.14
A simple four-colour map.

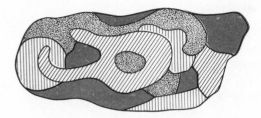

Fig. 11.15
A more complicated four-colour map.

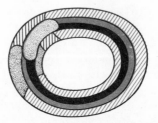

Fig. 11.16
A map drawn on a surface of genus 1 in which only six colours are needed.

For surfaces of genus 1, such as an inflated inner tube (torus), it has been proved that any map may be coloured by using *seven* colours, since seven regions may be drawn in which each one touches the remaining six. Fig. 11.16 is an illustration showing a case where six colours are necessary. The reader is invited to try to modify this to make it necessary to introduce a seventh colour. An actual surface such as a car inner tube or a lump of modelling clay would help the investigation.

Euler's Theorem. A pyramid on a triangular base (a tetrahedron) has 4 faces, 4 vertices and 6 edges. A pyramid on a square base has 5 faces, 5 vertices and 8 edges. A triangular prism has 5 faces, 6 vertices and 9 edges. A cube has 6 faces, 8 vertices and 12 edges. If a corner is sawn off a cube the resulting solid will have 7 faces, 10 vertices and 15 edges. For all such solids $F+V-E=2$, where F, V, and E represent the number of faces, vertices and edges respectively. This is easily pictured for the solid shapes mentioned but it can be stated more generally that if any closed surface (such as that of a lump of modelling clay) is divided into F regions by E arcs joining, in pairs, V points on the surface, such that at least two edges meet at each of the V points, then $F+V-E$ is independent of the method of dividing up the surface.

Electrical circuits. Electrical circuits are such that specific points on components must be joined by wires, but the exact lengths and shapes of the wire connexions are not determined by the needs of the electrician, so that the geometrical arrangement of a set of components may be modified without disturbing the electrical circuits. In fact some internal connexions in radio and television sets are made with flexible wire so that parts may be moved after the wiring has been completed. This is essentially a topological arrangement since it does not involve sizes, lengths, straight lines, ratios, etc., which enter into metrical and projective geometries.

Mammals and plants. In many respects mammals are topologically equivalent, differing only in the metrical geometry of their parts. The mechanisms of fertilization of plants, stamens, pistils, ovaries, etc., are topologically identical in all flowering plants (angiosperms). The variations between species are differences of shapes, sizes and proportions, that is, metrical and projective differences but not topological.

Paper-scissors-and-gum geometry

A flat rectangular piece of thin card, or fairly substantial paper, at once gives us a surface that is a plane and can be laid out flat on a desk top (Fig. 11.17 (*a*)). It can be rolled to form a cylinder (*b*). A cone (*c*) or the frustum of a cone such as the parchment part of many lampshades as in Fig. 11.17 (*d*) can be cut and then opened out to give a flat,

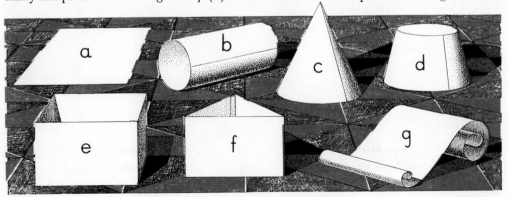

Fig. 11.17
Developable Surfaces.

i.e. plane surface. By folding and gumming paper, square (*e*) and triangular prisms (*f*) may be constructed without any stretching of the paper. A scroll shape (*g*) can also be made from flat paper without stretching or shrinking.

All the shapes illustrated in Fig. 11.17 are *developable surfaces* that can be made from a plane simply by bending or creasing. They form a very important group and many of their properties can be explored quite simply.

One very important surface which is not developable is that of a sphere. Because a sphere is not a developable surface, map making and map reading is quite complicated.

Complicated shapes can be made by cutting and gluing paper together so that a composite surface is made out of parts which themselves are developable surfaces, but which, as wholes, are not developable. A closed box or a cylinder with ends may be made from paper by cutting and gluing (Fig. 11.18).

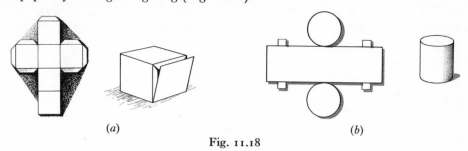

(*a*)   (*b*)

Fig. 11.18

For the ordinary person, by far the most interesting example of a composite surface, made up of component pieces all of which are developable surfaces, is a dress or a suit. Cutting out a dress from a paper pattern is an interesting and quite complex exercise in paper-and-scissors geometry. Similar tailoring is carried out in shipyards when the beautiful sweep of the hull of a ship is made from steel plates, riveting taking the place of the dressmaker's stitches.

Straight lines can be made accurately by creasing paper (Fig. 11.19).

Right angles can be made by folding and then refolding, so that the first fold lies along itself (Fig. 11.20).

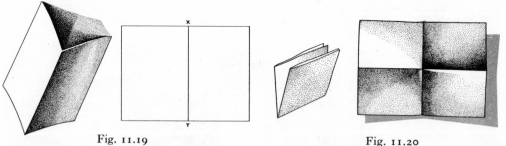

Fig. 11.19
A straight line by creasing.

Fig. 11.20
A right angle by two folds.

SYMMETRY

By cutting through a folded sheet of paper all that needs to be known about simple symmetry may be learned (Figs. 11.21 and 11.22).

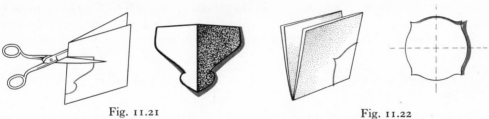

Fig. 11.21
Symmetry about *one* axis.

Fig. 11.22
Symmetry about two axes at right angles.

Although the scope of this approach is somewhat limited, a number of well-known geometrical facts can easily be illustrated with paper and scissors as the essential apparatus. The following five examples are quite familiar to anyone who has done any geometry.

EXAMPLES

1. *Any point, P, on the perpendicular bisector of the line joining two points A and B, is equidistant from A and B.*

Step (i) Mark points *A* and *B* on a sheet of paper and fold along *AB*.

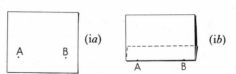

Step (ii) Fold the paper again so that *A* and *B* coincide. Open out again. This gives a crease, at right angles to that given by step (i), which is the perpendicular bisector of the line *AB*.

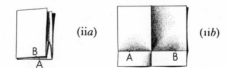

Step (iii) Choose any point *P* on the perpendicular bisector of *AB*. Fold along *AP* and then cut along this fold. Then fold along *BP* and cut along this fold. The paper will now look like that illustrated in (iii *b*).

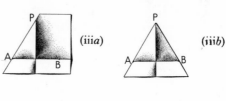

Step (iv) Fold again along the perpendicular bisector. *AP* and *BP* will coincide since the figure is, by construction, symmetrical about the perpendicular bisector of *AB*.

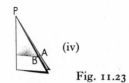

Fig. 11.23

2. By altering the sequence, the reader is asked to prove the converse of this proposition, namely, that *if P is any point equidistant from two points A and B, then P lies on the perpendicular bisector of A and B.*

3. *The perpendiculars from any point on the bisector of an angle to the arms of the angle are equal in length.*

This is left as an exercise for the reader, using methods similar to those set out in Example 1.

4. *The area of a triangle is equal to the area of a rectangle with half the height and on the same base.*

Make three creases in a sheet of paper and cut along the creases, thus cutting out a triangle.

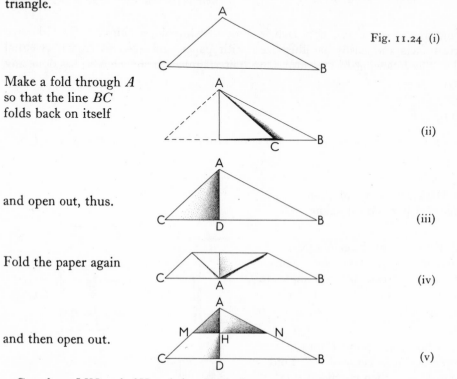

Make a fold through *A* so that the line *BC* folds back on itself

Fig. 11.24 (i)

(ii)

and open out, thus.

(iii)

Fold the paper again

(iv)

and then open out.

(v)

Cut along *MN* and *AH* and then stick the parts together on a sheet of paper to form the figure (vi).

(vi)

This illustrates the fact that the paper from which the triangle ABC was made can be used to make a rectangle of half the height and on the same base.

Note that the statement says "illustrates the fact that" only; rigid proof by this method is no easier than by the usual method.

5. Continuing from Fig. 11.24 (v) above, if this figure is creased along *MN* so that *A* coincides with *D*, and then *B* and *C* are folded over so that they also coincide with *D*

Fig. 11.24 (vii)

we have an illustration of the fact that the *three angles of a triangle add up to a straight line.*

These examples are familiar enough to all who have done any geometry, but paper-scissors-and-gum geometry does lead to new ideas, particularly in relation to basic ideas about surfaces. A sheet of paper has two surfaces, one of which could be coloured blue and the other red (Fig. 11.25).

Fig. 11.25

If a long strip of paper is gummed to itself to form a band or belt, it will be seen that one side of the paper is on the outside of the belt and the other is on the inside; one side could be coloured blue and the other red (Fig. 11.16).

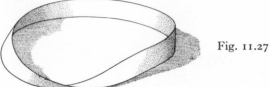

Fig. 11.26

THE MOEBIUS* STRIP

If, however, the paper is given a twist before gumming the ends together, a strip could be made like this (Fig. 11.27):

Fig. 11.27

Before reading any further, try to colour this so that one side of the paper is blue and the other side red.

You will find that if you begin colouring one side blue, you can go on colouring that side blue without any break in continuity until the whole paper is coloured blue. Further, the edge of the paper is one continuous curve.

We have in the Moebius strip the strange object which consists of one single continuous surface bounded by one continuous curve.

If the strip is now cut round the middle you will naturally expect to have two surfaces

Fig. 11.28

bounded by two edges. This is exactly what happens. Cut the strip and see what you obtain (Fig. 11.28).

* A. F. Moebius, 1790–1868.

Experiences such as this serve to indicate how much is often taken for granted, and that definitions of surfaces, and what is meant by both sides of a piece of paper, do need to be framed with care if they are to be used in any reasoning process.

Try also cutting the strip twice, along lines each one-third of the way across (Fig. 11.29).

Fig. 11.29

First write down what you expect to obtain before you actually do the cutting.

Other approaches to geometry

There are many other possible approaches to geometry. Obvious ones are paper, pencil and dividers, a geometry based on distances alone. We might use paper, pencil, straight-edge and dividers, lines and distances alone. Then there is the very important geometry based on paper ruled in squares. This, co-ordinate geometry, is one of the most versatile of all approaches to geometry. The best-known approach to geometry is the paper, pencil, straight-edge and pair of compasses geometry which is taught to all secondary school children. This is Euclidean Geometry.

MECCANO

Meccano is very useful in obtaining experience in connexion with angles, parallelograms and triangles. For example, if six long strips of Meccano are bolted together to form three parallel rods crossing over three parallel rods, they will make four parallelograms, and, by altering the angle between the two sets of rods, various shaped parallelograms can be formed such as (Fig. 11.30):

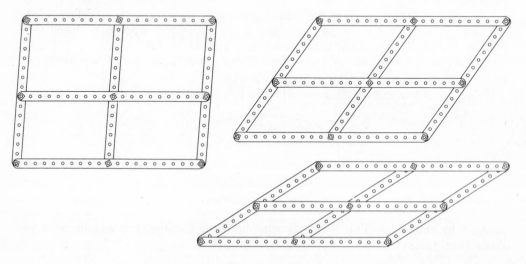

Fig. 11.30

From figures such as these it is obvious that the sides of the parallelograms remain the same length throughout, but that as one pair of opposite angles gets bigger, the other pair gets smaller, and such facts as "the opposite angles of a parallelogram are equal" are quite clearly shown in the various shapes obtained from this one set of Meccano strips. From the same figure it will be quite clear that as the strips are moved certain angles remain equal in all positions, and such well-known facts as "alternate angles are equal" and "corresponding angles are equal" are clearly demonstrated in this figure.

This figure which is built up from parallelograms is not rigid, and any attempt to build a structure based on parallelograms is always liable to collapse. On the other hand, if three strips of Meccano are bolted together to form a triangle, it is at once clearly felt that this triangle is a rigid figure, and even when the nuts are not screwed up particularly tightly it is not possible to deform the shape of a triangle. When three sides of a triangle are fixed, then the triangle is rigidly determined. It is also possible to construct a rigid triangle by anchoring two of the angles, in which case it is not even necessary to put a nut and bolt in the third angle of the triangle, so that two angles and one side are enough to fix the shape of the triangle. Again, if two strips of Meccano are bolted together, and the angle between these two sides is locked, then it is possible to cut out a third side of the triangle in quite flimsy paper and it again can be felt that two sides and the included angle are enough to ensure that a triangle so formed is quite rigid. Experience such as this is a very good preliminary to understanding the meaning of congruent triangles, and is a useful introduction to the study of geometrical problems concerned with straight lines and angles. By bolting two strips together and locking the angle between them it is possible to slide this angle round between two fixed supports and show that angles in the same segment of a circle are equal.

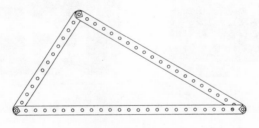

Fig. 11.31

USE OF PHOTOGRAPHS AS A HELP IN UNDERSTANDING GEOMETRICAL FACTS

Photographs should be used a great deal more in introducing ideas of geometry, and for a number of specific purposes in actually finding things out. One very simple example is that of finding the height of a tree.

Long before children are old enough to handle a clinometer, or theodolite (see p. 187), it is possible to find the height of a tree by the method shown in Fig. 11.32. If a photograph is taken of the tree, if possible from a fair distance, and again, if possible, from a height roughly half-way up the tree, as illustrated in the figure, then, on the photograph, the height from the ground to the top of the tree can be measured, and we will suppose that this height is 1·8 in., and the greatest width of the tree can also be measured, in this case, 1·4 in. It is then a simple matter to stand immediately below the point of the tree, on the extreme left, and mark the spot by a stone or peg, and then to walk across and stand underneath the part of the tree which sticks out farthest on the right-hand side and to mark this point on the ground with another stone or peg and then, with a tape-measure, to measure this distance. If this distance is 35 ft and h is the actual height of the tree, then the value of h will be given fairly accurately by the formula:

$$h = \frac{1\cdot8}{1\cdot4} \times 35 \text{ ft}$$

$$\therefore \quad h = \frac{\overset{9}{\cancel{1\cdot8}}}{\underset{7}{\cancel{1\cdot4}}} \times 35 \text{ ft}$$

i.e. $h = 45$ ft

Similar use may be made of photographs to estimate heights of houses, and similar lengths which are inaccessible to direct measurement.

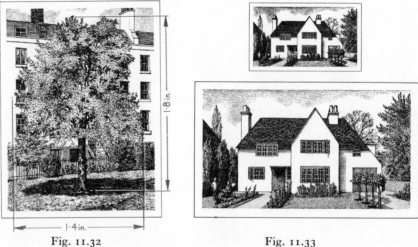

Fig. 11.32   Fig. 11.33

The example chosen supposes that the proportion of height to width of the tree is the same as the proportion of the height to width in the photograph, and it also supposes that this ratio is the same whatever the size of the photograph. This can be demonstrated quite simply if a small snapshot is enlarged so that three or four different-sized enlargements of the same photograph are made and corresponding lengths measured in each of these photographs. Angles should also be measured, and the following facts become quite clear: in all these photographs, when any length is divided by another length, the same ratio is obtained on whichever size of photograph the measurements were obtained, and angles are unchanged in all the photographs.

In the pictures (Fig. 11.33), it can be verified that in each case the roof slopes at 50° and the height of the house is half the length of the house. In each case the door is one-third of the height of the house, and in each case the angle between the two sloping sides of the gable is 70°. If various photographs are taken of parts of a building and these are available in several different-sized enlargements, a great deal of the geometry of similar figures can be discussed, and a number of distances and lengths, which are normally inaccessible, can be calculated very simply. From these photographs also, some of the rules of perspective can be demonstrated. For example, the lines on the photographs corresponding to lines which in the original are parallel will be seen to meet at eye level.

Euclidean Geometry

Until about the middle of the last century European geometers had for over two thousand years voluntarily restricted themselves to a development of geometry based only on paper, pencil, straight line and compasses. To understand how this came about we need to know something of Plato, who was born in Athens in 429 B.C. Plato was a most distinguished philosopher who gathered around him a body of men and founded the "Academy" about the year 380 B.C. So great a man was Plato that his authority was accepted by the academicians and he exerted an extraordinary influence on both contemporaries and successors. Plato believed that mathematics and philosophy were very closely connected and insisted that a study of geometry should be made by all who sought to become philosophers. Over the entrance to the Academy was inscribed

$$Μηδεὶς \ Ἀγεωμέτρητος \ Εἰσίτω$$

which may be translated "Let no one enter who is ignorant of geometry". Plato's philosophy was greatly concerned with ideals and with perfection. Perfect justice and perfect truth could not be achieved but were ideals to which things could approximate. His theory of forms also played an important part in his teaching and he was strict in his systematic use of a logical development from carefully expressed definitions, postulates and axioms. Plato seems to have accepted without question that a circle was a perfect figure. He also seems to have accepted without question that the orbits of heavenly bodies were circles. He takes the straight line as an example of an ideal; many things may approximate to straightness but none of them quite attains the ideal of perfect straightness. He uses straightness as an illustration of perfection in his theory of forms, together with other concepts of perfection including unity, 1, and the perfection of the circle. Geometry as developed in the Academy by Plato's successors became a strictly logical development based on postulates and axioms, making use of the perfect forms of the line and the circle. The perfection of the line and the circle was taken for granted by the Platonists: it was largely an aesthetic and metaphysical conception of perfection.

About the year 300 B.C., Ptolemy, who had succeeded Alexander the Great in the part of his empire centred on Egypt, opened the new university at Alexandria, and he turned to Athens for his staff. Euclid became the first head of the Mathematics department. He was a conscientious exponent of the geometrical traditions of the Academy of Plato and he compiled a comprehensive exposition of geometrical knowledge. It is a rigidly logical deductive system based on precisely defined axioms and postulates (self-evident theorems which are not deduced from more elementary theorems) admitting the use of only rulers and compasses for constructions on a plane surface. (The rulers are straight-edged, ungraduated.) Euclid's geometry is so complete, so systematic, so coherent in its logical development that it set a standard of integrity of accurate statement and intellectual honesty that put the study of geometry on a lofty pedestal as the perfect academic discipline. Euclid's text-book on geometry, written between 300 B.C. and 275 B.C. survived as the standard school text-book until the present century. A standard text-book cannot hold the field for over 2000 years without cramping the imagination to some extent, and it was only during the nineteenth century, after men such as Riemann and Lobatschewsky had come forward with non-Euclidean geometries, that more adventurous attitudes to space became possible. Today many fresh and stimulating approaches to geometry are available to students; nevertheless a thorough grounding in formal geometry based on Euclid is the surest foundation for such adventures.

Thus, it came about that for 2000 years western man agreed to explore space and deduce his geometry according to a set of rules which allowed the use of only ruler and compasses, paper and pencil. Mathematicians were given an example of perfection in logical development and accurate statement and at the same time they were restricted in their explorations by the rules of procedure, laid down in the fourth century B.C., imposed by the Platonic traditions of the Academy.

In England, Euclid's *Elements* was the standard text-book used for the teaching of geometry in schools until about the beginning of the twentieth century. The Mathematical Association was formed in 1871 for the purpose of reforming the teaching of Geometry and has published a number of reports* making suggestions for reforming geometry syllabuses. The most recent report, published in 1939, aims at something far more constructive than a mere dilution of Euclid, as will be seen from the following quotation from page 5 of the introductory chapter:

"*Intuition and Logic.* Geometrical power depends on two factors to one of which franker recognition needs to be given than is customary. That attention to reasoning is necessary is true enough, but traditionally such exaggerated importance has been attached to this factor that the other, which is certainly of not less importance, has been too much neglected.

"In the days when Euclid reigned supreme this was natural; the subject to be studied was not 'Geometry' but 'Euclid's Elements of Geometry', habitually abbreviated to 'Euclid' pure and simple.

"Now Euclid's great book is emphatically a logical, systematic treatise on the elements of the subject rather than a book on the subject itself: it is not concerned with the general body of geometrical facts known in his time, still less, of course, with the far wider field known today, but with the logical articulation of the simplest of those facts. So in days when for school purposes 'geometry' meant 'Euclid' it was not unnatural that examining bodies should allow 'Logic' as an alternative subject, for the very essence of Euclid is the logical examination of facts already well known, not a natural method of learning those facts in the first instance.

"Even today there are fields of advanced geometrical study in which the logical aspect is predominant or even exclusive. In geometries of four and more dimensions 'intuition' is unavailable and such geometries are therefore predominantly if not

---

* *Mathematical Association Reports:* 1919—"The teaching of Mathematics in Public and Secondary Schools"; 1923—"The Teaching of Geometry in Schools"; 1939—A Second Report on "The Teaching of Geometry in Schools" (reprinted 1954).

exclusively logical. In 'Axiomatik' the only safe method is deliberately to exclude intuition, lest unrecognized assumptions should slip in unawares.

"But in elementary school work we are faced with a different problem, viz. the first recognition of geometrical facts and the development of the power of geometrical perception. Until this has been to some extent acquired, attempts to reason on the facts are constantly hampered. The paradox may almost be ventured that in many cases until a fact is obvious argument will be of little avail.

"Our recognition of this is of course checked by the fact that under school conditions a boy will often say 'It is obvious' to cover ignorance: as teachers used to say 'Whenever I see the word "obvious" in a Euclid paper I know there is something wrong'. But it remains true about a very large proportion of geometrical propositions that unless they are 'obvious' to the boy, apart from 'proof', there is something very defective in his geometrical perception."

The geometry of such curves as the parabola discussed in Chapter 10 can best be explored after the figure has been drawn from numerical data plotted on squared paper. "Squared-paper geometry" was made possible by the work of René Descartes (1596–1650). His work has not only led to the understanding of many complicated curves and made possible the design of shapes, such as aerofoils, which have to fit in with specified conditions, but it has also helped very much in the understanding of the properties of algebraic functions. The use of "Cartesian co-ordinates", "Cartesian geometry" or "co-ordinate geometry" is outside the scope of this book, but no chapter on geometry would be complete without a reference to Descartes and his pioneer work in this field.

EXERCISES

1. Make a tracing of the essential features of a fairly large photograph which includes buildings or other features containing a number of horizontal and some vertical lines.

   Produce the lines which represent horizontal lines that are parallel to one another in the original building and verify that they meet at a point. Then produce the lines which represent another set of lines that are parallel to one another but not parallel to the first set; verify that they meet at a point. If possible find a third set of horizontal parallels represented in the photograph and produce these to meet at a point.

   Verify that the points of intersection all lie on a horizontal line at the level of the camera.

   Verify that all vertical lines are represented by lines which remain vertical.

2. Select a tree, a house and a bag. Describe their shapes as well as you can

   (i) without introducing numbers into your description,

   (ii) when you are free to introduce numerical data into your description if you wish to (by numerical data is meant expressions such as "twice as high as it is wide", as well as references such as "15 ft" or 45°).

   You should restrict your description to the shape of the object. If practicable, ask someone to try to pick out the tree or house or bag from others, from your description of its shape. Note the facts you describe.

3. Cut out any triangle. Bisect the angles by folding the paper so that adjacent sides lie along one another and crease the paper to mark the bisector. Verify that the three

bisectors of the angles pass through a single point. Call this point I. With centre I, open your compasses to the appropriate radius and draw the "incircle" of the triangle, lying inside the triangle and touching all three sides.

4. Draw, approximately, the shape of the wool in a single row of knitting. Then draw the next row and indicate how they interlock. Try to find how to indicate on your diagram the interlocking differences between two rows when the knitting is all "plain" or is "plain and purl".

5. Your reflection in a plane mirror is such that it looks like a person whose left hand moves when you move your right hand, whose left ear would look red if your right ear was red, and so on. We say that a mirror image is "laterally reversed". Explain why this is so and explain also why it is that left becomes right and right becomes left, but that "up" does not become "down" and there is no inversion in the vertical direction.

6. If you looked at two photographs of the same street, one taken in 1934 and the other in 1959, you could tell which was which from the different appearances of the motor cars. Assuming the pictures are too small for details to be picked out, describe the differences in general shape and outline between the two sets of motor cars.

   Again ignoring small details, could you do the same for women's clothes or for men's clothes?

7. Find some books or magazines or labels on tins of food about fifty years old. Look at the printing, both on title pages and in the text, and, using the vocabulary of shapes and space rather than aesthetics, describe the differences in lettering. If you can find a photograph of a station, taken before about 1910, or the destination board of an old motor omnibus, compare the lettering of the name of the station or the lettering on the omnibus with that of today, again restricting your considerations to geometrical language.

8. A mischievous boy put some flavouring matter on the tails of three equal-sized snakes, A, B and C. It was the sort of flavouring snakes enjoy. Snake A began to swallow the tail of snake B at the same time as snake B began to swallow the tail of snake C, who had at the same time begun to swallow the tail of snake A. It is the habit of this breed of snake to swallow things without chewing. Where would the swallowing process stop? Draw two sketches of the end position, one as seen from above and the other of a cross-section through the snakes.

12

Shapes and Sizes

Where there is uniformity and regularity, mathematics may be found. There is the type of uniformity of a million pennies, freshly minted, indistinguishable from one another, or the regularity of the uniform alternation of night and day, winter and summer, new moon and full moon for which precise times may be given. On the other hand, there is the type of regularity which makes possible the recognition of a distant oak tree or Lombardy poplar or hawthorn tree despite the fact that no two oaks are identical and prevailing winds may make considerable differences in the profiles of poplars or hawthorn trees. Bee-hives may differ in details, but it is usually possible to see a white object on the other side of a field and know that it is a bee-hive and not a shed or a box or a bungalow. Our judgments about birds, trees and animals are based upon appraisals of subtle relationships between size, shape and form. This theme has been expounded in very great detail in D'Arcy Thomson's two big volumes *On Growth and Form*, which are a feast of enjoyment for both mathematicians and biologists and should be in every school and college library.

Sizes

There are appropriate ways of exploring and describing various types of uniformity. On the one hand, precise statements such as "the diameter of a halfpenny is exactly one inch" or "the diameter of a size-8 drill is 0·199 in." may be made because the objects they describe conform to man-made standards. On the other hand, answers to questions such as "How big is a full-grown oak-tree?" or "How tall is an English man?" cannot be given in the same way. They are legitimate questions which call for serious answers such as, "Full grown, an oak tree varies in height from 60 to 130 feet, the difference depending upon situation; the tallest being those that have been drawn up, in forests, at the expense of their branches".* Udney Yule gives information about the sizes of English men which may be expressed in the form that their average height is 5 ft 7·46 in., two-thirds of all English men have heights between 5 ft 4·9 in. and 5 ft 10·0 in. and 95 per cent have heights between 5 ft 2·3 in. and 6 ft 0·6 in.†

The highly organized nature of our civilized world is obvious, but we do not always appreciate the importance to it of standardization. We take it for granted that if we buy an electric-light bulb in one shop it will fit into a socket bought in another shop or that our own particular bicycle-tyre pump will fit on to the valve of anyone's tyre. In order to secure the benefits of standardization the British Standards Institution was established in 1901, the same year in which the United States of America set up their National Bureau of Standards.

---

* *The Observer's Book of Trees and Shrubs.* W. J. Stokoe (F. Warne & Co.), p. 149.
† *An Introduction to the Theory of Statistics.* G. Udney Yule (Griffin & Co.), Chapter VII.

We carry around with us mental pictures of various sizes and it does not take very much effort to associate these sizes with the appropriate units. We should be able to recognize a six-foot wall or a three-foot cane, to know whether a bag of potatoes weighs about seven pounds or fourteen pounds, to distinguish between a two-gallon can and a one-gallon can, to have a rough idea of the length of a mile and to know roughly what an acre field looks like.

In the world around us we are able to observe directly grains of sand, trees, mountains, houses, boxes, cathedrals and office blocks, gnats, elephants, long walks, train journeys, full stops and printed letters, and speeds from that of a tortoise to that of a racing car; we can feel things like sandstone, custard or velvet and we can hear things like the buzzing of bees or thunder. Such things are directly accessible to our senses and they can be measured directly with rulers, tape measures, scales, watches supplemented by a few simple devices such as speedometers, and helped occasionally with binoculars, simple microscopes or audiometers.

We are aware, also, that there are things too small for us to see or too far away and too big to measure directly. Our ordinary units are appropriate for a range of sizes but they make a poor job of conveying concepts of size to us when related to things outside this range such as protons, mesons, electrons or neutrons or such as spiral nebulae. We may accept a statement that a meson, in its brief life measured in millionths of a second, may be associated with a term in an equation which relates to a mass of the order of $2 \cdot 5 \times 10^{-25}$ grammes, but this does not mean much to a man who can estimate the weight of a pound or a kilogramme and who can never have seen anything smaller than a tiny grain of dust containing millions of millions of atoms. We may accept a statement that a spiral galaxy is receding at 20,000 miles a second and is distant 2,500 million, million, million miles, but this description of a vast distance in terms of our everyday units helps very little in our intellectual problem of forming clear mental pictures of the magnitudes we seek to conceive.

Considerable intellectual problems arise in relation to quantities outside the range of our senses. Until the end of the nineteenth century, mathematics had been developed in the minds of men whose concepts were derived from this ordinary world of our senses, simply extended a little by optical microscopes and telescopes. The atom was smaller than anything visible through a microscope, but it was not different in kind from the matter they knew through their senses. Space, too, was simple; it had no properties save the emptiness in which material objects could have position. A sub-atomic particle was a contradiction of words for, by definition, an atom was the smallest particle of matter.

A revolution in thought had to take place before a mathematics of nuclear physics could evolve, and another revolution in thought made possible Einstein's concept of space-time structure. By similes and analogies, workers in these specialist fields try to explain their work in terms of concepts derived from the world of our senses, and their readers should appreciate the difficulties involved. In so far as they are describing phenomena inaccessible to our five senses, their task is as difficult as explaining to a blind man, in terms of sound and touch, things which can only be seen. Both writer and reader must exercise very great imagination and caution. For the person who does not work in these fields, mathematics remains both a self-consistent logical structure and a most powerful way of co-ordinating precise knowledge and understanding of the world in which we live.

ORDERS OF MAGNITUDE

Even if we agree to omit sizes outside the scope of our direct experiences, we are still left with the range from a grain of dust to the thousand or so miles which could make up a single journey. It is convenient to sub-divide this great range so that things which are of the same *order of magnitude* may be considered together and described in appropriate units. The usage of this somewhat informal classification may be illustrated by a few simple examples.

The thickness of paper is of the order of a tenth of a millimetre. Some paper is thicker than this and some thinner, but $\frac{1}{10}$ mm is the right sort of size. 1 mm is the order of magnitude of the thickness of cardboard, while $\frac{1}{100}$ mm is the order of magnitude of the thickness of very thin tissue.

Pebbles are of the order of inches, ordinary garden plants of the order of feet, bushes of 10 ft, forest trees of 100 ft, fair-sized hills of the order of 1000 ft, and high mountains of the order of 10,000 ft.

Shapes

Irregular shapes such as those of trees, animals, people, countries or clouds cannot be completely described in any simple manner. Diagrams, plans or maps may be drawn to illustrate them and selected measurements may be given. For example, the County of Lancashire may be illustrated by a map, drawn to scale; it may be described in general terms as extending about 88 miles in a North-south direction and as being about 50 miles wide from East to West in the South, narrowing to as little as 9 miles from East to West in a line about 6 miles south of Lancaster, and having an area of 1,033,076 acres in the administrative county. Such information is true; it gives an idea of the size, but is of very little practical use. Before seeking information, one should know for what purpose it is required and then use specific means of obtaining data. This will generally be found by breaking the irregular shape up into a number of the well-known regular geometrical shapes and making use of the properties of triangles, circles, pyramids, cones, cylinders and spheres and the relationships between lines and angles which are included in geometrical and trigonometrical studies.

SIMILARITY

"A piece of paper is 1·62 times as long as it is wide"; "A roof slopes up at 45° to the horizontal"; "A kite consists of an isosceles triangle with a semicircle described on its base": these are three statements which refer to shapes and not to size. If photographs of these three objects were taken, then the three statements would be true whatever the size of the enlargement of the negative. This is characteristic of shapes and we may make use of this idea to define similarity by saying that two objects are similar if they have the same shape. This definition implies two separate statements: first, that if two figures are similar all *angles* associated with one figure are *equal* to the corresponding angles in the other figure; secondly, the *ratio* of any two lengths in one figure is equal to the *ratio* of corresponding lengths in the other figure. Such statements are independent of the size of the figures, so that a figure of the order of magnitude of an inch may be similar to a figure of the order of magnitude of a mile. Because of this fact scale drawings, models, maps and charts are able to illustrate completely all details relating to shape.

Trigonometry

In the definition of similarity, it will be seen that two apparently distinct properties remain unaltered in any reduction or enlargement in the size of a photograph or in the scale of a figure. Angles are measured with protractors, which show the amount of turning required to move from one direction to another; ratios of lengths are obtained by measuring lengths with rulers and dividing one length by another. That both angles and ratios of length are equal in similar figures, and that both angles and ratios of length are altered when shapes are distorted, suggest that these are not independent properties and that there is some sort of functional relationship between them. The study of this relationship is the basis of trigonometry. In this paragraph we shall do no more than define the three ratios, sine, cosine and tangent, usually abbreviated to sin, cos and tan.

If XOY is a horizontal straight line, OP is a line inclined at an angle $A°$ to the line XOY, and Q is the point on XOY such that angle PQO is a right angle, then the trigonometrical ratios are defined as follows (Fig. 12.1):

$$\sin A° = \frac{QP}{OP}$$

$$\cos A° = \frac{OQ}{OP}$$

$$\tan A° = \frac{QP}{OQ}$$

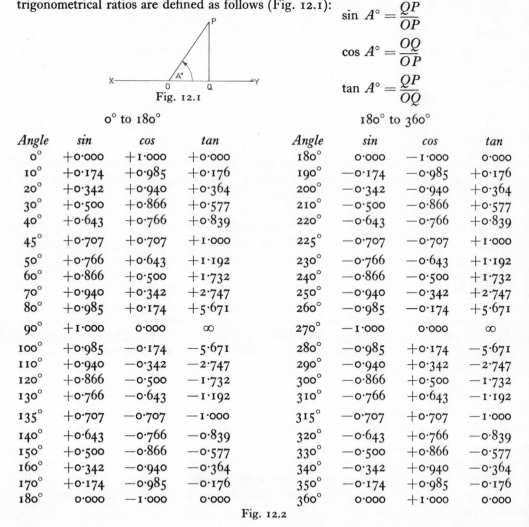

Fig. 12.1

0° to 180°				180° to 360°			
Angle	sin	cos	tan	Angle	sin	cos	tan
0°	+0·000	+1·000	+0·000	180°	0·000	−1·000	0·000
10°	+0·174	+0·985	+0·176	190°	−0·174	−0·985	+0·176
20°	+0·342	+0·940	+0·364	200°	−0·342	−0·940	+0·364
30°	+0·500	+0·866	+0·577	210°	−0·500	−0·866	+0·577
40°	+0·643	+0·766	+0·839	220°	−0·643	−0·766	+0·839
45°	+0·707	+0·707	+1·000	225°	−0·707	−0·707	+1·000
50°	+0·766	+0·643	+1·192	230°	−0·766	−0·643	+1·192
60°	+0·866	+0·500	+1·732	240°	−0·866	−0·500	+1·732
70°	+0·940	+0·342	+2·747	250°	−0·940	−0·342	+2·747
80°	+0·985	+0·174	+5·671	260°	−0·985	−0·174	+5·671
90°	+1·000	0·000	∞	270°	−1·000	0·000	∞
100°	+0·985	−0·174	−5·671	280°	−0·985	+0·174	−5·671
110°	+0·940	−0·342	−2·747	290°	−0·940	+0·342	−2·747
120°	+0·866	−0·500	−1·732	300°	−0·866	+0·500	−1·732
130°	+0·766	−0·643	−1·192	310°	−0·766	+0·643	−1·192
135°	+0·707	−0·707	−1·000	315°	−0·707	+0·707	−1·000
140°	+0·643	−0·766	−0·839	320°	−0·643	+0·766	−0·839
150°	+0·500	−0·866	−0·577	330°	−0·500	+0·866	−0·577
160°	+0·342	−0·940	−0·364	340°	−0·342	+0·940	−0·364
170°	+0·174	−0·985	−0·176	350°	−0·174	+0·985	−0·176
180°	0·000	−1·000	0·000	360°	0·000	+1·000	0·000

Fig. 12.2

Tables of these ratios, to four places of decimals and at tenth-of-a-degree intervals, are included in most books of mathematical tables. The table (Fig. 12.2) gives values at 10° intervals, sufficient to illustrate the pattern of the ratios, yet simple enough to allow all the ratios to be included together. The meaning of the + and − signs are explained by means of examples.

The signs used in conjunction with the trigonometrical ratios fit in with the conventions used with graphs, namely, that distances to the right of the origin are labelled + and those to the left are −, while those above the origin are + and those below are −. The diagrams (Fig. 12.3) illustrate the ratios corresponding to 60°, 120°, 240° and 300°. If, in each diagram, OP is drawn 2 cm long, the lengths of QP and OQ, with the appropriate signs, would be those indicated on the figure. The reader may verify that the value of the sin, cos and tan of each angle agrees with the values given in the tables.

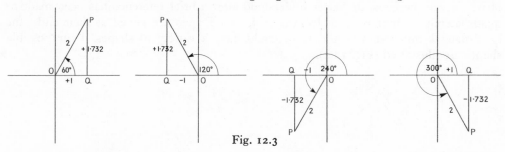

Fig. 12.3

For most problems in the elementary uses of trigonometry the values of the ratios for angles between 0° and 90° suffice, but it will be appreciated that there are many engineering and surveying problems when angles greater than 90° need to be introduced, and wherever there is rotation, angles from 0° to 360° are involved.

EXAMPLE

A roof slopes at 45° to the horizontal. The distance measured up the roof from the gutter to the ridge at the top of the roof is 15 ft. What is the height of the ridge above the level of the gutter?

$$\frac{GB}{GR} = \cos 45° \quad \therefore \quad GB = GR \times \cos 45°$$

$$= 15 \times 0{\cdot}707 \text{ ft}$$

$$= 13{\cdot}6 \text{ ft.}$$

The answer to a question such as this could, of course, be obtained just as easily and accurately by scale drawing, but where greater lengths are involved and great accuracy is required, tables may be used to obtain any required degree of accuracy and they are not subject to the errors which may arise from drawings.

There are two simple formulae which are very useful:

1. In any triangle the lengths of the sides are proportional to the sines of the angles opposite to them, thus in the triangle ABC,

$$\frac{BC}{\sin A} = \frac{CA}{\sin B} = \frac{AB}{\sin C}.$$

2. In any triangle ABC,

$$\cos A = \frac{CA^2 + AB^2 - BC^2}{2 \cdot CA \cdot AB}$$

with similar formulae for $\cos B$ and $\cos C$, namely,

$$\cos B = \frac{AB^2 + BC^2 - CA^2}{2 \cdot AB \cdot BC}$$

$$\cos C = \frac{BC^2 + CA^2 - AB^2}{2 \cdot BC \cdot CA}.$$

TRIANGLES

Geometers, surveyors and engineers make considerable use of triangles, the importance of which will, perhaps, be better understood after a brief reference has been made to quadrilaterals. If four rods, of lengths 4, 5, 6 and 7 cm are joined at their ends, the quadrilateral which they would form could have a variety of shapes. Four possible shapes are illustrated (Fig. 12.4).

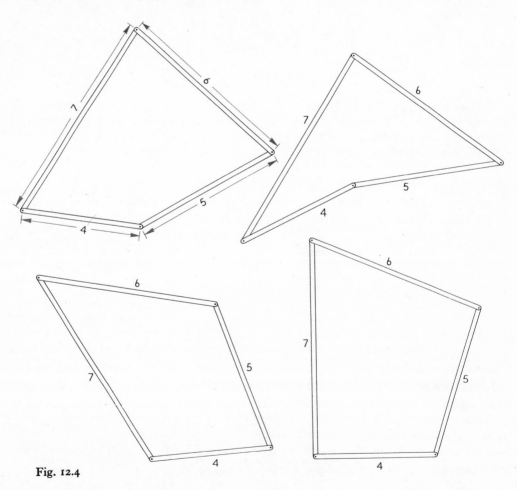

Fig. 12.4

It will be seen that these shapes are quite different and that if the rods are bolted at the corners so that the angles are not held rigid, any one of these quadrilateral shapes could be deformed to take the shape of one of the others. Anyone who has played with Meccano will know that, however much the nuts and bolts at corners are tightened, they will work loose and the structure will cease to be rigid.

A good example of this lack of rigid shape of quadrilaterals is trellis work. A length of trellising may be bought as a compact piece, with the slats touching one another and no open spaces between them. It may then be opened out to form the familiar pattern of squares or it could be opened a little less to give a diamond trellis. When such a piece of trellis is in place, firmly screwed to supporting posts, it will become the rigid support for climbing plants which we are used to seeing in gardens. The rigidity, however, is imposed on the trellis by the supporting posts and is not inherent in the criss-cross structure itself.

Fig. 12.5

A five-sided, a six-sided and in fact every many-sided framework will behave in the same way if jointed at the corners. The only simple shape made out of jointed strips (i.e. strips of which the corner bolts do not lock the angles) that is intrinsically rigid is the triangle. A triangle whose sides are of given lengths can have one, and only one, possible shape. This geometrical fact finds practical applications in strutting and reinforcing, in the use of guy ropes and props; it explains the diagonal bar on farm gates and the cross-girdering of rigid structures, including cranes, girder bridges and even such immense structures as the Eiffel Tower (Fig. 12.5).

The principle of these tie bars is illustrated very simply by the quadrilateral already discussed. Of all the possible shapes which could be made with four rods of lengths 4, 5, 6 and 7 cm, one of them will be such that the distance from the intersection of the 4-cm and the 5-cm rods to the intersection of the 6-cm and 7-cm rods is exactly 8 cm. If an 8-cm rod is bolted across this diagonal the quadrilateral is then equivalent to two triangles and it is quite rigid (Fig. 12.6). It is suggested that this quadrilateral be made out of Meccano or some such material and then the diagonal bar be joined so that the rigidity of the structure can then be tested. Although, mechanically, the rigidity of a triangle made out of bars or rods or strips of fixed length is quite fundamental to structural work, draughtsmen and surveyors find it convenient to make use of other sets of facts which determine uniquely the shape and size of a triangle.

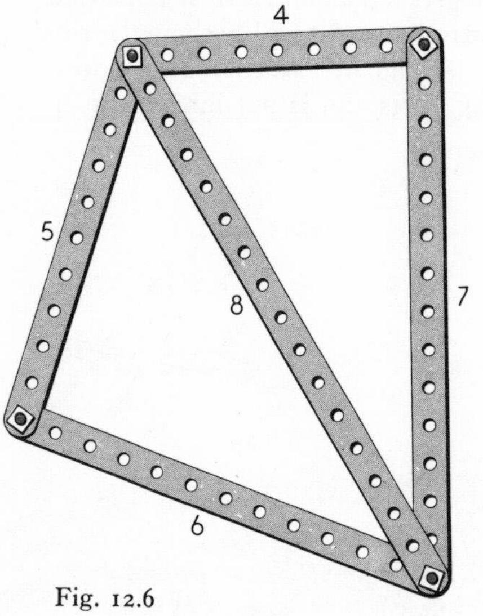

If AB and AC are two rods, of lengths 5 cm and 6 cm respectively, and they are bolted together at A, the angle being locked by means of a small plate, then the length of BC will be determined precisely (Fig. 12.7). If $\angle A = 60°$ a careful drawing will give the length as about 5·57 cm. The cos formula for the

Fig. 12.6

triangle given on page 184 was

$$\cos A = \frac{CA^2 + AB^2 - BC^2}{2 . CA . AB}$$

and the table gives cos 60° = 0·500

$$\therefore \quad \tfrac{1}{2} = \frac{36 + 25 - BC^2}{2 . 6 . 5}$$

i.e. $\tfrac{1}{2} = \dfrac{61 - BC^2}{60}$

or $1 = \dfrac{61 - BC^2}{30}$

i.e. $30 = 61 - BC^2$

so that $BC^2 = 31$

and $BC = \sqrt{31} = 5\cdot5676.$

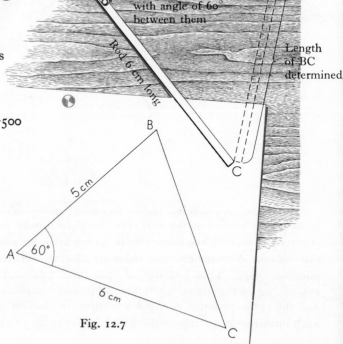

Fig. 12.7

Thus, either by scale drawing or by trigonometry, a knowledge of the lengths of two sides of a triangle and the size of the angle between them enables the third side to be determined exactly.

Surveyors may set about the job of mapping an area by beginning at two points, B and C, the distance between which they have measured extremely accurately. They then set up an instrument called a theodolite at B and at C and from these points measure the bearings of some point such as the top of a church steeple or a pole set up for the purpose of marking a particular place. A theodolite consists essentially of a telescope mounted on a base which can be levelled by means of a spirit-level and aligned by means of a compass. Protractor scales enable the direction in which the telescope is pointing to be read off. Another scale enables the angle of elevation above or depression below the horizontal to be determined. Making use of the fact that a triangle can be defined without ambiguity when the length of one of its sides and the size of two of its angles are known, the position of the top of the church steeple can be determined relative to the base points B and C. For example, a surveyor sets up his theodolite at a place B, and erects a pole at another place C which is exactly 4 chains (88 yards) due East of B, and he sights the corner, A, of a field which is roughly North-east of B. He finds that the angle CBA is 48° and then moves his theodolite to C and finds that the angle BCA is 62°. This information is sufficient to place A exactly on a plan on which the positions of the base points B and C have been marked.

If we take an actual example, using one side and two angles of a triangle, in the Chilterns, just to the north of Thame, are the two villages of Chearsley and Lower Winchendon. The church tower of Lower Winchendon is exactly a mile and a half in a direction N. 30° E. from the church tower at Chearsley. These two towers may be plotted on a map, as in Fig. 12.8, in which 1 mile is represented by 1 inch, that is, in which the scale is $1 \frac{\text{mile}}{\text{inch}}$.

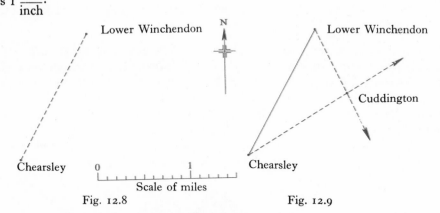

Fig. 12.8   Fig. 12.9

From Chearsley church, the church tower of Cuddington bears N. 60 E., and from the church at Lower Winchendon, Cuddington church tower bears S. 26° E. When these two lines of bearing are drawn, their point of intersection is the position of the church at Cuddington (Fig. 12.9).

Only one triangle can possibly be drawn from the information given. From any two of the three landmarks now mapped, two bearings may be obtained to place exactly the position of a fourth landmark. Progressing in this way it is possible to extend the map indefinitely until the whole country has been mapped. This is the process of "triangulation" by which surveyors map a region from some initial base-line, by covering it completely with accurately constructed triangles. It is because a triangle can without ambiguity be completely defined by three of its elements that such a network of triangles gives an accurate mapping of a whole area. All measurements obtained from scale drawings can be checked by calculations; this will ensure that no error made at one point of a systematic triangulation gives rise to subsequent cumulative errors as the mapping is extended.

The breaking down of complex shapes into triangles is of great importance in a wide variety of contexts, and the properties of triangles figure largely in systematic geometry courses. Once the engineers' structures, the cartographers' maps and the geometers' figures have been broken down to triangles, the draughtsman's drawing-board and his trigonometrical tables can be used to obtain lengths and angles to any required degree of accuracy.. The intimate association of trigonometry with triangles is implied in the name, *tri* = three, *gonia* = angle, *metrein* = to measure, which is simply Greek for "measuring triangles". In passing, it is interesting to note that the Greek mental picture of an angle was a knee (Greek: *gonu*, Latin: *genu*, French: *genou*) whereas the Romans pictured an angle (*angulus*) as bent, like an ankle.

A fact about triangles which must be known before any use is made of any other properties is the simple observation that the sum of the angles is 180°.

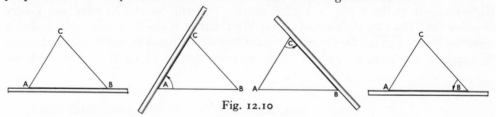

Fig. 12.10

If a ruler is placed along the side AB of a triangle ABC and is then turned through the angle A so that the ruler lies along AC, and it is then turned through the angle C so that it lies along CB and is then turned through the angle B so that it lies along BA, then clearly it will have turned through the angles $A + B + C$ and it is now lying along the same side of the triangle, BA, as when the experiment began, but it will be the other way up, having turned through 180° (Fig. 12.10).

The same fact, *the sum of the angles of a triangle is 180°*, can also be demonstrated by cutting out a triangle in paper and folding the paper as in Fig. 12.11.

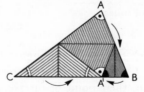

Fig. 12.11

Having established the angle sum of the triangle as 180°, it is clear that if *two* angles of a triangle are known, the third can be calculated. Returning to the three villages of Chearsley, Lower Winchendon and Cuddington, the known facts about the triangle are that the side AB joining Chearsley (A) to Lower Winchendon (B) is of length 1·5 miles; angle $CBA = 60° - 30° = 30°$ and angle $ABC = 30° + 26° = 56°$. The remaining angle $CAB = 180° - (30° + 56°) = 94°$. Using the formula on page 183

$$\frac{BC}{\sin A} = \frac{CA}{\sin B} = \frac{AB}{\sin C}$$

we have

$$\frac{BC}{\sin 30°} = \frac{CA}{\sin 56°} = \frac{1·5 \text{ miles}}{\sin 94°}$$

i.e.

$$\frac{BC}{0·5000} = \frac{CA}{0·8290} = \frac{1·5 \text{ miles}}{0·9976}$$

giving $BC = 1·5 \times 0·5 \div 0·9976 = 0·7518$ mile

$CA = 1·5 \times 0·8290 \div 0·9976 = 1·246$ mile

which confirms the lengths of the lines in the diagram and expresses them with greater accuracy than is possible from the drawing itself.

Shapes and sizes in the world around us

Armed with the knowledge that by breaking up complex figures into triangles or finding triangles to fit facts about objects and by making use of scale drawings or trigonometry to obtain further information, we are in a position to begin to explore some of the shapes and sizes of things in the world around us.

HOW BIG ARE TREES?

We have already referred to oak trees as being between 60 ft and 130 ft high. How can we find the height of an actual tree with the minimum of bother? We do not require very great accuracy; three or four feet more or less do not make much difference when we are concerned with trees where there is much variation between individuals. We shall find out more about the heights of trees by measuring several trees fairly accurately than by spending about the same time in measuring one tree very accurately.

Fig. 12.12

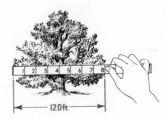

120 ft

There are several ways of setting about the job of estimating the height of a tree. Probably the easiest way is to stand about 120 yards away from a large oak tree, hold a ruler vertically at arm's length, slide the thumb along the ruler until the top of the ruler coincides with the line of sight of the top of the tree and the thumb with the base of the trunk, and note the graduation on the ruler at the edge of the thumb nail. Then, with the ruler still at arm's length, but now horizontal, and in a position so that it appears to lie across the widest part of the tree, again take a reading (Fig. 12.12). Then go over to the tree, place a stick or stone under the extremity of a branch on one side of the tree, and pace out how far it is to the farthest point under the outermost branch on the other side.

In this example:

$$\begin{aligned} \text{vertical height on ruler} \quad &= \quad 7 \text{ in.} \\ \text{horizontal length on ruler} &= \quad 8 \text{ in.} \\ \text{greatest width of tree} \quad &= 120 \text{ ft.} \end{aligned}$$

Making use of the fact that corresponding sides of similar triangles are in the same ratio, we have:

$$\frac{\text{height of tree}}{7 \text{ in.}} = \frac{\text{width of tree}}{8 \text{ in.}}$$

$$\therefore \quad \text{height of tree} = \tfrac{7}{8} \times \text{width of tree}$$
$$= \tfrac{7}{8} \times 120 \text{ ft}$$
$$= 105 \text{ ft.}$$

Another way of estimating the height of a tree is by comparing the length of the shadow it casts with the length of the shadow cast by a pole of known height. This is much more effective with slim trees such as Lombardy poplars than with spreading trees such as oaks or cedars for which the "top" of the shadow is not likely to be the shadow of the top of the tree. Measure the length of the shadow and the length of the shadow cast by a stake whose height can be measured easily (Fig. 12.13). Then, because the triangles are similar, the ratio of lengths will be the same, giving:

$$\frac{BC}{CA} = \frac{DE}{EA} \quad \text{i.e.} \quad \frac{6}{17} = \frac{h}{280 \text{ ft}}$$

so that

$$h = \tfrac{6}{17} \times 280 \text{ ft}$$
$$= 100 \text{ ft (approximately).}$$

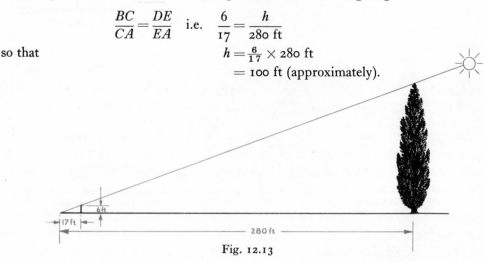

Fig. 12.13

Another possible way of forming a fairly accurate idea of the height of a tree is to take a photograph of a friend standing beside it. If the height of the person beside the tree is known, it is just a matter of measuring how many times the picture of the friend goes into the height of the picture of the tree (Fig. 12.14):

height of Sylvia $= 5$ ft 4 in.

height of Sylvia's photograph $= 1 \cdot 25$ in.

height of photograph of tree $= 4 \cdot 75$ in.

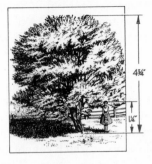

Fig. 12.14

Then $\dfrac{\text{height of tree}}{4 \cdot 75} = \dfrac{5 \text{ ft 4 in.}}{1 \cdot 25}$

$\therefore$ height of tree $= \dfrac{4 \cdot 75}{1 \cdot 25} \times 5$ ft 4 in.

$= 3 \cdot 8 \times 5$ ft 4 in.

$= 20$ ft $3 \cdot 2$ in.

Height of tree is about 20 ft.

From a variety of measurements of this nature, which are not difficult to make, it becomes clear that there is a large population of trees whose heights are mainly in the range 80 to 120 feet which could survive together in mixed woodlands from the point of view of growing tall enough to share in the sunlight. There is another large population of trees that attains heights up to about 30 feet or a little more, such as alders, crab-apples, hawthorns and rowans, which could not compete with the forest trees, but which are nevertheless real trees, being larger than the bushes which attain heights of merely 10 to 15 feet. These smaller trees have their place in hedges and parkland, where there is no density of tall trees, and on the fringes of woodlands.

Although many different species of tree are of similar height when fully grown, their profiles differ widely. Since the whole process of life and growth depends upon the area of leaf surface exposed to the light and air, the shape of a tree is as important to it as its height. The regularity of shape as well as of size is of great help in recognizing species of trees and has played a very great part in art. Hobbema's *Avenue at Middelharnis* is a wonderful study of trees and perspective, owing much of its appeal to the proportions of the trees. Constable uses more solid trees such as oaks, elms and beeches to furnish his landscapes, which were painted on enormous canvases, whereas Van Gogh makes much more use of the families of smaller trees such as the cypress.

We are so accustomed to living among trees that we are apt to overlook the importance of the framework they provide for our lives. Occasionally we are reminded of this background by a chance experience such as going into a wood where the trees are the "wrong" size. The juniper trees in the Pennine Way, near High Force in upper Teesdale, make a charming scene where Oberon, Titania and their attendant fairies would look appropriate. The giants of the wood are scarcely ten feet tall, but the junipers are slender, gracefully proportioned and full grown, making a setting which would be suitable for miniature houses in its glades, where children should be playing. The whole scene is saved from being scrub by the maturity of the little tree shapes and the consistency of the dwarf proportions. Sometimes models have a similar effect, and from some viewpoints, such as Box Hill, the distant scene below looks all so small that it might be a vast panoramic model.

BUILDINGS

Those who live in towns will take the scale of their environment from the sizes of buildings. There are two distinct reasons for being interested in the sizes of buildings; one is simply that of understanding the meaning of simple descriptive sentences, and the other is a contribution to aesthetic appreciation.

In a sentence such as "It is proposed to build a block of offices with a frontage of 120 ft and 75 ft in height, finished in Portland stone" the various parts of the sentence convey specific information. It is no more difficult to acquire a mental picture of a "75-ft high building" than it is to acquire a mental picture of a "red-brick building" or a "Portland stone building". There is, however, a widespread tendency to turn a blind eye and a deaf ear to dimensions, and the simple statement of sizes often fails to convey a clear picture. There may be an intellectual understanding of the meaning of the number 75 and a fair mental picture of a "foot", but "75-ft high building" is a simple concept which cannot be derived from a seventy-five-fold mental multiplication of the concept of a "foot". The ordinary person knows many buildings very well. These may include his own house, a cinema, a school, the local town hall, a church and other obvious buildings in the neighbourhood, but he is unlikely to have put approximate measurements to them. By using methods similar to those already described for trees it is not difficult to assign approximate heights to these familiar buildings. Once this has been done direct concepts will have been formed which correspond to the descriptions "20-ft high", "50-ft high", "100-ft high", etc., which will then evoke responses as readily as other words such as "red", "brick", "stone", "book", etc., in common usage.

In recognizing the importance of buildings as major items of our environment we cannot ignore that there are very beautiful buildings and some whose utter ugliness affronts the most undiscriminating eye. The impression made by a building depends upon a complex variety of factors including the relationship to neighbouring buildings, colour, size, outline, shape, decoration or choice of materials used in construction. Many of these items interact with one another, and appreciation of building design will be incomplete without some study of all the contributory factors. Of these factors those involving shapes and sizes, and their relations with one another, are very important. A glance at Figs. 12.15, 12.16 and 12.17 will illustrate the purely dimensional aspects, colour, embellishments and functional considerations having been excluded.

 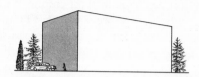

Fig. 12.15

These represent the plain outlines of buildings. The one on the left is 100-ft tall and 62-ft wide and that on the right 62-ft tall and 100-ft wide. They illustrate the "Golden Section" referred to in Chapter 13. Both look rather gaunt blocks.

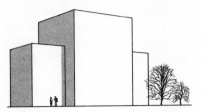

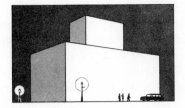

Fig. 12.16

These two buildings are identical with those in Fig 12.15, but additions have been made
without altering the main blocks.

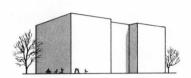

Fig. 12.17

These two buildings have the same overall dimensions as the first two simple blocks,
but subtractions have been made to break up the whole block into sections which can
be looked at in relation to one another.

The treatment of the tall building on the left of Fig. 12.17 has not been very successful.
The reader might like to experiment in a variety of ways, keeping to the dimensions
originally given and, avoiding small-scale embellishments, varying the way in which
the simple block is broken up, until a satisfying profile has been obtained. After this has
been done the reader should measure the various heights and widths and seek some
numerical pattern and then compare the final picture with some buildings designed
by trained architects and study how they have approached the problem.

PERSONAL MEASUREMENTS

It was pointed out, in Chapter 2, that the inch, the foot, the yard and the mile were
either directly or indirectly based upon personal measurements. As well as these basic
units, much of the furniture, household equipment and other paraphernalia are based
upon personal measurements. As a preliminary to examining the sizes of things in the
house, it would be a good plan for the reader to know something about his or her own
measurements. Most people know their own height and weight. The inside leg measurement is necessary information for buying a pair of trousers for a man, the height of the
waist line above the ground is useful information for women in relation to skirt lengths.
The distance between the knee and the sole of the foot is relevant to the height above the
floor for the seats of chairs. The height of eye above the ground, waist to shoulders and
length of arms complete the up-and-down measurements. In *Man and the Vertebrates*
by A. S. Romer (Pelican Books) interesting comparisons are made between these various
measurements in European man, African man and various anthropoid apes, and
diagrams illustrating the relative sizes of head and body from birth to adulthood are to
be found in many books on health, physical education, medical topics and dress.

Circumferences at certain specific places round the bodies of a number of female film stars are much publicized. It was interesting to find that a young man knew precisely the girth of the currently popular pneumatic blonde but had not the remotest idea of the number of square feet of lovely wife he was about to marry. When asked to give some approximate figure he gave an answer which could mean either that he was about to marry a babe a few months old or was only aware of what was left uncovered by quite a modest swimsuit. The problem of making an estimate of the surface area of a human body is not difficult but it does call for a certain amount of ingenuity. It is suggested as an exercise for the reader. The volume of the human body is very easily obtained. We know from experience in a swimming bath that we have just about the same density as water, since with our lungs inflated we float with a very small fraction of our volume above the water and with deflated lungs we just about sink. Our density is, therefore, about that of water, namely, $62\frac{1}{2}$ lb per cubic foot. A person who weighs nine stone, or 126 lb, has, therefore, a volume of about two cubic feet.

Apart from a fairly comprehensive knowledge of ourselves, which, after all, is the controlling factor in the design of most things made for our comfort and convenience, our information about other objects should be the appropriate information, related to the purpose for which the information was obtained. For some purposes we need to know heights, for others, lengths and breadths, and for yet others, areas and volumes. We need to distinguish between regular shapes and irregular shapes and we need also to have ideas about how irregular shapes can be represented approximately as straightforward combinations of regular shapes.

LINEAR DIMENSIONS

By linear dimensions we mean the properties of objects which depend simply upon measurements of length and not upon areas or volumes. The following exercises illustrate the use of simple linear measurements.

1. Stand in front of a wall and go through the motions of washing up, washing through some simple garments and washing hands and face. Note where your hands have been and decide how high above the floor a sink should be for the greatest comfort, avoiding unnecessary bending of the back.

2. Decide how high a door-handle should be so that it can be reached by a three-year-old without standing on tip-toe and by a six-foot-tall man without stooping. If this is not possible, decide upon the best compromise height.

3. How wide could a dinner table be so that plates and condiments can be passed politely across the table, gracefully and without undue stretching? If one of the diners is a normal-sized eleven-year-old, how much difference would this make?

4. Measure the size of the pages of this book and the size of the part of the page filled with printing. Calculate the ratio of the longer to the shorter side in each case. Look at a number of books and select one which strikes you as having the most pleasing proportions.

5. Measure the width of a roll of wallpaper. Measure the length and breadth of your bedroom. Calculate how many widths of wallpaper are required to go round the four walls of the room. Then measure the height of the room and, assuming that there are no horizontal joins in the vertical strips of wallpaper stuck on the walls, and that a roll contains between 34 and 35 feet of paper (allowing for the wastage at the ends of the

roll), calculate how many strips are required to paper the walls. Look in a decorator's window, select a paper that you like and estimate how much it would cost to buy paper for your room.

6. Ask a five- or six-year-old child, an eleven- or twelve-year-old and an adult to sit down. Measure the distance from the bottom of the heel to the underside of the thigh when the lower part of the leg is vertical, then measure the distance from the back of the knee to the base of the back and decide upon suitable chair sizes for them. When they are seated on suitable chairs, measure also the height above the floor to elbow level and form some opinion as to suitable heights for tables.

Circles all have the same shape, that is, they are similar to one another. Any *ratios* of lengths associated with circles will, therefore, be independent of the size of the circles and so will be the same for all circles. The ratio of great importance in geometry is $\dfrac{\text{circumference of circle}}{\text{diameter of circle}}$. This is the number 3·14159 . . . which is given the symbol π ("pi" the Greek letter corresponding to the sound "p"). This relation may be written in the form

$$\text{circumference of circle} = \pi \times \text{diameter}$$

or, since the diameter is twice the radius of a circle, it may be written in the familiar form

$$\text{circumference} = 2\pi \times \text{radius}$$

and remembered in the symbolic form

$$C = 2\pi r.$$

The world on whose surface we live is an almost perfect sphere. The slight flattening at the poles, often mentioned in Geography books, is no more than $\frac{1}{300}$ of the earth's radius and quite undetectable on even a large-sized drawing of a globe. If a globe were cut through by a series of parallel planes, very much as it would be if put through a bacon-cutting machine, these sections would be circles whose radii became smaller and smaller. A circle whose centre is at the centre of the sphere is called a "great circle" and its radius is equal to the radius of the sphere. Any other circle on the sphere is called a "small circle" (Fig. 12.18).

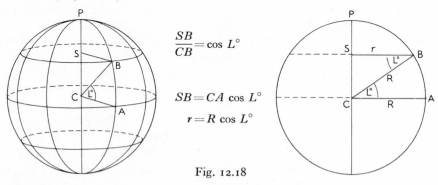

$$\frac{SB}{CB} = \cos L°$$

$$SB = CA \cos L°$$

$$r = R \cos L°$$

Fig. 12.18

If C is the centre of the earth, P is one of the poles, A a point on the equator, S the centre of a small circle whose plane is parallel to the plane of the equator, and B is the point on this small circle where it is cut by the meridian AP, then angle ACB is the "latitude" of P.

$$\angle CBS = \angle ACB \quad \text{(alternate angles)}$$
$$= \text{latitude of } B$$
$$= L° \quad \text{(say)},$$
$$\frac{SB}{CB} = \cos L°$$

or
$$SB = CB \cos L°$$

which may be expressed in the form

radius of parallel of latitude = (*radius of earth*) × cos (*latitude*).

As a consequence of this, in a map such as Mercator's projection, in which the meridians are represented by parallel lines at right angles to the line representing the equator, the scale increases with latitude. In Mercator's projection, distance on earth will be proportional to (distance on map) × cos (latitude). (*See* Fig. 6.5, p. 69.)

Areas

The area of a surface is measured by the number of units of area which will fit into the surface. The common units of area are the square inch (in²) or square centimetre (cm²) for small areas, the square foot (ft²), and the acre or the square mile for larger areas.

For rectangular shapes the number of square inches which can be fitted into a rectangle is equal to (the number of inches in the length) × (the number of inches in the breadth). This has already been discussed in Chapter 6. Other areas, either of regular figures or irregular surfaces, must be broken up or fitted together to reduce them to rectangular areas.

AREA OF A TRIANGLE

Let ABC be a triangle, D the foot of the perpendicular from C to AB, and M the mid-point of CD. The line through M parallel to AB cuts AC and BC in H and K respectively. It will be found that H is the mid-point of AC, and K the mid-point of BC (Fig. 12.19). If the triangles HMC and KMC are cut out and placed, as in the figure, with the triangle HMC now in the position HPA and triangle KMC in the position KQB, the rectangle $ABQP$ will have the same area as the original triangle ABC (Fig. 12.20). This rectangle has the same base AB as the triangle ABC, but half its height.

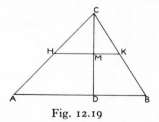 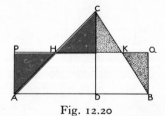

Fig. 12.19   Fig. 12.20

The area of a triangle is equal to the area of a rectangle with the same base but with half the height.

AREA OF A TRAPEZIUM

A trapezium is a quadrilateral with *one* pair of opposite sides parallel.

The area of a trapezium may be obtained in a way very similar to that which gave the formula for the area of a triangle. *ABCD* is the trapezium with *AB*∥*DC*. From the vertex *C* a line is drawn perpendicular to the opposite side *AB*, cutting *AB* at *E*. *M* is the mid-point of *CE*. The line through *M* parallel to *AB* cuts *AD* at *H*, and *BC* at *K*. It will be found that *H* is the mid-point of *AD*, and *K* of *BC*. If the triangle *CMK* and the trapezium *CMDH* are cut out and placed, as in Fig. 12.21, with *CMK* in the position *BQK*, and *CMHD* in the position *RPHA*, it will be seen that the area of the original trapezium *ABCD* is equal to the area of the rectangle *RBQP*. The base, *RB*, of this rectangle is composed of *RA*, which is equal to the side *CD* of the original trapezium, together with *AB*, the side of the original trapezium parallel to *DC*. The height of the rectangle is equal to half the height of the original trapezium.

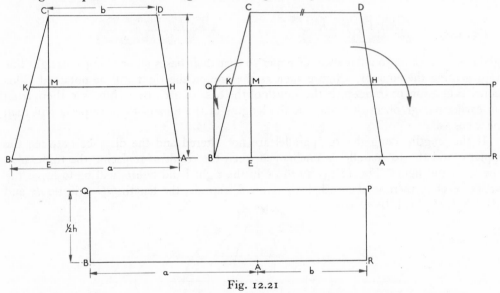

Fig. 12.21

The area of a trapezium is equal to the sum of the parallel sides times the distance between them divided by two.

Since this is the formula for the area of a trapezium, it follows that two trapezia with their parallel sides of the same lengths and with the same perpendicular heights will be equal in area.

This fact will help in appreciating the construction of maps which represent areas accurately. Most atlases use the Sanson-Flamsteed equal-area projection for some of their maps of the world, or for maps of large portions of the earth's surface. When the density of population, the proportion of land under grass or arable crops or forest, or simply the area of different countries is to be compared, equal-area projections must be used.

The figure on the left of Fig. 12.22 represents a globe on the surface of which are drawn parallels and meridians at 10° intervals. If we imagine all the areas between the equator and 10° N. separated by the 10° meridians, to be cut from the surface of the

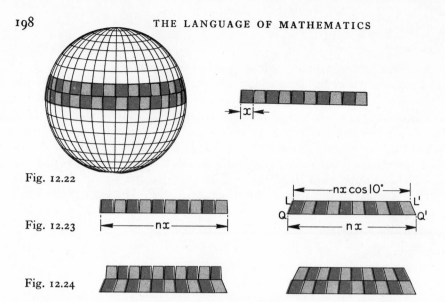

Fig. 12.22

Fig. 12.23

Fig. 12.24

globe and stuck on to a flat sheet of paper so that their bases all lie along a straight line representing the equator, a figure such as the one on the right will be obtained. This consists of a row of trapezia. If the length of the base of each trapezium is x, then, from an earlier paragraph in this chapter, the lengths of the tops of these trapezia will each be $x \cos 10°$.

If the lengths along the $10°$ parallel are not altered and the distance between the equator and the $10°$ parallel is unchanged, then the result of replacing the trapezia in the left-hand figure (Fig. 12.23) by those in the right-hand figure, will be to leave the area of each of them unchanged. If there are n trapezia, the length QQ' will be nx and the length LL' will be $nx \cos 10°$.

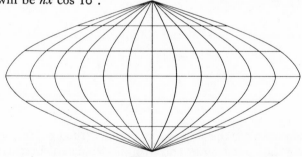

Fig. 12.25
Sanson-Flamsteed's projection.

A similar treatment of the elements of the globe between $10°$ and $20°$ N. will lead to Fig. 12.24.

This may be continued until the whole of the northern hemisphere is represented by an unbroken area, this time on flat paper and not on a globe. The southern hemisphere may be treated in the same way.

If the points on the meridians are now joined by a smooth curve, the ordinary Sanson-Flamsteed projection is obtained. The actual meridians are *exactly* graphs of the function $\cos L$, where L is the latitude.

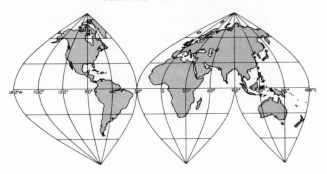

Fig. 12.26

A Sanson-Flamsteed map of the world looks something like an onion and there are considerable distortions of shape at the extreme edges of the map (Fig. 12.25). This is overcome by constructing a "divided" map in which the centres of the land masses, both south and north of the equator, are made the centres of Sanson-Flamsteed projections (Fig. 12.26). Such a map has an equator which is a single line, evenly divided for longitude with parts of the whole projection constructed to include South America, Africa and Australasia as accurately as possible in the Southern hemisphere, and North America and Eurasia in the northern hemisphere, and with breaks in the whole map occurring in the oceans.

AREA OF A CIRCLE

Of the many ways of obtaining a value for the area of a circle, we shall mention only two. The most elementary method is by counting squares; counting all whole squares systematically and then pairing off parts of squares so that the parts can be added to

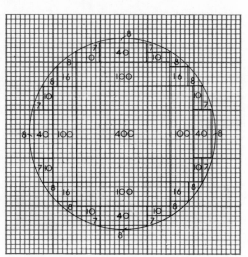

Fig. 12.27

Circle of radius 2 in. drawn half size.

make whole squares. Fig. 12.27 illustrates this method for a circle of radius 2 in. giving an area of 1256 small squares $= 12\cdot56$ in.^{2} (Radius)$^2 = 4$ in.^{2}, so that by counting squares we obtain the formula

$$\text{area of circle} = 12\cdot56 \text{ in.}^2 = 3\cdot14 \times 4 \text{ in.}^2 = 3\cdot14 \times r^2.$$

The other method we discuss here shows that the area should be equal to $\frac{1}{2}$ (circumference) $\times$ (radius) or πr^2.

The circle is divided into a number of sectors by drawing a diameter, then a diameter at right angles to this, then dividing the quadrants again by two more diameters at 45° to these and then inserting four more diameters at $22\frac{1}{2}$° and so on, bisecting each sector in turn. Fig. 12.28 illustrates the process when the circle has been divided into 16 equal sectors. If these sectors are now cut out and arranged as in Fig. 12.29, it will be seen that the sectors fit together to give a figure which is very little different from a parallelogram.

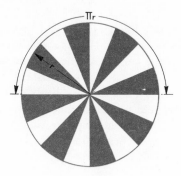

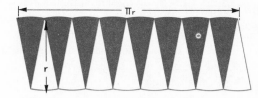

| Fig. 12.28 | Fig. 12.29 |

The area of this figure will be $\dfrac{\text{(sum of parallel sides)} \times \text{(distance between them)}}{2}$. The parallel sides consist of the arcs of the sectors which between them add up to the whole circumference of the circle, that is, to $2\pi r$. The distance between the parallel sides is the radius of the circle. The area of the figure, which is the same as that of the circle, will, therefore, be

$$\frac{2\pi r \times r}{2} = \pi r^2.$$

This figure is clearly not quite a parallelogram, but Fig. 12.30 (a) which is made by dividing

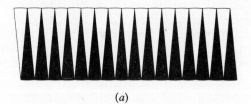

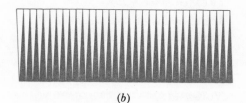

| (a) | (b) |
| Fig. 12.30 |

the circle into 32 sectors is a better approximation to a parallelogram and, in theory, the process could be continued to give closer and closer approximations as the number of sectors is increased indefinitely.

AREAS OF ZONES OF A SPHERE

If the reader will imagine a football which just fits
into a cylindrical waste-paper holder and will try
to picture the effect of putting all this through a
bacon-slicing machine, he will see that there will
be sections of the sphere and sections of the
cylinder (Fig. 12.31). It is a fact that the area of
the surface of the sphere cut off between two
parallel planes is equal to the area cut off from the
surface of the circumscribing cylinder between
the same two planes.

Thus, if we consider a section of the surface of
a sphere of radius R bounded by two planes which
are a distance h apart, the surface area of the
curved surface cut off from the sphere will be
equal to the curved surface of a cylinder of
radius R and height h (Fig. 12.32).

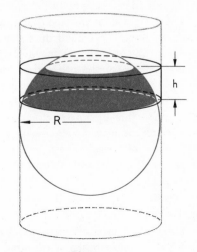

Fig. 12.31

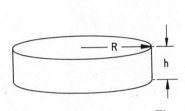

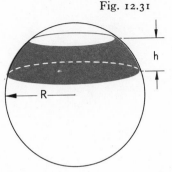

Fig. 12.32

Such a surface can be opened out to a rectangle of width $2\pi R$ and height h, which has
an area $2\pi Rh$.

A whole sphere, of radius R, will have
a height of $2R$. Its surface area will,
therefore, be $2\pi R.2R$, that is,
area of surface of a sphere $= 4\pi R^2$.

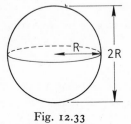

$$2\pi R \times 2R = 4\pi R^2$$

Fig. 12.33

AREA OF THE SURFACE OF A CONE

If the radius of the base of a
cone is R and its *slant height* $= l$
then
area of curved surface of a cone $= \pi Rl$.

Fig. 12.34

Volumes

Volumes are measured as numbers of cubic centimetres, cubic inches or cubic feet and
occasionally as cubic yards. A cubic inch is the volume of a cube, each of whose sides is
one inch in length.

If a rectangular solid has edges of lengths 3, 4 and 5 inches, then it is clear that this
could be built up from $3 \times 4 \times 5 = 60$ one-inch cubes, so that its volume would be

described as being 60 cubic inches. If the reader will draw on a sheet of paper a rectangle 3×4 inches, he will see that this has an area of 12 square inches and that 12 one-inch cubes could be placed on the paper so that they just covered the rectangle, forming a layer, 12 cubic inches in volume and one inch in height. If five such layers were placed one on top of the other they would form the solid of height 5 inches and containing 5×12 cubic inches. For any shaped solid which, when placed on a table, would have vertical sides, the area of the base gives the number of cubic inches in a layer one-inch high, so that for any such solid, of height h (i.e. built up from h layers one-inch thick), the volume would be (area of base) $\times$ (height).

The volume of a cylinder whose cross-section is a circle of radius r, and whose height is h, will be (area of base) $\times$ (height) $= \pi r^2 \times h$.

VOLUME OF A PYRAMID

By using wood or modelling clay, or making pyramids by sticking cardboard faces together, it is easily demonstrated that a rectangular solid can be built up from *three* pyramids with bases of the same area and with equal heights (Fig. 12.35).

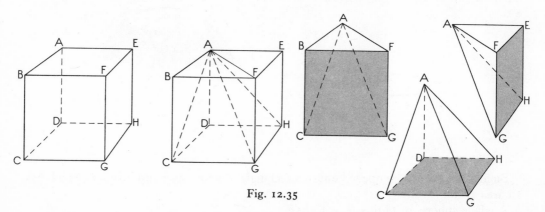

Fig. 12.35

From this construction it will be seen that the volume of any pyramid is equal to

$$\frac{(\text{area of base}) \times (\text{perpendicular height})}{3}.$$

A *cone* may be thought of as being made up of a large number of pyramids, and its volume, like that of a pyramid, may be expressed in the form

$$\text{volume of cone} = \frac{(\text{area of base}) \times (\text{perpendicular height})}{3}.$$

VOLUME OF A SPHERE

The formula for the volume of a sphere follows very simply from that of the area of its surface, for if a small circle is drawn on the surface, and the points of the circumference of this small circle joined to the centre of the sphere, the volume of the small cone so formed will be $\frac{1}{3}$ (area of base) $\times$ (height). But all such cones that could be drawn would have the same height, namely, the radius, R, of the sphere and so each would have a volume equal to $\frac{1}{3}$ (area of base) $\times$ R.

The whole surface area of a sphere is equal to $4\pi R^2$. If the sphere is regarded as being made up of tiny cones of height R whose vertices are at the centre of the sphere (Fig. 12.36), the sum of the areas of all their bases would be the surface of the sphere, so that the volume of a sphere is equal to

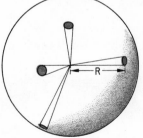

$$\tfrac{1}{3} \text{ (surface area)} \times R$$
$$= \tfrac{1}{3} \times 4\pi R^2 \times R = \tfrac{4}{3}\pi R^3.$$

Fig. 12.36

The volume of a buoy-shaped solid consisting of a cone surmounted by a spherical cap would, by the same reasoning, have a volume equal to $\tfrac{1}{3}$ (area of curved surface) $\times R$.

We have already seen that the surface area of a zone of a sphere is equal to $2\pi R \times h$, where h is the height of the zone, therefore the area of the whole buoy-shaped solid

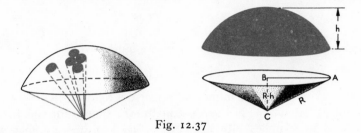

Fig. 12.37

would be $\tfrac{1}{3}$ $(2\pi Rh) \times R = \tfrac{2}{3}\pi R^2h$. The volume of the spherical cap itself is the volume of the buoy-shaped solid minus the volume of the cone (Fig. 12.37).

Theorem of Pythagoras

The ancient Egyptians knew that if a triangle had sides in the ratio of $3:4:5$ then one of its angles was a right angle. They also knew that (area of square of side 3 in.) + (area of square of side 4 in.)

$$= 9 \text{ in}^2 + 16 \text{ in}^2 = 25 \text{ in}^2$$
$$= \text{(area of square of side 5 in.)}.$$

The credit for establishing the general case has traditionally been given to Pythagoras (569 B.C. to 500 B.C.), who is known to have travelled in Egypt before settling down at Crotona, in southern Italy, where he founded his school of mathematicians and philosophers.

The theorem may be stated in the form: "The square on the hypotenuse of a right-angled triangle is equal to the sum of the squares on the other two sides." This may be put in the form: "If ABC is a triangle such that the angle CAB is a right angle, then $BC^2 = CA^2 + AB^2$."

A simple way of demonstrating the theorem is to cut out of card, or plywood, or plastic, four identical triangles in which one of the angles is a right angle. If we call the lengths of the sides a, b and c, then two equal squares of side $(b+c)$ can be shown to contain either

(four triangles abc)   plus a^2 . . . .   Fig. 12.38 (a)
or   (four triangles abc)   plus b^2+c^2 . . . .   Fig. 12.38 (b)

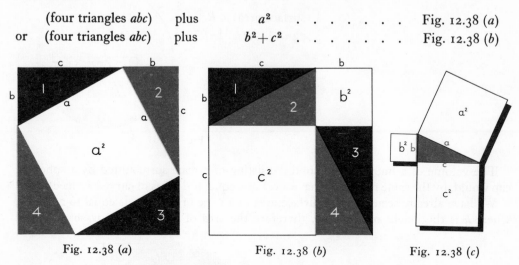

Fig. 12.38 (a) Fig. 12.38 (b) Fig. 12.38 (c)

Since the total areas in each case are the same, we must have

$$a^2 = b^2 + c^2.$$

The reader is invited to check numerically that the following sets of three numbers are such that the square on one of them is equal to the sum of the squares on the other two and then to draw triangles with sides proportional to these numbers and to check that these are right-angled triangles:

3, 4, 5:   5, 12, 13:   8, 15, 17:   12, 35, 37:   16, 63, 65:   7, 24, 25:   20, 21, 29:   28, 45, 53.

The theorem of Pythagoras plays a very important part in geometry and trigonometry. Since the definitions of sin, cos and tan involve the ratios of lengths measured along sides of a right-angled triangle, the three trigonometrical ratios are relations between three lengths which satisfy a Pythagorian relationship.

If a, b, c are the lengths of the sides of a right-angled triangle, where $\angle B = 90°$,

then $\sin A = \dfrac{a}{b}$ and $\cos A = \dfrac{c}{b}$

but Pythagoras tells us that $b^2 = a^2 + c^2$ for a right-angled triangle

so that $\dfrac{b^2}{b^2} = \dfrac{a^2}{b^2} + \dfrac{c^2}{b^2}$

i.e. $1 = \left(\dfrac{a}{b}\right)^2 + \left(\dfrac{c}{b}\right)^2$

which may be written $1 = \sin^2 A + \cos^2 A.$

This relation is true for all angles.

Circles and Ellipses

THE CIRCLE

Plato regarded the circle as a "perfect shape". With a less exacting definition of perfection than that of Plato, we may say normally that the circle is a shape that is pleasing to the eye in many designs, but that it is an inescapable and dominant part of our environment. When the hands on the *round* dial of our alarm clocks reach a certain position, the mechanism, mainly composed of *round* wheels, sets off an alarm bell which wakes us; we open our eyes and, through the *round* black pupil in the centre of our *round* blue or brown iris in our eyes, we see the bedroom, bright with the light from the *round* sun. We switch on the current, which comes to us through wires of *circular* cross-section from a power station in which *circular* dynamos are rotating, to the *round* kettle, and boil water which comes to us through *round* pipes, and then we make tea in a *round* tea pot and drink it from *round* cups, made on a revolving potter's wheel. Our morning cup of tea is followed by a wash from a basin in which a *round* plug has been placed in a *round* plug-hole. After washing, we have breakfast, which may include an egg, whose shell is *round* in one plane and, when fried, has a *round* yolk. On our way to work we travel on a bus with *round* wheels, and we pay for our journey with *round* pennies. From the moment we are born until the last *round* screw is turned to secure our coffins, the *round* circular shape dominates our lives.

The reader might profitably spend a little while asking why so many things are circular. The answers will include considerations of the methods of manufacture, convenience of usage, aesthetic qualities of the circular shape, strength of the finished article or, as with wheels, the geometrical properties of the circle which alone conform to the nature of the object being considered.

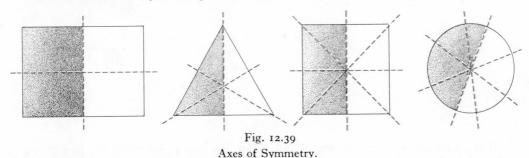

Fig. 12.39
Axes of Symmetry.

A rectangular peg would fit into a rectangular hole in two positions (Fig. 12.39), a peg with an equilateral triangular section would fit into a hole of this shape in three positions, a square peg will fit into a square hole in four positions, but a round peg is in no way restricted to any particular position in a round hole. This very simple fact of everyday experience is of the utmost consequence to our material civilization, for it means that the peg may be twisted round in the hole. This property makes possible the twisting of a drill in a hole, the turning of a bolt, thread sliding smoothly along thread, the gliding of clay through the skilled fingers of a potter as he fashions cups and vases on a potter's wheel, the turning of wheels upon their bearings, the functioning of water and gas taps, the turning of wood and metal in lathes, and the operation of hinges on doors and gates and of the joints in our own skeletons.

THE ELLIPSE

Although we know that pennies, wheels and the tops of round tables are circular, the images they form on the retinas of our eyes are foreshortened. The portrayal of circles in paintings and in photographs is by ellipses. An ellipse may be constructed by drawing a diameter AA' across a circle, drawing lines A_1Q_1, A_2Q_2, A_3Q_3, etc., at right angles to AA', as in Fig. 12.40, and then marking the points P_1, P_2, P_3, etc., which are such that

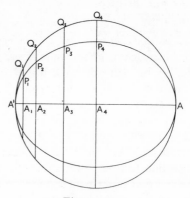

$$\frac{A_1P_1}{A_1Q_1} = \frac{A_2P_2}{A_2Q_2} = \frac{A_3P_3}{A_3Q_3} = \cdots$$

Fig. 12.40

The curve joining the points P_1, P_2, P_3, etc., will then be an ellipse.

The line AA' will be the longest line which may be drawn in the ellipse and it is called the *major-axis*. The mid-point of this line is called the centre, S, of the ellipse. The line at right-angles to AA' through S is the *minor-axis*, BB' of the ellipse. The usual convention is to call the length AS, a and the length BS, b (Fig. 12.41).

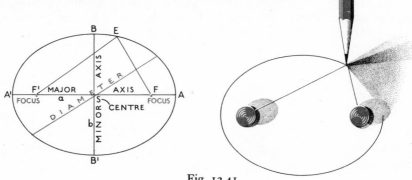

Fig. 12.41

There are two important points, F and F', on the major axis called the foci of the ellipse. The focus, F, may be found by opening a pair of compasses to length a and, with centre B, marking off the point F on AS such that $BF = AS = a$. Similarly the focus F' is on SA' such that $BF' = a$.

The foci F and F' have the property that if E is *any* point on the circumference of the ellipse, then $FE + F'E = \text{constant} = 2a$.

This property provides the simplest way of constructing an ellipse. Take a piece of thread, tie in it two knots at a distance $2a$ apart, stick a drawing-pin through each knot and press the drawing-pins through the paper and into a drawing-board underneath. Then, with the thread kept taut, slide the point of a pencil round the thread.

Any line through the centre of the ellipse, cutting the circumference at points P and Q, is called a *diameter* of the ellipse, and the centre of the ellipse will be the mid-point of the diameter.

If *TPT'* is a line which touches the ellipse at *P*, it is called a *tangent* to the ellipse. One property of the tangent to an ellipse is that the two focal distances *FP* and *F'P* make equal angles with the tangent at *P* (Fig. 12.42).

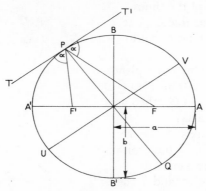

Fig. 12.42

If *PQ* is a diameter of the ellipse and *TPT'* the tangent at *P*, and another diameter *UV* is drawn parallel to *TPT'*, then the two diameters *PQ* and *UV* are called conjugate diameters. Conjugate diameters have many very interesting properties which may be explored in any book about projective geometry, but from an elementary point of view they are the lines in a photograph or a perspective drawing of a foreshortened circle which correspond to two perpendicular diameters of this circle. The illustration of a

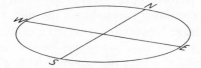

Fig. 12.43

perspective view of a compass (Fig. 12.43) shows the lines *NS* and *EW* as conjugate diameters of the ellipse which is the foreshortened view of the circle.

Planets

Many of the properties of ellipses were worked out by the ancient Greeks and remained interesting but little used facts until the sixteenth century, when our understanding of the movements of planets in the solar system rapidly developed. Even before the invention of telescopes, a celebrated Danish astronomer, Tycho Brahe (1546–1601), painstakingly recorded the times and elevations of the passages of the major planets across his transit circle, leaving his successors a vast quantity of data accurately observed and systematically recorded. From this, Johann Kepler (1571–1630) was able to deduce that each of the planets moved round the sun in a path which was an ellipse with the sun at one of the foci. Rouse Ball* credits Kepler with introducing the word "focus" in this context, *focus* being the Latin word for fireplace or hearth, and the sun being the source of light and heat for the planets of the solar system.

* *A Short Account of the History of Mathematics.* W. W. Rouse Ball (Macmillan).

Among the properties of planetary motion in an ellipse there are two of importance for timekeeping and estimations of speeds and distances: (1) the line joining the sun to any planet sweeps out equal areas in equal times, and (2) the squares of the times taken by the various planets to complete circuits of their orbits is proportional to the cubes of major axes.

(1) If S represents the sun, and a planet takes the same time to move from P to Q as it takes to move from P' to Q', then area $PSQ =$ area $P'SQ'$ (Fig. 12.44).

Fig. 12.44

(2) If VV' is the major axis of the orbit of Venus, JJ' the major axis of the orbit of Jupiter, t the time taken by Venus to complete a circuit of her orbit, and T the time for Jupiter to complete a circuit of Jupiter's orbit, then

$$\frac{t^2}{(VV')^3} = \frac{T^2}{(JJ')^3}.$$

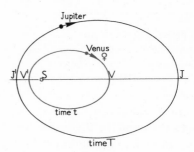

Fig. 12.45

Kepler showed separately that each of the planets conformed to these geometrical descriptions.

At about the same time, Galileo (1564–1642) propounded new ideas about the nature of forces and Descartes (1596–1650) introduced the new techniques of algebraic or co-ordinate geometry. Sir Isaac Newton (1642–1727) was able to unite all this work and describe celestial mechanics in terms of his simple laws of motion and his law of gravitational attraction, "two bodies attract one another with a force proportional to the product of their masses and inversely proportional to the square of the distance between them". This may be written

$$\text{Force of attraction} = \gamma \frac{M.m}{r^2} \quad \text{(Newton's Law of Gravitation)}$$

where γ is a constant quantity whose value is approximately

$$1 \cdot 05 \times 10^{-9} \frac{\text{ft}^3}{\text{sec}^2.\text{lb}} \quad \text{or} \quad 1 \cdot 2 \times 10^{-1} \frac{\text{miles}^3}{\text{day}^2.\text{tons}} \quad \text{and}$$

M and m are the masses of the two bodies and r is the distance between them.

Newton's concept of the universe as a single mechanical system, throughout which common mechanical laws held good, was a revolution in thought which for ever places Newton among the great men of the world. It is not easy in the twentieth century to appreciate the greatness of this concept, and it may come as a surprise to many people to be reminded that until about three hundred years ago the motions of heavenly bodies were generally described in terms which had hardly progressed from the days of Ptolemy of Alexandria, who died in A.D. 168. John Milton's *Paradise Lost*, published in 1667, is the last great work of art to use the symbolism of the Ptolemaic system of astronomy. Without going into details it can be said that this was based on a separate description of the motion of each planet, supposedly constrained to move in a crystal sphere in a path which was described exclusively in terms of circles. There was little justification for the restriction of the path to one made out of circles, whose centres moved round circles, which moved round other circles, all on the crystal spheres, other than the thought, derived from Plato, that circles were perfect shapes and that God (or the gods, according to the religion of the astronomer), would, of course, use only what was perfect for the motion of the heavenly bodies which He, or they, controlled. Newton's enunciation of the law of universal gravitation not only extended the field of science into outer space, it served also to reinforce the fundamental faith of scientists that the whole complex pattern of the natural universe may be described in terms of a set of consistent natural laws to which there are no exceptions. They may have to be content with partial explanations in some instances and to say that in our present state of knowledge some phenomena cannot be described completely in terms of the accepted laws, but today, if a supposed law of nature is contradicted by some observable facts, either the observations must be proved to be at fault or the law must be scrapped; there is no escape by excluding any physical objects from the realm of scientific enquiry. Furthermore, the analysis of physical laws conforms to the strict procedures of mathematical logic.

One should not credit Newton with more than his fair share of the work of establishing the nature of scientific thought. Man had been groping towards such a concept of science ever since the days of the great Greek philosophers. It is true to say that Newton's work is the greatest single landmark on the road.

There has been a fresh approach to the problems of the nature of space and the mechanics of the cosmos during this century, by Einstein. The great American telescopes at Mount Wilson and Palomar have extended observational astronomy to the giant extra-galactic nebulae hundreds of millions of light-years distant, and measurements of an accuracy undreamed of in Newton's day have led to some modification of Newton's laws. Nevertheless, for calculations within the solar system, Newton's laws hold good for all but the most exacting calculations.

Patient work by astronomers has extended our knowledge of the universe during the three centuries since Newton's day, but surprisingly little of this is taught in schools. The last few years have seen developments which have captured the public imagination and been given front-page publicity in the Press. Rockets have penetrated far into space, artificial satellites have been successfully launched, at least one Russian and one American "probe" have escaped completely from the earth's gravitational field and are moving in independent orbits round the sun, and men have now returned safely to earth after being in orbit.

Satellites

If a weight were being swung round and round at the end of a string and the string broke, the weight would fly off at a tangent (Fig. 12.46).

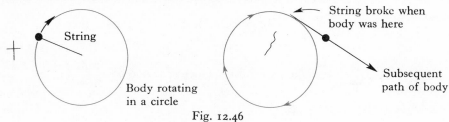

Fig. 12.46

In order to keep a body moving round in a circular path a force has to be supplied continuously to it, directed towards the centre of the circle. This *centripetal* force is provided by the string in the example just given. Without the string, the weight would go on in a straight line but the tension in the string keeps it going in a curved path. The faster the body moves, the greater the tension in the string. In the case of planets moving round the sun, and the moon moving round the earth, the gravitational pull between the two heavenly bodies plays the same role as the tension in the string.

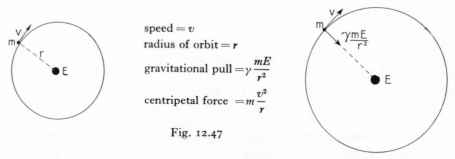

$$\text{speed} = v$$
$$\text{radius of orbit} = r$$
$$\text{gravitational pull} = \gamma \frac{mE}{r^2}$$
$$\text{centripetal force} = m \frac{v^2}{r}$$

Fig. 12.47

The centripetal force required to keep a body of mass m moving round a circle of radius r with a speed v is $m\dfrac{v^2}{r}$.

If E is the mass of the Earth, m is the mass of a satellite and r is the radius of the satellite's orbit, then the gravitational pull of the Earth on the satellite is given by Newton's formula, $\gamma \dfrac{mE}{r^2}$. When the satellite is orbiting uniformly the speed and distance are such that the gravitational force just provides exactly the correct centripetal force to keep the satellite in its orbit, thus

$$m\frac{v^2}{r} = \gamma \frac{mE}{r^2}. \qquad \cdots \cdots \cdots \quad \text{Fig. 12.47}$$

Cancelling both sides of this equation by m and multiplying both sides of the equation by r^2 gives

$$v^2 r = \gamma E.$$

THE MOON

We know the motion of the moon very accurately. In round figures its distance from the earth is 250,000 miles and it takes $27\frac{1}{3}$ days to complete a circuit of its orbit round the earth. The circumference of its orbit is 2π times its radius $= 2\pi \cdot 250{,}000$ miles $= 500{,}000\pi$ miles which it travels in $27\frac{1}{3}$ days. Its speed, v, is, therefore, $\dfrac{500{,}000\pi \text{ miles}}{27 \cdot 3 \quad \text{day}}$ or $\dfrac{500{,}000\pi}{27 \cdot 3 \times 24} \dfrac{\text{miles}}{\text{hour}} = 2400 \dfrac{\text{miles}}{\text{hour}}$ (approximately). For the moon, therefore, $v^2 r$ has the value

$$\left(2400 \frac{\text{mile}}{\text{hour}}\right)^2 \times (250{,}000 \text{ miles}) = 1{,}440{,}000{,}000{,}000 \frac{\text{miles}^3}{\text{hours}^2}.$$

This, therefore, is the value of γE.

ARTIFICIAL SATELLITES

We are now in a position to answer the question "How fast must be the speed of launching of an artificial satellite which will go into a stable orbit 500 miles above the earth's surface?"

Radius of Earth = 3960 miles   ∴   distance of satellite from centre of earth = 3960 + 500 miles = 4460 miles.

If speed is v, then

$$v^2 \times 4460 \text{ miles} = 1{,}440{,}000{,}000{,}000 \frac{\text{miles}^3}{\text{hours}^2}.$$

Dividing both sides of the equation by 4460 miles gives

$$v^2 = 323{,}000{,}000 \frac{\text{miles}^2}{\text{hours}^2}.$$

Taking the square root of both sides of the equation gives

$$v = 18{,}000 \frac{\text{miles}}{\text{hour}} \text{ (approximately)}.$$

If we calculate the speed required for an earth satellite 1000 miles above the earth's surface we obtain

$$v^2 \times 4960 \text{ miles} = 1{,}440{,}000{,}000{,}000 \frac{\text{miles}^3}{\text{hours}^2}$$

giving $v = 17{,}000 \dfrac{\text{miles}}{\text{hour}}.$

If we calculate the speed necessary to keep a satellite in orbit 2000 miles above the earth's surface, we have

$$v^2 \times 5960 \text{ miles} = 1{,}440{,}000{,}000{,}000 \frac{\text{miles}^3}{\text{hours}^2}$$

giving $v = 15{,}600 \dfrac{\text{miles}}{\text{hour}}.$

These may be set out in the table

Height of satellite above Earth's surface (miles)	Speed of Satellite (mile/hour)	Time taken to complete orbit (hr)
500	18,000	1·56
1000	17,000	1·833
2000	15,600	2·40
250,000 (Moon)	2,400 (Moon)	27·3 days (Moon)

The last column is obtained by calculating the circumference, $2\pi r$ of the orbit, and dividing this distance by the speed. For example, for the satellite 500 miles above the earth, $r = 4460$ miles, so the total length of one circuit of its orbit will be $2\pi \times 4460$ miles = 28,023 miles, so that time taken $= \dfrac{28{,}023 \text{ miles}}{18{,}000 \frac{\text{mile}}{\text{hour}}} = 1 \cdot 56$ hours.

Elliptical orbits

The calculations just made have been for the simplified cases of circular orbits. In fact no planetary orbits are perfectly circular. Newton showed that the law of inverse squares for gravitational attraction was compatible with the movement of a planet or satellite in a stable elliptical orbit. The circle is, of course, a particular case of an ellipse in which the two foci coincide at a point which is the centre of the circle. For simple calculations we have only to replace the radius of the circle in the above formulae by half the major axis of an ellipse. Thus, if half the major axis of an elliptical orbit of a satellite of the earth is 4460 miles, then the time to complete a circuit of the orbit will be 1·56 hours. The velocity of the satellite when passing the end of the major axis will be 18,000 miles/hour.

ACTUAL ARTIFICIAL SATELLITES

On January 31st 1958 the United States of America announced the successful launching of an artificial satellite called "Explorer". The orbit of the "Explorer" was markedly

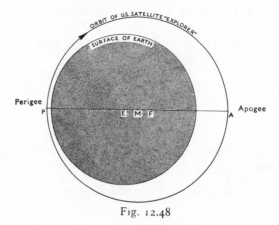

Fig. 12.48

elliptical, whereas the orbits of the two U.S.S.R. satellites "Sputnik I" and "Sputnik II" were almost circular.

For the "Explorer", the English newspapers gave the information that the nearest approach to the earth (perigee) was 230 miles, the farthest distance from the earth (apogee) was 1700 miles. Knowing that the radius of the earth is 3960 miles, this gives all the information necessary to draw the ellipse.

The data may be expressed in the form

Distance from focus of ellipse to one end of major axis = 3960 + 230 miles = 4190 miles.
Distance from focus to other end of the major axis = 3960 + 1700 miles = 5660 miles.
∴   total length of major axis = 9850 miles
and distance between foci = 5660 − 4190 miles = 1470 miles.

Fig. 12.48 is drawn to the scale of 1 cm to 2000 miles, but the reader will find it easier to use a larger scale than this. The procedure for drawing a diagram twice this size is

(i) Make two knots in a piece of thread so that the knots are as near to 9·85 cm apart as is possible to arrange. Pierce the knots with drawing-pins and check that the two pins are just under 10 cm apart in case the knots slipped when the pins were pushed through them.

(ii) Mark two points E and F on the paper as nearly as possible 1·47 cm apart, and insert the two drawing-pins firmly through the paper at E and F and into something such as a drawing-board.

(iii) Keeping the thread taut, slide a pencil round the thread.

(iv) The pencil will have traced out an ellipse which represents the orbit of the satellite. Complete the diagram by drawing a circle with centre E and radius 3·96 cm to represent the earth (radius 3960 miles).

THE MINOR AXIS OF THE ORBIT

If M is the mid-point of the major axis, then a perpendicular to the major axis through M will cut the ellipse in B and B'. MB will be equal to the length of the minor axis (Fig. 12.49). $EF = 1470$ miles $\therefore ME = 735$ miles. EB is half the length of the thread

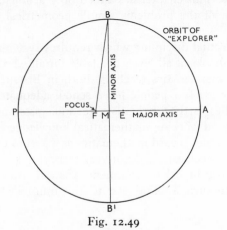

Fig. 12.49

used in the construction of the ellipse. Its length will, therefore, be 4925 miles. Since $\angle EMB = 90°$, we may use the theorem of Pythagoras to obtain the length of the minor axis.

$$MB^2 + ME^2 = BE^2 \quad \text{(Pythagoras} \ldots \angle EMB = 90°)$$
$$\therefore \quad MB^2 + (735 \text{ miles})^2 = (4925 \text{ miles})^2$$
$$\therefore \quad MB^2 = (4925^2 - 735^2) \text{ miles}^2 \qquad (4925^2 = 24,255,625$$
$$= 23,715,400 \text{ miles}^2 \qquad 735^2 = \underline{\quad 540,225}$$
$$\therefore \quad MB = 4870 \text{ miles.} \qquad \qquad 23,715,400)$$

For this ellipse, then, major axis $= 4925$ miles

minor axis $= 4870$ miles

a difference of 55 miles or only about 1·1 per cent, which is too small to be noticed with the naked eye and too small to be measured in a diagram constructed by such homely apparatus as thread and drawing-pins.

The time taken will be the same as the time taken to complete a circular orbit of radius 4925 miles. The reader is left to verify that this is about 1·8 hours or 108 minutes.

The observed time quoted by the newspapers on February 1st 1958 was 106 minutes "after allowance had been made for the rotation of the earth".

This chapter is entitled "Shapes and Sizes". It has been possible to sample only a few of the sizes and shapes of the things around us, but we have ranged from the circular pupil of an eye, with a diameter of about a tenth of an inch or less, up to the orbit of the moon, which has a diameter of about half a million miles, and we have discussed shapes ranging from the regular shape of a circle to the complex shape of a tree. A study of shapes and sizes is an attempt to understand more about the space in which we live and move and the shapes we see about us. A willingness to take out rulers and measure, to make judgments about sizes, shapes and proportions and to look critically at such shapes as those of smoothing irons, motor cars, houses, office blocks and cathedrals is to be expected of intelligent people who take a lively interest in their environment. This should lead to appreciation of design and a critical appraisal of both art and industrial products. The active interest in shape and size may well provoke enquiry into formal geometrical relationships. This chapter has aimed only at illustrating the scope of geometrical ideas and a few of the problems simple geometrical analysis will help us to understand.

Geometry is an intellectual discipline which requires systematic study, but there are plenty of geometry text-books at all levels available for all who are interested. There is, however, a shortage of mathematics teachers, both in Britain and America, and as a consequence of this, far too few people leave school adequately stimulated to pursue their mathematical studies further. Scientists, technologists and technicians know that they have to acquire a good working mathematical knowledge for their work, but many other intelligent people do not regard mathematics as a part of the way of thinking about everyday things, and as a necessary and not very terrifying key to the understanding of many facets of our non-technical environment. Instead, they are content to muddle along without it and to turn a blind eye to the numerical and logical aspects of everyday life.

13

The Fibonacci Sequence and the Golden Section

THE SEQUENCE of numbers

$$1 \quad 1 \quad 2 \quad 3 \quad 5 \quad 8 \quad 13 \quad 21 \quad 34 \quad 55 \quad 89 \quad 144 \quad 233 \quad 377 \quad \cdots$$

is such that each term is the sum of the two terms which immediately precede it; thus
$5 + 8 = 13$ and $8 + 13 = 21$ and so on. Starting from 1, the next term, $0 + 1$, is also 1,
the next term, $1 + 1 = 2$, and so the whole sequence can be built up very easily by
simple addition. The sequence is named after Leonardo Fibonacci of Pisa (born 1175)
and has some very interesting applications.

Before discussing some of the less obvious Fibonacci sequences which occur in nature,
we can illustrate the sequence by a very simple example. If sums of money amounting
to whole numbers of nickels are paid, and the only coins used for payment are nickels
and dimes, then, if o represents a nickel and O represents a dime, the number of ways
in which such sums of money may be paid out may be represented schematically as
follows:

Amount to be paid	Possible arrangements of coins making payment	Number of arrangements
5¢	o	1
10¢	oo, O	2
15¢	ooo, oO, Oo	3
20¢	oooo, ooO, oOo, Ooo, OO	5
25¢	ooooo, oooO, ooOo, oOoo, oOO, Oooo, OoO, OOo	8
	etc.	

The reason why this follows the development of the Fibonacci sequence is clear when
we note that 25¢ may be regarded as five nickels or one dime three nickels, so that the
25¢ arrangements consist of

ooooo, oooO, ooOo, oOoo, oOO   obtained by paying one nickel and then one of the
ways of paying four nickels, and

Oooo, OoO, OOo . . . . .   obtained by paying one dime and then one of the
ways of paying three nickels,

so that the number of ways for each amount is the sum of the numbers of ways for the two
previous amounts.

Ancestry of a male bee

A male bee, called a drone, has a mother but no father. After a nuptial flight, the fertilized
eggs laid by a female bee hatch into females, either workers or queens. Males hatch from
unfertilized eggs. If the genealogical tree of a male bee is traced backwards, it will be
seen that the number of ancestors in any one generation is a Fibonacci number (Fig. 13.1).

This is one of the instances in nature where simple arithmetic can be displayed with precision because we have traced development backwards. A single, live drone must have had only a mother and one of her grandmothers must have had a successful nuptial

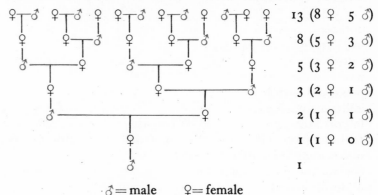

13 (8 ♀   5 ♂)

8 (5 ♀   3 ♂)

5 (3 ♀   2 ♂)

3 (2 ♀   1 ♂)

2 (1 ♀   1 ♂)

1 (1 ♀   0 ♂)

1

♂ = male   ♀ = female

Fig. 13.1

flight and laid a fertilized egg. In other situations, e.g. when discussing the development of a plant or the growth of weed on a pond, or if one is analysing the descendants of a bee rather than its ancestors, the changes and chances of natural life impose an element of variation upon a regular pattern of development. So it is that in Nature there is a rich variety as well as an underlying uniformity.

Flowers

Each species of flower has a basic pattern of development, and a corresponding number pattern, typical of a species but not always precisely followed in every single plant of the species. Although there are families which follow other patterns (notably plants with symmetrical development and four-petalled flowers) the numbers of the Fibonacci sequence play an outstanding part in the description of flowers.

Two-petalled flowers are not common. One example is the tiny Enchanter's Nightshade.

Three petals are associated with members of the lily family and with irises.

Five-petalled flowers are the most common of all and there are hundreds of species, both wild and cultivated, with five petals.

Eight-petalled flowers are not so common as five-petalled, but there is quite a number of well-known species with eight.

Thirteen, *twenty-one* and *thirty-four* petals are quite common and a few are mentioned in the next two paragraphs.

RANUNCULUS FAMILY

In this family the common buttercup has *five* petals; so have some delphiniums, larkspurs and columbines. The lesser celandine has *eight* and so have some delphiniums, while the trollius (globe flower) and some double delphiniums have *thirteen*. These are all Fibonacci numbers, but there do not seem to be many in this family with numbers above this. I did, however, count the number of petals in a large double garden peony and found it to be 235. This is surprisingly near to the Fibonacci number, 233. It would be unwise to make general statements from the result of the counting of petals on a single flower, but one may say that this particular individual developed in such a way that its petal arrangement followed the pattern shown by the smaller members of the family. It is also pertinent to mention that the deviation of 235 from the number 233 is a smaller fraction (less than one in a hundred) than one might expect for an individual variation from a general pattern of development.

COMPOSITAE

The daisy family contains flowers whose heads consist of a number of tightly packed florets. The florets in the centre of each head do not have any petals, but the outer ring of ray florets, white in the common daisy, yellow in heleniums, shades of red in pyrethrums and with a wide range of colours in cultivated Michaelmas daisies, illustrates the Fibonacci sequence extremely well.

Five is rare in this family; the humble wall-lettuce is the only one I have come across.

Eight is also fairly uncommon; *squalid senecio*, related to the ragwort, is one which can be found in some parts of England, and *field senecio*, found fairly easily on the North and South Downs, is another.

Thirteens are common, including *ragwort*, *corn marigold*, *mayweed* and several of the *chamomiles*.

Twenty-ones include garden flowers and wild flowers, some heleniums and asters, succory or chicory, doronicum and some hawk-bits.

Thirty-four is the commonest number for the family. Ordinary field daisies, ox-eye daisies, some heleniums, gaillardias, plantains, pyrethrums and a number of the hawk-bits and hawkweeds have about thirty-four rays. The white or coloured parts which radiate from the outer ring of florets in the head of a flower such as a daisy are not strictly petals, but many readers may think of them as petals and one would not be likely to be misunderstood, in popular parlance, if one said that some daisies had thirty-four petals. It may help some readers who are not botanists to explain that it is these parts which are being counted. If the "petals" are counted

on a number of daisies growing on a lawn, there might be some with thirty-one, some with thirty-two, a few more with thirty-three and a majority with thirty-four. In saying that daisies have thirty-four "petals" one is generalizing about the species—but any individual member of the species may deviate from this general pattern. There is more likelihood of a possible under-development than over-development, so that thirty-threes are more common than thirty-fives.

Fifty-five. Some field daisies have fifty-five "petals", having developed one stage further than those with thirty-four. This may also be true of heleniums.

Both *fifty-fives* and *eighty-nines* are common with Michaelmas daisies. I counted one Michaelmas daisy and found it had 157. Taking another flower from the same plant I carefully removed the rays, starting with the outermost, and after removing 144 I found that a further thirteen sprang from a ring of florets within the head and were quite distinct from the other 144, being incurling where the others grew outwards. The 157 was thus the sum of two Fibonacci numbers, and, as it happened, two numbers which were exactly members of the sequence.

Other orders show Fibonacci numbers in other ways. For example, the milkwort has two large sepals, three smaller sepals, five petals and eight stamens. Although lilies and irises and the daffodil family are associated with threes and sixes in their flowers, I found that a clump of *Alstromerias* in my garden had one plant with *two* flowers growing on each of *three* stalks and that where these three stalks grew out from the top of the main stem a whorl of *five* leaves grew out radially; while another plant had *three* flowers on each of *five* stems with a whorl of *eight* leaves at the base of the flower stalks. In the clump as a whole there were other variations, mainly three flowers on three stalks with five leaves or three flowers on five stalks with five leaves. Fours and sixes and sevens were missing.

The association of Fibonacci numbers and plants is not restricted to details of flowers. A new shoot commonly grows out at the axil, the point where a leaf springs from the

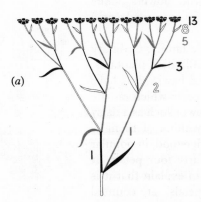

Fig. 13.2

main stem of the plant. Further leaves and branch shoots then grow from both the main and the branch stems, and so the number of leaves or nodes where new shoots appear in the next stage of development is the sum of those from the main and branch stems. The development is illustrated by the schematic diagram of a simple plant, the sneezewort (Fig. 13.2). A careful comparison between this and the genealogical tree of the bee shows a similarity of structure: the main stem of the plant corresponds to the main female line of descent, and the branchings of the plant correspond to the matings with male bees in the genealogical tree. It would be difficult, admittedly, to find an actual plant so perfectly exhibiting the Fibonacci sequence as that in the drawing. In nature, the plant receives its sunlight mainly on one side, it is exposed to winds from some other direction, sudden cold spells may retard growth at some stages of development, and all these facts may lead to departures in a given plant from the general pattern of the species so that, as usual, the pattern of development is a general pattern, modified in any particular individual plant. It is clear, however, that normally the shoots and flower heads will approximate to Fibonacci patterns.

This schematic diagram has been drawn as though all the shoots branched out parallel to the plane of the paper and the plant were flat. This illustrates well enough the development which leads to Fibonacci numbers but it suppresses the characteristic of a majority of plants that successive leaves and shoots develop round the main stem, so that if one shoot is on the north side of the plant the next may be at 60° round from the north, the next at 120° round from the north, and so on spiralling round the main stem as successive stages develop (Fig. 13.3 (b)). If we were to cut off such a plant just above the root and put the bottom of the stem through a ring and carefully pull the plant down through the ring, we should bunch the flowering head together rather tightly and we should expect to find a number of florets packed together, the number being one of the Fibonacci series and the arrangement being spiral in form. As will be shown in the next paragraph, the Fibonacci sequence is very closely related to a sequence of powers, or an exponential sequence, and the combination of this with a succession of equally spaced radii suggests the equiangular spiral which was discussed in Chapter 9. Now the composite head of one of the daisy family is composed of many tiny florets which are packed very tightly together. The diagram below (Fig. 13.3 (a)) was constructed geometrically from two families of intersecting equiangular spirals and it illustrates the arrangement of the

centre of a flower head. The equiangular spiral does, in fact, describe very accurately the pattern of the florets within the heads of the daisy family and such flowers as the scabious. A pattern which was constructed from the intersection of 21 spirals with 34 spirals is shown in Fig. 9.34, on page 143, and compared with a photograph of a flower head, Fig. 9.33.

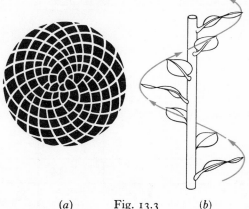

(a)   Fig. 13.3   (b)

Ratio of successive terms of a Fibonacci sequence

If the ratios of successive terms of the sequence are calculated:

$$\tfrac{1}{1}=1\cdot0,\ \tfrac{2}{1}=2\cdot0,\ \tfrac{3}{2}=1\cdot5,\ \tfrac{5}{3}=1\cdot66,\ \tfrac{8}{5}=1\cdot6,\ \tfrac{13}{8}=1\cdot625,\ \tfrac{21}{13}=1\cdot6154\ldots,$$

$$\tfrac{34}{21}=1\cdot61905\ldots,\quad \tfrac{55}{34}=1\cdot61765\ldots,\quad \tfrac{89}{55}=1\cdot61818\ldots,\quad \tfrac{144}{89}=1\cdot61798\ldots,$$

$$\tfrac{233}{144}=1\cdot618055\ldots,\quad \tfrac{377}{233}=1\cdot618025\ldots,\quad \tfrac{610}{377}=1\cdot618037\ldots,\quad \tfrac{987}{610}=1\cdot618033\ldots$$

they approach nearer and nearer to a number $1\cdot618034\ldots$ which is a very old friend. It was of interest to the Greeks in the Classical period because of its connexion with the "Golden Section" which played a part in design and architecture. The precise quantity is

$$\frac{1+\sqrt5}{2}=1\cdot618034\ldots$$

One reason why the Fibonacci series has been neglected in schools is that, in spite of its extremely simple law of development, the formula for the n-th term of the sequence has a rather forbidding appearance:

$$u_n=\frac{1}{\sqrt5}\left\{\frac{1+\sqrt5}{2}\right\}^n-\frac{1}{\sqrt5}\left\{\frac{1-\sqrt5}{2}\right\}^n$$

When this somewhat awkward quantity is worked out for the various terms the $\sqrt5$'s do cancel quite simply. The first few terms are obtained as follows:

$$u_0=\frac{1}{\sqrt5}-\frac{1}{\sqrt5}=0;$$

$$u_1=\frac{1}{\sqrt5}\left\{\frac{1+\sqrt5-1+\sqrt5}{2}\right\}=\frac{2\sqrt5}{\sqrt5\times2}=1;$$

$$u_2=\frac{1}{\sqrt5}\left\{\frac{1+2\cdot\sqrt5+5-1+2\cdot\sqrt5-5}{4}\right\}=\frac{4\cdot\sqrt5}{\sqrt5\times4}=1;$$

$$u_3=\frac{1}{\sqrt5}\left\{\frac{1+3\cdot\sqrt5+3\cdot5+5\cdot\sqrt5-1+3\cdot\sqrt5-3\cdot5+5\cdot\sqrt5}{8}\right\}=\frac{16\cdot\sqrt5}{\sqrt5\times8}=2.$$

As higher terms are calculated, the arithmetic becomes very much heavier, but the general pattern is retained; all the terms with $\sqrt5$ in them cancel and simply leave the Fibonacci whole numbers.

$$\frac{1}{\sqrt5}=0\cdot4472136\ldots,\qquad \frac{1+\sqrt5}{2}=1\cdot618034\ldots$$

The sequence obtained from $u_n=0\cdot4472136\times(1\cdot618034)^n$ will give an exponential curve (Fig. 13.4), and after the first four terms the Fibonacci sequence v_n is virtually indistinguishable from this exponential sequence of numbers:

$n=1$	2	3	4	5	6	7
$u_n=0\cdot7236$	$1\cdot1708$	$1\cdot8944$	$3\cdot0652$	$4\cdot9597$	$8\cdot0249$	$12\cdot9846$
$v_n=1$	1	2	3	5	8	13

(continued opposite)

$n =$ 8	9	10	11	12	13
$u_n =$ 21·0095	33·9941	55·0036	88·9977	144·0014	232·9991
$v_n =$ 21	34	55	89	144	233

The continuous curve is the graph of the function

$$y = 0 \cdot 4472 \times (1 \cdot 61803)^x$$

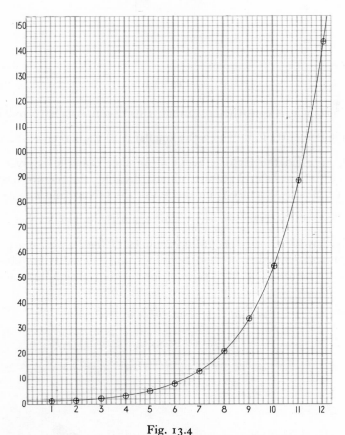

Fig. 13.4

The points ⊕ represent the Fibonacci numbers.

The Fibonacci numbers are, therefore, a set of whole numbers which satisfy almost exactly an exponential law of growth associated, not with whole numbers such as we may get from counting the leaves, branches, flowers and similar features of a plant, but with the growth of continuous measurable quantities such as heights, lengths and velocities. This is interesting because it is an unexpected relationship to the exponential law which is known to be typical of most biological growth.

The table above and the accompanying graph (Fig. 13.4) illustrate this unlooked-for compatibility between continuous and discrete quantities.

The Golden Section

Tastes may vary, but many people asked to select one of the shapes shown in Fig. 13.5 for note-paper or for the frame of a picture would choose the third. It is not too square and not too elongated.

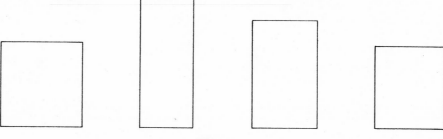

Fig. 13.5

The third rectangle is constructed so that if its height is called h and its width w the $\dfrac{w}{h} = \dfrac{h}{w+h}$. This proportion, in which the smaller is to the larger as the larger is to the sum of both, is called the Golden Section. Another example is given in the sketch below (Fig. 13.6). The central feature, almost dividing the picture into two parts, is placed so that if b is its distance from the left of the picture and a is its distance from the right of the picture, then $\dfrac{a}{b} = \dfrac{b}{a+b}$. This again is the Golden Section. The Greek architects, who have left many beautiful examples of their classical art, were aware of this proportion and a number of their buildings illustrate it. It has also been used in many well-known paintings. If both sides of the equation are multiplied by $b\,(a+b)$ we obtain $a \,.\, (a+b) = b^2$ which can be written in the form

$$a^2 + ab = b^2 \quad \text{or} \quad b^2 - ab - a^2 = 0.$$

Fig. 13.6

Since we are interested in the ratio $\dfrac{b}{a}$, the equation may be expressed as a quadratic equation in $\dfrac{b}{a}$ in the form

$$\frac{b^2}{a^2} - \frac{b}{a} - 1 = 0$$

and the two solutions of this equation are

$$\frac{b}{a}=\frac{1+\sqrt{5}}{2} \quad \text{and} \quad \frac{b}{a}=\frac{1-\sqrt{5}}{2}$$

i.e. $\frac{b}{a}=1\cdot618034\ldots$ and $\frac{b}{a}=-0\cdot618034\ldots$

The first of these solutions gives us the Golden Section.

The reader should verify that

$$1\cdot618034 \times 0\cdot618034 = 1 \text{ and that } 1\cdot618034 \times 1\cdot618034 = 2\cdot618034$$

(both correct to five places of decimals). The ratios

$$\frac{0\cdot618034}{1}, \quad \frac{1}{1\cdot618034} \quad \text{and} \quad \frac{1\cdot618034}{2\cdot618034}$$

are all examples of the Golden Section ratio (they are, of course, equal to one another).

Idle Fancy

In text-books mathematicians write seriously, proving things, solving equations and presenting mathematical proofs with elegance and assurance. Because there is little point in going into print, in a mathematics book, if there is nothing businesslike to say, the reader who is not a mathematician is rarely given an opportunity of letting the fancy roam in a mathematical context. This is a pity.

If the thirteen ancestors of the male bee in the sixth generation before him are set out as in the table on page 216, but the females are left white and the males coloured black, they will look like this

○ ● ○ ● ○ ○ ● ○ ● ○ ● ○ ○

If the flowers on new shoots in the diagram of the little plant in Fig. 13.2 are coloured black and the flowers on older stems are left white, they will look like this

○ ● ○ ● ○ ○ ● ○ ● ○ ● ○ ○

and both of these look very much like an octave on a pianoforte keyboard, the thirteen elements corresponding to the thirteen semitones of the chromatic scale (Fig. 13.7).

Fig. 13.7

This resemblance between two naturally occurring examples of thirteen elements in a Fibonacci development and a pianoforte keyboard draws attention to a number of facts about musical scales.

Mankind has a specialized physiological structure in the ear which enables different sounds and combinations of sounds to be heard with remarkable discrimination. Over the two or three thousand years during which man has made musical instruments, various conventions have grown up for the tuning of these instruments and, within the last few centuries, for the writing of musical scores. These conventions have developed in such a way that what we call music gives pleasure when it reaches the brain through the mechanism of the human ear. These conventions cannot, therefore, be regarded as completely arbitrary since they must in some way be compatible with the physiology of the hearing mechanism. In the chapter in which reference was made to the equiangular spiral, the relation between the exponential sequence and the sensitive hair-like receptors in the cochlea was mentioned, and in this present chapter attention has been drawn to the closeness of a Fibonacci sequence to points on an exponential curve. It is not surprising to see that there is a suggestion of a Fibonacci development about our musical conventions. The *chromatic scale* contains *thirteen* notes, the eight white notes and five black notes, in a full octave.

The ordinary octave such as the octave in C-major contains *eight* notes, the eight white notes on a keyboard which constitute the octave.

One of the earlier European scales was the "pentatonic scale" which contained *five* notes. The five notes D, E, G, A, B constitute such a scale and a number of well-known airs may be played using just these. Fig. 13.2 suggests the following diagram:

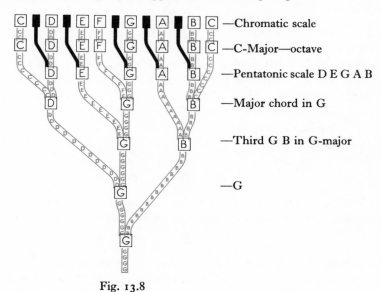

Fig. 13.8

The succession of this development is as follows:

      1. G.

      2. G B—a harmonious "third", a pleasing and simple harmony.

      3. D G B—the notes Soh, Doh, Me in key G.

      5. D E G A B—a pentatonic scale with correct intervals.

      8. C D E F G A B C—the octave in key C.

    13. The full thirteen notes of the chromatic scale.

This is the sort of progression of increasing sets of notes which is musically very tidy and in line with the conventional development of western music.

This proves nothing, and any charge that the plant development could have been drawn out in other ways which led to different patterns of notes, could not be answered.

(Actually if the last set of branch stems all branched to the right instead of to the left the notes would be B C C♯ D D♯ E F F♯ G G♯ A A♯ B, the correct chromatic scale but starting at a different note.)

The point of this section about scales is the very simple one that theories of harmony and musical form have to take into account both the physiological structure of the ear, which is related to the exponential sequences, and the individual notes, which have been standardized according to musical conventions which have developed over the years. That these conventions have many properties characteristic of the Fibonacci sequence may or may not be a coincidence. The idea gives scope for play, building up various scales by methods exactly paralleling the genealogical trees of bees and the growth of plants. Some musician may one day study the development of musical conventions from some fresh angle and suggest a reason for this association of ideas. The main reason for including it here is simply that it is quite a light-hearted example of assorted data being linked together systematically. The finding of such patterns is mathematically very satisfying.

14

Statistics

DISRAELI ONCE made the mischievous remark: "There are lies, damned lies and statistics." Instead of its being deservedly treated as a bright remark, scoring a transient debating point, it has entered the language as an aphorism and been given a totally undeserved currency that is doing a great deal of harm. It is the reverse of the truth, and a form of words closer to suggesting the truth would be that "There are lies, damned lies and numerical statements made by people ignorant of statistics". Statistics make possible the systematic testing of numerical data for relevance, reliability and validity. The usefulness, importance and honesty of a number used to describe some fact can be assessed only if its relations to the whole context are carefully studied, and it is the duty of a statistician to make such studies and present evidence in a form that will enable considered judgments to be based upon it.

We may say, by way of introduction, that if we are presented with a large set of numbers relating to something, we begin by looking for some pattern in the numbers and, if we find one, we compare it with similar sets of numbers to see whether they, too, show the same sort of pattern. Experience shows that some patterns are common to several sorts of numerical information and that there is a number of standard patterns we may expect to find with certain types of data.

The heights of men provide a suitable first example for two reasons. In the first place, a height is something that we can visualize quite easily, and it helps, in describing a numerical pattern, if we can see the quantities as well as the numbers they represent; and, in the second place, heights are familiar quantities, easily checked and within everyone's experience.

Fig. 14.1

The majority of men are of middling height. There are very few very short people and there are very few very tall people, and an average sample of people would vary in size in the sort of way here illustrated.

226

This is a general picture which in general terms agrees with our experience. If we now try to be more precise and we measure the heights of a 100 men, perhaps 100 students in a college or 100 men employed in a factory, and list their heights in *inches*, we obtain a set of numbers such as

$59\frac{1}{2}$, $60\frac{1}{2}$, 61, $61\frac{1}{2}$, 62, 62, $62\frac{1}{2}$, $62\frac{1}{2}$, 63, 63, 63, $63\frac{1}{2}$, $63\frac{1}{2}$, $63\frac{1}{2}$, 64, 64, 64, 64, $64\frac{1}{2}$, $64\frac{1}{2}$, $64\frac{1}{2}$, $64\frac{1}{2}$, $64\frac{1}{2}$, 65, 65, 65, 65, 65, $65\frac{1}{2}$, $65\frac{1}{2}$, $65\frac{1}{2}$, $65\frac{1}{2}$, $65\frac{1}{2}$, $65\frac{1}{2}$, 66, 66, 66, 66, 66, 66, $66\frac{1}{2}$, $66\frac{1}{2}$, $66\frac{1}{2}$, $66\frac{1}{2}$, $66\frac{1}{2}$, $66\frac{1}{2}$, $66\frac{1}{2}$, 67, 67, 67, 67, 67, 67, 67, $67\frac{1}{2}$, $67\frac{1}{2}$, $67\frac{1}{2}$, $67\frac{1}{2}$, $67\frac{1}{2}$, $67\frac{1}{2}$, $67\frac{1}{2}$, 68, 68, 68, 68, 68, 68, $68\frac{1}{2}$, $68\frac{1}{2}$, $68\frac{1}{2}$, $68\frac{1}{2}$, $68\frac{1}{2}$, $68\frac{1}{2}$, 69, 69, 69, 69, 69, $69\frac{1}{2}$, $69\frac{1}{2}$, $69\frac{1}{2}$, $69\frac{1}{2}$, $69\frac{1}{2}$, 70, 70, 70, 70, $70\frac{1}{2}$, $70\frac{1}{2}$, $70\frac{1}{2}$, 71, 71, 71, $71\frac{1}{2}$, $71\frac{1}{2}$, $71\frac{1}{2}$, 72, 72, $72\frac{1}{2}$, 73, $73\frac{1}{2}$, $74\frac{1}{2}$ inches.

A glance at this table will show that there are many more men with heights between 64 and 69 inches than between 59 and 64 or 69 and 74 inches, but to appreciate the pattern it is valuable to present the numbers in some form that will enable the whole sequence of numbers to be visualized at a glance. In the diagram below (Fig. 14.2) each ● represents one man and the ●'s are put against the appropriate heights.

Fig. 14.2

The shape of this representation also shows quite clearly that there are many men in the middle range of heights and that the numbers thin off on either side. There is also a symmetry about the shape, centred on 67 in. (5 ft 7 in.). One could count also that two-thirds of the men have heights from 64 to 70 in., that is, within three inches of the mean, and that all but four, that is, 96 per cent, are within six inches of the mean height.

The shape of the distribution of heights could be shown in a slightly condensed way, by grouping heights together in classes. We might class the three measurements 59 in., $59\frac{1}{2}$ in., 60 in. together, the three heights $60\frac{1}{2}$ in., 61 in., $61\frac{1}{2}$ in. together, and so on. This would give a representation such as Fig. 14.3.

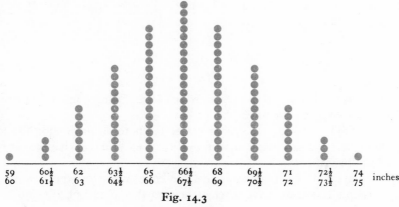

Fig. 14.3

Heights of 100 men.

In such a distribution the class which contains the most members, represented by the highest column, is called the *mode*. The middle member of the whole group is the *median*; in this case both the 50th and 51st out of 100 have a height of 67 in., which is the median height.

If we now find another hundred men, measure their heights and draw a column graph to illustrate the distribution of heights, we should normally expect to find that, with minor variations, we had a diagram that fitted very closely to the one illustrated above. This would be true only if we chose an ordinary group of English men. A group of English women would show exactly the same sort of distribution but would be farther to the left in the diagram, all their heights being proportionately somewhat smaller. We should expect a similar distribution, but all the members a great deal smaller, if we measured a group of Pigmies in the Congo region, and the whole group to be somewhat taller if we measured Scandinavians. If the group were selected at random, whatever the actual sizes involved, we should expect to find that the range in which two-thirds of the people were found to lie was about half the range which contains 95 per cent, this being a consistent property of attributes "normally" distributed. The word "normally" is here used in a particular sense, which will be apparent later.

The distribution of heights illustrated in the diagram below has been invented to illustrate the point to be made in this paragraph and is not quoted from actual measurements. Sometime, round about Easter-tide, ninety-nine men were dining together one Saturday evening. As they stood around just before sitting at their places, their heights were observed and they were found to be distributed as in Fig. 14.4:

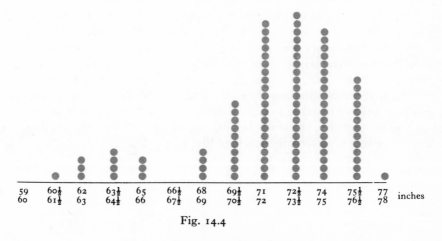

Fig. 14.4

The question is, "What was the occasion which brought these ninety-nine men together to dine on this Saturday evening?"

The answer to this question is given in the footnote on page 230. Try to guess the answer, and when you have done so, turn over the page and see what the distribution was concocted to illustrate.

The importance of this exercise is that we know what to expect from an ordinary sample of people. Here we have a set of heights that does not fall into this ordinary pattern, and the evidence that the group of people has been selected in an unusual sort of way is within the figures themselves. This being so, we may not draw conclusions about the whole population from a study of this group; we may use the figures to make statements only about the particular group.

Normal Distribution

The heights of people are "normally" distributed, and the percentage of the population within any prescribed limits of height is known and can be read from the graph of a *normal* curve, or from the tables giving the ordinates of the curve and areas under the curve, printed in statistics text-books and statistical tables. The weights, as well as the heights, of people are distributed in much the same way, so are the sizes of animals of the various species, so are plants. The importance of the normal curve in understanding biology cannot be exaggerated, and some of the best-known and most widely used statistical tables have been prepared by workers whose interests have been mainly biological. This type of distribution is not, however, especially associated with any particular field of study but is, somewhat surprisingly, applicable to problems arising from both pure chance and precision engineering. A batch of electric light bulbs, made in the same factory to the same specifications, will not all burn out after exactly the same number of hours of burning. There will be a mean (or average) life, and a majority of the bulbs would be expected to last about this length of time; but a few will burn out quite a long time before this and a few will last a lot longer. This last sentence has been worded in a very vague way, using everyday words in their everyday, imprecise way. What does "quite a long time" mean? This sort of language is adequate for the individual customer who buys a bulb occasionally and months, or years, later has to replace it. The manufacturer needs to be able to assess the quality of his products accurately, for he knows that in the long run it will be the reliability and relatively consistent performance of the articles he markets, in combination with their price, which will bring him prosperity. This efficiency can come only with precise knowledge of the behaviour of what he produces. Industry is very much interested in statistics, and it is the "normal" distribution curve that is fundamental to a great deal of statistical technique.

If the time shown by a hundred clocks, chosen at random in a town, were recorded at the instant of the last "pip" at six o'clock by the B.B.C. time signal, then one would expect some to be fast, some to be slow, but the distribution of their errors to be a "normal" distribution. If this were not so, one would expect something unusual about the sample of the chosen hundred. In the particular case of clocks, it is possible that a number of them might be electric clocks, tied to the master clock at the power station and all sharing a particular error deriving from a single cause. An analysis of the distribution of errors should then reveal a double population, one of independent mechanisms with errors independently derived, and the other with a consistent error not normally distributed. The wear found after a certain time in the bearings of any one model of motor car would also be expected to be normally distributed, and if any one batch of a production model showed an abnormal distribution of wear, car manufacturers might well make special arrangements about replacements for certain parts.

Examples of "normal" distributions could be drawn from a multitude of contexts, and the very close approximation to normal distributions of many of the most closely studied populations has been thoroughly well established.

(a) APPROXIMATELY NORMAL DISTRIBUTIONS

If a batch of watches is set so that they show exactly the correct time at noon on a certain Monday, their times again compared with a noon time-signal a week later, and again compared with the correct time at noon on the following Monday, we might expect the following percentage distributions of the watch errors (Figs. 14.5 and 14.6).

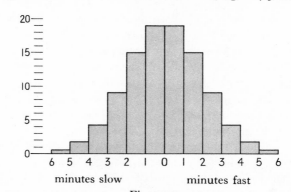

Fig. 14.5
Watch errors after *one* week.

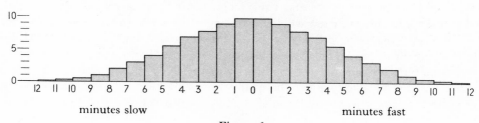

Fig. 14.6
Watch errors after *two* weeks.

These two column graphs, or "histograms", are essentially the same shape, but since in a fortnight, watches will have gained or lost about twice what they gain or lose in a week, the second histogram is spread out over twice the length of base. Again, since in a fortnight only about half the number of watches will be within a minute of the correct time compared with the number which keep within this error in a week, the height of the second histogram is only about half the height of the first one. There will, therefore, be a variety about the appearances of these histograms, their detailed dimensions depending upon the number of things being measured and the intervals taken for plotting the variable quantity. A histogram for errors in watches after a fortnight, taking two minutes, four minutes, six minutes fast or slow as the grouping limits, would produce a figure just like the one for one week with one-minute intervals.

If, instead of 100 watches and one-minute intervals, we had chosen 500 watches and twelve-second intervals (five times the number and one-fifth of the time interval) we should obtain a histogram whose outline would look like Fig. 14.7.

Answer to question on page 228:

The ninety-nine men were the crews of eleven boats taking part in the Head-of-the-River Race and consisted of eleven coxes and eighty-eight oarsmen.

If we had chosen a million watches and a ten-thousandth of a minute as our class interval, we should have the outline of a histogram in which the steps were so very small they would not be distinguishable by eye and the diagram would look like a very smooth curve.

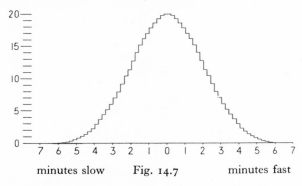

minutes slow   Fig. 14.7   minutes fast

(b) THE NORMAL DISTRIBUTION

The larger the population and the smaller the class interval, the more nearly the outline of a histogram approaches a smooth curve. There exists a precisely defined continuous curve which is called the "Normal Curve" (Fig. 14.8). When some attribute of a large number of individuals is *normally distributed*, the tops of the columns of the histogram illustrating the distribution will lie approximately on this normal curve. The larger the population and the smaller the class intervals, the nearer will the outline of the histogram lie to the normal curve. For any sample selected from a population, we do not expect an exactly normal distribution, and the smaller the sample the less regular the distribution to be expected.

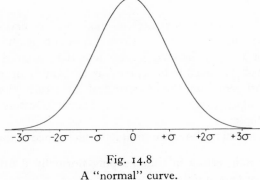

Fig. 14.8
A "normal" curve.

A normal curve is defined by an algebraic equation which has the form

$$y = A\, e^{-cx^2} \quad (c \text{ is a positive constant}).$$

Standard Deviation

If we suppose that we have two batches, each consisting of 1000 watches, and in one batch the regulators are set somewhere near the centre of the scale, but in the second batch the regulators have been adjusted to reduce the amount gained or lost, we should expect the deviation from mean time, after a week, to be very much greater for watches in the first batch than for watches in the second batch. In the diagrams below (Figs. 14.9 and 14·10), two histograms are drawn to illustrate the two sets of errors, and superimposed on them are the best-fitting normal curves.

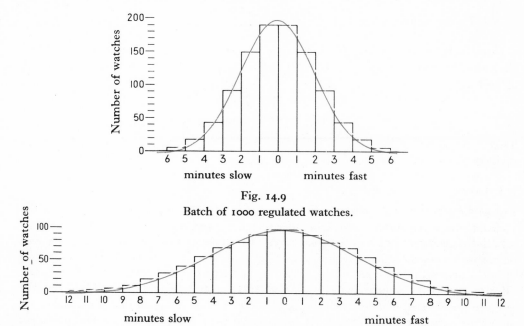

Fig. 14.9
Batch of 1000 regulated watches.

Fig. 14.10
Batch of 1000 unregulated watches.

Both these distributions are approximately normal and the curves drawn in are normal curves. They differ in the spread of the curve and in the heights of the ordinates. In testing any samples or any populations, it is obvious that we need some agreed method of measuring the spread. We need to be able to say that the error in time-keeping of one batch of watches is different from the other and, if the information is to be of any use, to be able to put some figure to it which quickly and accurately describes the performance of the samples as a whole.

The two samples referred to above are completely described in the following sentences:

> Regulated batch, errors in time-keeping normally distributed with standard deviation of two minutes per week.

> Unregulated batch, errors normally distributed with standard deviation of four minutes per week.

For a population of known size the precise details of the distribution are known if the standard deviation is known. The standard deviation is given the Greek letter "sigma" as its symbol.

$$\text{Standard deviation} = \sigma$$
$$\text{Total number} \quad = N$$

Then, in the equation $y = A\,e^{-cx^2}$,

$$A = \frac{0.4\,N}{\sigma} \text{ and } c = \frac{1}{2\sigma^2}.$$

NOTE. The actual value of A is $\dfrac{N}{\sigma\,.\,\sqrt{2\pi}} = \dfrac{0.3989N}{\sigma}$.

If one of the watches in the batch is x minutes fast, or $(+x)$, and there are N watches altogether (in this case $N = 1000$) then the standard deviation of the distribution, σ, is given by

$$\sigma^2 = \frac{\Sigma\,x^2}{N}.$$

That is, the square of the standard deviation is the sum of the squares of all the deviations divided by the total number of cases.

EXAMPLE

I usually travel on the same bus each morning, and shortly before the end of my journey I change buses. On forty-eight successive weekday mornings I counted the number of standing passengers or the number of vacant seats on each of the buses, but on two occasions I walked the last part of the journey.

On the FIRST BUS

		No. of occasions
Standing passengers	5	1
	4	1
	3	3
	2	5
	1	8
	0	12
Vacant seats	1	8
	2	5
	3	3
	4	1
	5	1

On the SECOND BUS

		No. of occasions
Standing passengers	6	1
	5	2
	4	4
	3	4
	2	4
	1	5
	0	6
Vacant seats	1	5
	2	4
	3	4
	4	4
	5	2
	6	1

Find the standard deviation of the two distributions and comment on them.

It is quite obvious that these two distributions are symmetrical and that the average number of passengers carried is exactly equal to the number of seats. The number of standing passengers on any occasion is, therefore, the deviation of the number of passengers above the mean, and the number of vacant seats is the deviation, on that occasion, below the mean. If there are 2 standing passengers on 5 occasions, we say that the *frequency* of class $+2$ is 5.

By definition, if σ is the standard deviation, then $\sigma^2 = \dfrac{\Sigma x^2}{N}$.

(If we take the case of two standing passengers, for this $x = +2$, $x^2 = 4$ and there are five occasions when the deviation is $+2$, so that the contribution of these items to the total of Σx^2 is 4×5.)

FIRST BUS

Deviation x	Frequency f	$f.x^2$
$+5$	1	25
$+4$	1	16
$+3$	3	27
$+2$	5	20
$+1$	8	8
0	12	0
-1	8	8
-2	5	20
-3	3	27
-4	1	16
-5	1	25
	48	192

SECOND BUS

Deviation y	Frequency f	$f.y^2$
$+6$	1	36
$+5$	2	50
$+4$	4	64
$+3$	4	36
$+2$	4	16
$+1$	5	5
0	6	0
-1	5	5
-2	4	16
-3	4	36
-4	4	64
-5	2	50
-6	1	36
	46	414

$$N_x = 48 \qquad \Sigma x^2 = 192$$
$$\sigma^2 = \frac{192}{48} = 4$$
$$\sigma = 2$$

$$N_y = 46 \qquad \Sigma y^2 = 414$$
$$\sigma^2 = \frac{414}{46} = 9$$
$$\sigma = 3$$

The two histograms show that there is less variation in the number of passengers who use the first bus. The standard deviation enables us to put a figure to this "less" variation and say, precisely, that the standard deviations are 2 passengers and 3 passengers respectively.

The Normal Distribution Curve

Total number of individuals in the population $= N$.

The standard deviation of the distribution $= \sigma$.

The frequency corresponding to score x is y.

Then if the distribution is normal,

For

$x = \sigma \times$	0·0	0·1	0·2	0·3	0·4	0·5	0·6	0·7	0·8	0·9
$y = \dfrac{N}{\sigma} \times$	0·399	0·397	0·391	0·381	0·368	0·352	0·333	0·312	0·290	0·266

For

$x = \sigma \times 1.0$	1.1	1.2	1.3	1.4	1.5	1.6	1.7	1.8	1.9
$y = \dfrac{N}{\sigma} \times 0.242$	0.218	0.194	0.171	0.150	0.130	0.111	0.094	0.079	0.066

For

$x = \sigma \times 2.0$	2.1	2.2	2.3	2.4	2.5	2.6	2.7	2.8	2.9	3.0
$y = \dfrac{N}{\sigma} \times 0.054$	0.044	0.036	0.028	0.022	0.018	0.014	0.010	0.008	0.006	0.004

This enables the normal curve to be drawn accurately for any distribution for which N and σ have been calculated. The histogram of an observed distribution may be drawn and compared with the appropriate normal curve.

In the first bus distribution of passengers, $\sigma = 2$ and $\dfrac{N}{\sigma} = 24$, we may take enough points to draw in a rough idea of the normal curve by taking

$$x = 0 \qquad y = 24 \times 0.399 \qquad (x=0, y=9.6)$$
$$x = 2 \times 0.5 \qquad y = 24 \times 0.352 \qquad (x=1, y=8.45)$$
$$x = 2 \times 1.0 \qquad y = 24 \times 0.242 \qquad (x=2, y=5.81)$$
$$x = 2 \times 1.5 \qquad y = 24 \times 0.130 \qquad (x=3, y=3.12)$$
$$x = 2 \times 2.0 \qquad y = 24 \times 0.054 \qquad (x=4, y=1.30)$$
$$x = 2 \times 2.5 \qquad y = 24 \times 0.018 \qquad (x=5, y=0.43)$$
$$x = 2 \times 3.0 \qquad y = 24 \times 0.004 \qquad (x=6, y=0.10)$$

We have now the actual information about the observed numbers of passengers travelling in the first bus and the co-ordinates of the *normal* curve with the same mean and standard deviation and we can put them on the same diagram and compare them (Fig. 14.11).

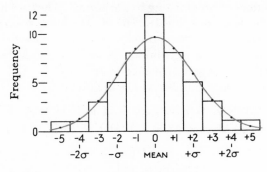

Fig. 14.11

Histogram of distribution. Normal curve with same Mean and Standard Deviation.

For the second bus we need to compare the histogram with a normal curve with standard deviation $\sigma = 3$ and $N = 46$ (Fig. 14.12).

$$\frac{N}{\sigma} = \frac{46}{3} = 15\cdot33$$

$x = 0$	$y = 15\cdot33 \times 0\cdot399$	$(x = 0, \quad y = 6\cdot13)$
$x = 3 \times 0\cdot5$	$y = 15\cdot33 \times 0\cdot352$	$(x = 1\cdot5, y = 5\cdot40)$
$x = 3 \times 1\cdot0$	$y = 15\cdot33 \times 0\cdot242$	$(x = 3\cdot0, y = 3\cdot71)$
$x = 3 \times 1\cdot5$	$y = 15\cdot33 \times 0\cdot130$	$(x = 4\cdot5, y = 1\cdot99)$
$x = 3 \times 2\cdot0$	$y = 15\cdot33 \times 0\cdot054$	$(x = 6\cdot0, y = 0\cdot83)$
$x = 3 \times 2\cdot5$	$y = 15\cdot33 \times 0\cdot018$	$(x = 7\cdot5, y = 0\cdot28)$
$x = 3 \times 3\cdot0$	$y = 15\cdot33 \times 0\cdot004$	$(x = 9\cdot0, y = 0\cdot06)$

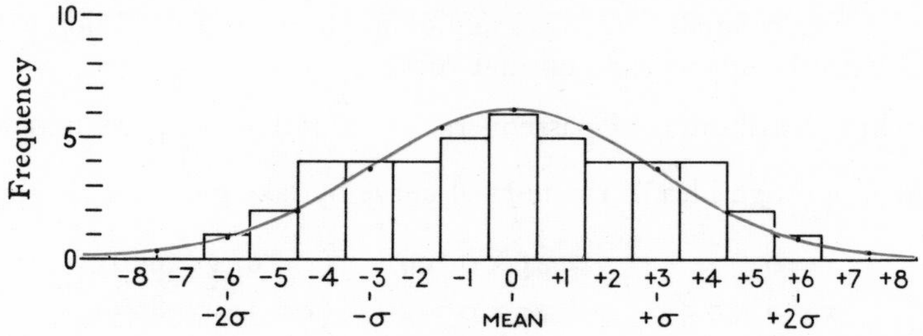

Fig. 14.12

Histogram of distribution. Normal curve with same Mean and Standard Deviation.

These two examples illustrate the process of fitting a normal curve to a given distribution. They also illustrate how a normal curve may correspond to a distribution which is fairly large at the centre and does not extend very far on either side of the mean, giving a tall curve which quickly decreases on either side of the mean (leptokurtic); or a distribution having a greater standard deviation, a smaller proportion of cases near the mean, and extending farther on either side, to give a curve which is flatter at the top (platykurtic).

The illustrations used so far have been artificially constructed to show symmetrical properties and distributions approximating to the normal. They are like the distributions to be expected from very large samples. In general, when we are considering only fairly small samples we expect irregularities and only rough approximation to the normal.

Here is an example of an actual distribution. A group of students was given the task of writing a code number against a sequence of letters "H = 1, F = 2, K = 3, Z = 4, M = 5." "Write the appropriate number under each letter

F K M Z H M K Z H F K Z M F H K F H M Z M Z F H K

M Z K F H Z K M H Z M K F K H F Z M Z M H F K H F, etc."

(There were eight lines of this nature and the students were given $1\frac{1}{2}$ minutes. The object was to investigate the rate of learning, and fatigue.) On the sixth trial, the number of letters coded by individual students was 132, 127, 125, 123, 122, 122, 121, 120, 119, 119, 116, 114, 114, 113, 112, 111, 111, 110, 108, 105, 105, 105, 103, 103, 103, 102, 102, 100, 100, 97, 96, 96, 95, 95, 94, 93, 93, 92, 90, 88, 87, 87, 85, 82.

When working with as many individuals as this it is convenient to group them together. This simplifies the arithmetic with not enough loss of accuracy to make any significant difference to the statistics finally found. Here we can group together the numbers from 80 to 84, 85 to 89, 90 to 94 and so on. When we have done this we can label the middle class 0, the class above this $+1$, and the class below 0, -1 and so on.

There is 1 member of the class 80 to 84 (actual number is 82).

There are 4 members of the class 85 to 89 (actual numbers 85, 87, 87, 88).

There are 5 members of the class 90 to 94 (actual numbers 90, 92, 93, 93, 94) etc.

In this way we can draw up a table as follows:

Class	Frequency f	Number of Class x	$f.x$	$f.x^2$
130–134	1	$+5$	$+5$	25
125–129	2	$+4$	$+8$	32
120–124	5	$+3$	$+15$	45
115–119	3	$+2$	$+6$	12
110–114	7	$+1$	$+7$	7
105–109	4	0	0	0
100–104	7	-1	-7	7
95–99	5	-2	-10	20
90–94	5	-3	-15	45
85–89	4	-4	-16	64
80–84	1	-5	-5	25
	44		-12	282

In the $f.x$ column the sum of the plus terms is $+41$ and the sum of the minus terms is -53; $(+41-53=-12)$.

TO FIND THE "MEAN" OR AVERAGE MARK

Each person above the mean contributes a $+$ score to column $f.x$. Thus, each of the 5 people in class $+3$ (120 to 124) contributes a score of $+3$ classes, and between them they contribute $+15$. Altogether the $+$ and $-$ scores come to -12. The average difference from the middle of class "0" is $\frac{-12}{44}$ or -0.27 classes. The mean of the distribution is therefore 0.27 *classes* below the middle of the range 105 to 109. Each class corresponds to 5 marks (105, 106, 107, 108, 109) so the actual mean in *marks* is $107-0.27\times5$ or $107-1.35$ or 105.65 or $\underline{105.6}$ (to one place of decimals).

TO FIND THE STANDARD DEVIATION

Taken from the middle of class 0, the sum of the squares of the deviations (in terms of *classes*) is 282. The mean value of this is $\frac{282}{44}=6.41$. This has been taken from the middle of class 0, which is 0.27 classes above the correct mean, and a correction has to be made to the 6.41, giving $\sigma^2=6.41-(-0.27)^2=6.41-0.07=6.34$. From square root tables, $\sigma=2.52$ classes.

For *classes*, $\sigma=2.52$. Each class spans 5 marks, so that for *marks* the standard deviation will be 2.52×5 or 12.6.

We can quickly draw up the table giving the normal curve for the same population, $N=44$, and the same standard deviation, $\sigma=2.52$.

$$\frac{N}{\sigma} = \frac{44}{2 \cdot 5} = 17 \cdot 6$$

$x = 0$	$y = 17 \cdot 6 \times 0 \cdot 399$	$(x = 0, y = 7 \cdot 00)$
$x = 2 \cdot 5 \times 0 \cdot 4$	$y = 17 \cdot 6 \times 0 \cdot 368$	$(x = 1, y = 6 \cdot 44)$
$x = 2 \cdot 5 \times 0 \cdot 8$	$y = 17 \cdot 6 \times 0 \cdot 290$	$(x = 2, y = 5 \cdot 13)$
$x = 2 \cdot 5 \times 1 \cdot 2$	$y = 17 \cdot 6 \times 0 \cdot 194$	$(x = 3, y = 3 \cdot 40)$
$x = 2 \cdot 5 \times 1 \cdot 6$	$y = 17 \cdot 6 \times 0 \cdot 111$	$(x = 4, y = 1 \cdot 95)$
$x = 2 \cdot 5 \times 2 \cdot 0$	$y = 17 \cdot 6 \times 0 \cdot 054$	$(x = 5, y = 0 \cdot 95)$
$x = 2 \cdot 5 \times 2 \cdot 4$	$y = 17 \cdot 6 \times 0 \cdot 022$	$(x = 6, y = 0 \cdot 39)$
$x = 2 \cdot 5 \times 2 \cdot 8$	$y = 17 \cdot 6 \times 0 \cdot 008$	$(x = 7, y = 0 \cdot 14)$

(We have chosen intervals of 0·4 for values of $\frac{x}{\sigma}$ for obtaining the ordinates of the normal curve, so that using $\sigma = 2·5$ gives whole numbers for x.)

The corresponding histogram and normal curve are shown in Fig. 14.13.

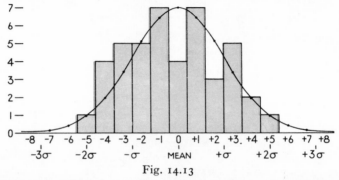

Fig. 14.13

Histogram and normal curve for distribution of scores from 44 people.

With a population as small as this there is not a very close correspondence in detail between the outline of the histogram and the normal curve, but it must be recognized that if only as few as four people in classes -3 or -4 scored a few points more and were brought up to class 0, it would make a very close approximation to the normal distribution. With small populations of only forty or fifty, we do not expect anything much closer than this.

When dealing with much larger numbers, the small irregularities even themselves out. Professor Vernon's *Graded Arithmetic-Mathematics Test* was given to over 1800 young women between the ages of eighteen and twenty years. The marks obtained in this test are tabulated at the top of page 239. Using these figures and working in *classes*

$$\text{Mean} = \frac{+32}{1834} = 0 \cdot 02 \text{ classes above the middle of class 0}$$
$$\sigma^2 = \frac{4676}{1834} - (+0 \cdot 02)^2 = 2 \cdot 55 - 0 \cdot 0004 = 2 \cdot 55$$
$$\sigma = 1 \cdot 60.$$

To plot the corresponding normal curve we have $\dfrac{N}{\sigma} = \dfrac{1834}{1 \cdot 6} = 1146.$

Actual mark obtained	Number of people f	Class f	f.x	f.x²
21 to 25	2	−5	−10	50
26 to 30	4	−4	−16	64
31 to 35	75	−3	−225	675
36 to 40	224	−2	−448	896
41 to 45	383	−1	−383	383
46 to 50	488	0	0	0
51 to 55	393	+1	+393	393
56 to 60	152	+2	+304	608
61 to 65	57	+3	+171	513
66 to 70	34	+4	+136	544
71 to 75	22	+5	+110	550
	1834		+32	4676

Class Interval = 5 marks.

(For $\sigma = 1.6$ we get values of x nearly equal to whole numbers if we choose

$$\frac{x}{\sigma} = 0.6,\ x = 0.96 \qquad \frac{x}{\sigma} = 1.2,\ x = 1.92 \qquad \frac{x}{\sigma} = 1.9,\ x = 3.04 \qquad \frac{x}{\sigma} = 2.5,\ x = 4.)$$

$$x = 0 \qquad\qquad y = 1146 \times 0.399 \qquad (x = 0, \quad y = 457)$$
$$x = 1.6 \times 0.6 \qquad y = 1146 \times 0.333 \qquad (x = 1, \quad y = 382)$$
$$x = 1.6 \times 1.2 \qquad y = 1146 \times 0.194 \qquad (x = 1.9, y = 223)$$
$$x = 1.6 \times 1.9 \qquad y = 1146 \times 0.066 \qquad (x = 3, \quad y = 76)$$
$$x = 1.6 \times 2.5 \qquad y = 1146 \times 0.018 \qquad (x = 4, \quad y = 21)$$
$$x = 1.6 \times 3.0 \qquad y = 1146 \times 0.004 \qquad (x = 4.8, y = 4)$$

The histogram showing the actual distribution, and the normal curve for a distribution of 1834 and standard deviation of 1·6 are shown in the accompanying figure (Fig. 14.14).

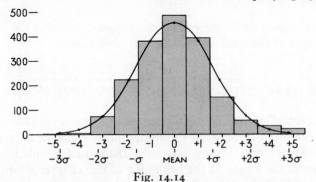

Fig. 14.14

Histogram showing the distribution of marks obtained by 1834 students on Vernon's *Graded Arithmetic-Mathematics Test*, together with the normal curve drawn for $N = 1834$ and $\sigma = 1.6$.

The whole of this calculation, the histogram and the normal curve have been based upon the frequencies in the classes. If actual marks are used, then

(i) *Mean*. The middle of class o corresponds to 48 marks.

$$+0.02 \text{ classes} \rightarrow 0.1 \text{ marks} \therefore \text{ mean mark} = 48 + 0.1 = \underline{48.1}.$$

(ii) *Standard deviation*. The standard deviation is 1.6 classes $= 1.6 \times 5$ marks
$$= 8 \text{ marks}.$$

$-\sigma$ corresponds to the mark 40.1
$+\sigma$ corresponds to the mark 56.1

Between these two marks the details of the distribution are

Mark	41	42	43	44	45	46	47	48	49	50	51	52	53	54	55	56
Number of people	70	62	85	74	92	79	91	106	94	118	93	113	76	67	44	46

which gives a total of 1310 with a score between $+\sigma$ and $-\sigma$.

1310 is $\frac{1310}{1834} \times 100$ per cent $= 71.4$ per cent of the total population.

For a perfectly normal distribution 68 per cent lie within $+\sigma$ and $-\sigma$.

AREA UNDER THE NORMAL CURVE

The height of each column of a histogram represents the number of people or objects belonging to the class defining the column. All columns are drawn the same width, so that the area of each column is proportional to the number of people it represents. Thus, the area under the whole histogram represents the total number of people, or objects, in the population described. As a population more and more closely approximates to a normal distribution so the histogram approximates more and more closely to a normal curve, and it is clear that the area under a normal curve represents the total population to which it corresponds. The area between the mean position, in the middle of the curve, and the ordinate corresponding to a particular value of the variate will represent the number of people, or objects, characterized by values of the variate between these limits. The following table gives the proportions of the area under the normal curve between a few selected values of the variate.

Table showing the areas under the normal curve, measured from the ordinate $x = 0$ to $x = x$, as percentages of the total area under the *whole* curve

$x/\sigma =$	0.00	0.25	0.50	0.75	1.00	1.25	1.50	1.75	2.00	2.25	2.50	2.75	3.00
area $=$	0.00	9.87	19.15	27.34	34.13	39.44	43.32	45.99	47.72	48.78	49.38	49.70	49.865

Thus, 34.13 per cent of the population lie between the mean position and one standard deviation above the mean or between the mean and one standard deviation below the mean. Thus, 68.26 per cent of any normally distributed population lie within one standard deviation of the mean. At the beginning of this chapter information was given about the heights of English adult males. Their mean is 5 ft 7 in., the standard deviation is 3 in. and they are normally distributed. Thus, we expect 68.26 per cent of the male population to have heights within the range 5 ft 4 in. and 5 ft 10 in.

47·72 per cent lie between the mean and $+2\sigma$ and 47·72 per cent lie between the mean and -2σ, so that 95·44 per cent lie within two standard deviations of the mean. In heights, this means that 95·44 per cent of the population have heights between 5 ft 1 in. and 6 ft 1 in.

49·865 per cent lie between the mean and either $+3\sigma$ or -3σ so that 99·73 per cent lie between $+3\sigma$ and -3σ. In other words, only 0·27 in 100 or 1 in 370 do not lie within three standard deviations of the mean.

Measurement of Intelligence

If we are wishing to obtain information about the number of teeth a person has we can simply count them. This is the simplest type of numerical assessment of all. If we wish to describe his height we measure it in an agreed unit, centimetres or inches, a centimetre or an inch being defined in terms of physical objects, the standard unit of length which is carefully preserved in each country. Rulers or measuring rods are standardized against the official unit. The same procedure is used for measuring weights. The establishment of an agreed unit for measuring "intelligence" is a much more difficult matter. Our present system of describing "intelligence" was developed in Paris in the early years of this century by Alfred Binet. His *Étude Expérimentale de l'intelligence* dates back to 1905, when the science of statistics was itself also in its infancy. Binet developed a number of tests, covering a variety of fields of ability, and found, for instance, that he could devise a test which a majority of eight-year-old children could perform but which defeated a majority of seven-year-old children. This test he assigned to the eight-year-old level. In this way he produced a battery of tests associated with each age group. A child who could do a majority of eight-year-old tests but not nine-year-old tests was assigned a "mental age" of eight years. Some bright seven-year-olds were found to have a "mental age" of eight, some duller nine-year-olds also had mental ages of eight or even seven. By dividing the "mental age" by the actual or "chronological age" he obtained a ratio, which, when expressed as a percentage, he called the "Intelligence quotient" or I.Q.

Thus, a nine-year-old child with a "mental age" of 11 would have an I.Q. given by $\frac{11}{9} \times 100 = 122$. Binet also discovered that the I.Q. of a child remained fairly constant; an I.Q. obtained at the age of eight would not be very different from an I.Q. measured three years later. After a child has reached the age of about fifteen years the development of intelligence levels off in much the same way that height and weight begin to stop increasing and stay at the size they will be when he is an adult. The mental age does not increase much above that attained at the age of about fifteen.

In the early work of Binet his criteria for associating a test with a particular age were not very precise by present-day standards, but the principles of mental measurement in terms of mental age and intelligence quotients that he introduced found wide acceptance and form the basis of most systems of test standardizations in use with children today.

Over the years, Binet's tests have been revised, the Terman-Merrill revision carried out at Stanford University, California, being one that is still very widely used. These later revisions make full use of modern statistical techniques in their standardizations. Defined as suggested by Binet, it is found that in an unbiased population I.Q.s are normally distributed. Terman and Merrill give the standard deviation of I.Q.s obtained from tests on 2904 children between the ages of 2 and 18 as 16·4 on a combination of their L and M versions of the test. In England we have a number of tests which have been standardized with a mean of 100 and a standard deviation of 15. This is true of the Moray House tests which are widely used for eleven-year-old children by Local Education Authorities who are responsible for deciding which schools will provide each child with the most appropriate secondary education.

Variations in the types of test will, of course, give somewhat different standard deviations, but for the range of growing children, the distribution of abilities, as determined by tests of the Binet type, may be described as normally distributed with a mean I.Q. of 100 and a standard deviation of 15. After the age of about 15 the quotient $\frac{\text{mental age}}{\text{actual age}}$ cannot be used, and intelligence tests for adults, after being duly tested for reliability, may have their marks converted into I.Q. scores by scoring the tests so that the mean mark is 100 and $\sigma = 15$.

From the areas under the normal curve given in Fig. 14.15 it will be seen that 27·3 per cent of a population lie between the mean and 0·75 σ, so that 22·7 per cent (i.e. 50 per cent − 27·3 per cent) of a population, which is normally distributed, will have deviations greater than 0·75 σ. If, for intelligence, $\sigma = 15$, $\frac{3}{4} \times 15 = 11\frac{1}{4}$, then if about $22\frac{1}{2}$ per cent of children are given a grammar school education, an I.Q. of about 111 will be about the grammar school border-line. If we were to take $\frac{1}{2}$ σ above the mean, or an I.Q. of $107\frac{1}{2}$ as the lower limit for grammar school entry, our table gives 19 per cent between the mean and $\frac{1}{2}$ σ, so that 69 per cent would be below this level and 31 per cent above. On the other hand, a level of entry as high as 115, or $+\sigma$, places 84 per cent below and only 16 per cent above this level.

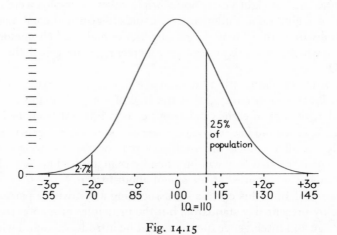

Fig. 14.15

25 per cent of a normally distributed population lie above 0·68 σ. Since 0·68 × 15 = 10·2, a quarter of the population will have intelligence quotients greater than 110. This is something like the proportion of grammar school places provided in the 1950's.

To provide grammar school places for all above an I.Q. of 105 or 0·34 σ would involve providing places for 37·7 per cent of the population, that is, providing places for an extra 12·7 per cent.

Almost exactly 700,000 children were born in 1949, so that to increase the number of places sufficiently to accommodate children with I.Q.s between 105 and 110, for children aged 11 in 1960, would involve building rooms and finding teachers for an additional 12·7 per cent of 700,000 = 89,000 children. There are few children with I.Q.s greater than 145. If we take the grammar school range of I.Q.s as from 110 to 145 (approximately the present range) there is a range of ability of 35 units of I.Q. in this 25 per cent of the population, whereas there is a range of only 10 units of I.Q. in the 25 per cent of the population between 100 and 110, so that if classes were to be divided so that the range of ability in a class was the same, classes would be three-and-a-half times as big for the middle range of abilities as for the two extremes of high and low I.Q.s. This consideration is not regarded as of great significance in most arguments about the sizes of classes, but it should not be completely ignored.

Provision made for children with low I.Q.s varies from area to area in the country. An I.Q. of 70 is about the lower limit for children in ordinary schools, and special schools are usually provided for children of I.Q. 70 and below. This is about two standard deviations below the mean, so that only 2·3 per cent of the population are catered for in this way.

However much we may dislike finding ourselves catalogued and sorted, provision of buildings and teachers must be made on a very large scale, and a thorough understanding of the normal distribution enables reasonably accurate estimates to be made of the proportion of the whole population that will be affected by particular changes and of the overall implications of alterations in educational policy.

Correlation

THE SCATTER-DIAGRAM

If two sets of figures are such that each item of one set can be associated with one item of the other set, then this mapping of one set on to the other can be represented on a diagram. Here are three examples.

EXAMPLES

1. Two boys take the outside temperatures at two-hourly intervals at the same time and at the same place. One thermometer is graduated in degrees Fahrenheit and the other in degrees centigrade. Their readings are

°F	43	44	46	51	54	57	55	49	44	47	53	56	62	64	60	55	60	64	66
°C	6	$6\frac{1}{2}$	8	$10\frac{1}{2}$	12	14	13	$9\frac{1}{2}$	$6\frac{1}{2}$	$8\frac{1}{2}$	12	$13\frac{1}{2}$	17	18	$15\frac{1}{2}$	13	$15\frac{1}{2}$	18	19

If a scatter-diagram is drawn we obtain the set of points representing the relationship between the two sets of numbers shown in Fig. 14.16.

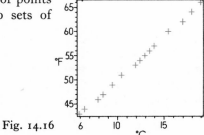

Fig. 14.16

2. Forty-five students were given two "intelligence tests" one; was Group Test 33 of the National Institute of Industrial Psychology, and the other the Moray House "Adult I" test. These are both tests which contain several different types of question and contain a majority of verbally presented material.

| Group Test 33 | 156 | 180 | 164 | 173 | 154 | 157 | 184 | 162 | 153 | 163 | 141 | 157 | 134 | 159 | 175 |
| Moray House AdI | 66 | 98 | 91 | 94 | 84 | 85 | 98 | 68 | 75 | 82 | 61 | 82 | 66 | 84 | 94 |

| Group Test 33 | 144 | 155 | 159 | 161 | 142 | 165 | 150 | 174 | 162 | 171 | 146 | 161 | 173 | 170 | 156 |
| Moray House AdI | 78 | 75 | 78 | 71 | 70 | 86 | 81 | 89 | 92 | 90 | 77 | 76 | 87 | 86 | 89 |

| Group Test 33 | 174 | 179 | 163 | 177 | 158 | 172 | 138 | 136 | 168 | 177 | 174 | 176 | 147 | 171 | 161 |
| Moray House AdI | 89 | 95 | 78 | 94 | 70 | 85 | 65 | 70 | 87 | 86 | 79 | 78 | 88 | 93 | 89 |

The scatter-diagram shown in Fig. 14.17 is obtained from these marks.

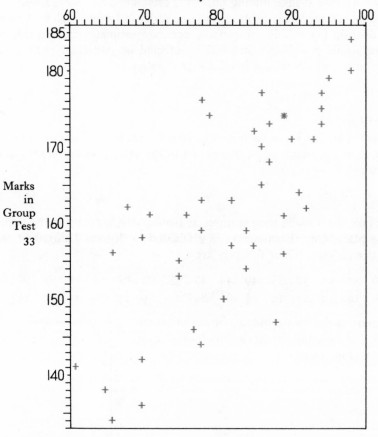

Fig. 14.17

3. The same forty-five students as in Example 2 were asked to write down the number of their house in the street in which they lived. Where the students' house numbers were greater than 100 the hundreds were ignored and only the tens and units were included. (Actually there were fifty-four students who took the tests but nine of these had no number for their houses.) The two sets of numbers, Moray House Test score and house number, were as follows:

Moray House AdI 66 98 91 94 84 85 98 68 75 82 61 82 66 84 94 78 75 78 71
House number   47 23 36 79 20 58 54 70 54 77 85 8 14 44 7 92 69 37 96

Moray House AdI 70 86 81 89 92 90 77 76 87 86 89 89 95 78 94 70 85 65 70
House number   45 84 12 25 51 28 9 76 30 69 94 4 99 77 39 84 12 32 15

Moray House AdI 87 86 79 78 88 93 89
House number   54 42 56 93 88 62 15

The scatter-diagram shown in Fig. 14.18 is obtained from these two sets of figures.

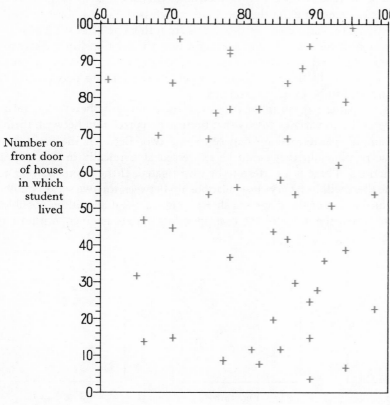

Fig. 14.18

In the first of these examples the points all lie on a straight line. In the second example it will be seen that the top left-hand corner and the bottom right-hand corner of the diagram are empty and that the majority of points are not very far away from the leading diagonal of the diagram. In terms of the quantities represented, we can say that no one with a high mark in one test has a very low mark in the other, and a majority have marks on the two tests which are not very different in their relative values. In the third example there is no obvious pattern at all in the arrangement of points in the scatter-diagram, and there is no relationship between the two sets of numbers represented.

Where the points on a diagram lie very close to a well-defined straight line or curve, we expect to find an algebraic equation relating the two sets of numbers. In Example 1, this is the equation

$$f = 1 \cdot 8\, c + 32$$

where f is the temperature in $^\circ$F and c is the temperature in $^\circ$C. Once such a relationship is established the whole precise machinery of algebra can be used and the treatment is no longer a problem of statistics. In practice, such relationships cannot always be dismissed as easily as this because there are likely to be errors of observation in the reading of instruments and, in experiments more complex than the simple reading of two thermometers, there will probably be various disturbing factors that will give rise to points which do not lie exactly on a well-defined line. Statistical analysis may well be useful in such cases to determine, on the one hand, which is the line of best fit and, on the other, to investigate the nature of the deviations from this line of best fit. However, in two variables which do lie very close to a straight line, the relationship is likely to be algebraic, and when one variable is known the corresponding value of the other variable can be determined exactly. In this case there is a perfect relationship between the two variables, which are said to be exactly correlated.

Where there is no pattern or form to the scatter-diagram and there is no relation whatsoever between the two variates we say that there is no correlation between them.

The second example is intermediate between these two. Between the two variates there is no precise relationship that could be expressed algebraically in terms of any simple usable equations. There is a pattern to be investigated. If the points lie very near to the diagonal line there will be a very close relationship between the two sets of numbers represented, and in the first of the diagrams shown (Fig. 14.19) it should be possible to predict one variate, when the value of the corresponding variate is given, within fairly

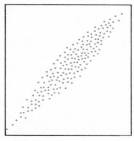

Fig. 14.19
High correlation.

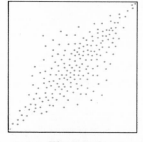

Fig. 14.20
Medium correlation.

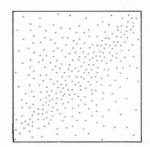

Fig. 14.21
Low correlation.

narrow limits. The second figure (Fig. 14.20) shows points less closely packed along the diagonal, but very obviously distributed fairly regularly about this diagonal with no extreme case of considerable deviation from the diagonal (both upper-left and lower-right corners are empty). Fig. 14.21 shows some pattern in so far as the upper-left and lower-right corners are slightly less populated than the other two corners, but there is much more scatter than in Fig. 14.20.

We need to be able to describe this gradation from perfect correlation to no correlation at all, and for this purpose we can calculate a "correlation coefficient". This is a number r_{xy} which has the value "1" for perfect correlation, "0" for no correlation, and has intermediate values which indicate the degree of correlation between the two variates.

COEFFICIENT OF CORRELATION

The derivation of the formula for calculating the coefficient of correlation is outside the scope of this book, and for proof of the formulae the reader is referred to any of the books listed at the end of this chapter. Even though we are not going through the algebra of deriving the formula, we can quite easily see how it gives us the sort of answer we should expect.

The nearer a point lies to the leading diagonal, the more it contributes to a high correlation, so that points in the top-right and bottom-left corners contribute towards, and points in the top-left and bottom-right corners count against, a high correlation (Fig. 14.22).

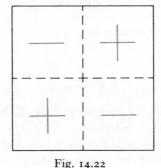

Fig. 14.22

Since, whether there is any correlation or not, we expect a large proportion of any normally distributed population to congregate towards the middle of a distribution, for this reason a number of people would be near the middle of the diagram whether there was any high correlation or not, and those who have high or low scores in one distribution will give a clearer indication of the degree of correlation than the middling ones. We do, therefore, want to "weight" the squares in some way so that those near the diagonal count for more than those farther away from it and those near the corners of the diagram count for more than those nearer to the middle.

This arrangement is achieved by dividing the vertical and horizontal axes into classes, as was done when the standard deviation was calculated, and giving each square the weight obtained by multiplying the two classes together. The meaning of this will be clear from Fig. 14.23. The square outlined is in class -3 for x and class $+2$ for y, so that its weighting is $-6 = (-3) \times (+2)$.

Class y

-25	-20	-15	-10	-5	o	$+5$	$+10$	$+15$	$+20$	$+25$	$+5$
-20	-16	-12	-8	-4	o	$+4$	$+8$	$+12$	$+16$	$+20$	$+4$
-15	-12	-9	-6	-3	o	$+3$	$+6$	$+9$	$+12$	$+15$	$+3$
-10	-8	-6	-4	-2	o	$+2$	$+4$	$+6$	$+8$	$+10$	$+2$
-5	-4	-3	-2	-1	o	$+1$	$+2$	$+3$	$+4$	$+5$	$+1$
o	o	o	o	o	o	o	o	o	o	o	o
$+5$	$+4$	$+3$	$+2$	$+1$	o	-1	-2	-3	-4	-5	-1
$+10$	$+8$	$+6$	$+4$	$+2$	o	-2	-4	-6	-8	-10	-2
$+15$	$+12$	$+9$	$+6$	$+3$	o	-3	-6	-9	-12	-15	-3
$+20$	$+16$	$+12$	$+8$	$+4$	o	-4	-8	-12	-16	-20	-4
$+25$	$+20$	$+15$	$+10$	$+5$	o	-5	-10	-15	-20	-25	-5

Class $x =$ | -5 | -4 | -3 | -2 | -1 | o | $+1$ | $+2$ | $+3$ | $+4$ | $+5$ |

Fig. 14.23

The formula for the coefficient of correlation is

$$r_{xy} = \frac{\dfrac{\Sigma\, xy}{N}}{\sigma_x . \sigma_y}$$

and so we need to calculate the value of the sum of all the terms $x.y$ and the mean and standard deviation of both the distributions.

We begin by grouping the scores in classes, as when we calculated the standard deviation. Our central square of the scatter-diagram will correspond to the middle of each of the Class "o" groups of the variates. Since this does not, necessarily, coincide with the two means exactly, there is a small correction term, as there was for the calculation of the standard deviation.

The correlation between the marks obtained in the Group Test 33 and the Moray House "Adult I" tests is worked out in full. The range of marks for the Moray House Test is roughly from 60 to 100, so that all the marks will fit into eleven groups of 4 marks with Class "o" including the mark of 80. The range of marks for Group Test 33 is from 134 to 183, so that these will all fit into eleven groups of 5 marks, centred on 160. A square (Fig. 14.24) is marked out with eleven columns and eleven rows, labelled along the top with the marks for the Moray House Test arranged in classes. The Group Test 33 marks are set out down the left-hand side, also arranged in classes. Each person is represented by a star in the appropriate square. The numbers in each row and each column are counted and the totals put in the column or row labelled f. Along the bottom the class labels, -5, -4, -3, etc., are put at the foot of each of the columns, in the row labelled x, and the classes corresponding to the Group Test 33 marks are set out in the column headed y. The rows labelled $f.x$ and $f.x^2$ provide the information required for calculating the mean and standard deviation of the x's, and the columns headed $f.y$ and $f.y^2$ collect the information required for the mean and standard deviation of the y's. The final column, labelled fxy, is required for collecting the product terms xy for calculation of the correlation coefficient.

Marks in Moray House test.

Marks in Group Test 33	58–61	62–65	66–69	70–73	74–77	78–81	82–85	86–89	90–93	94–97	98–101	f	y	fy	fy^2	fxy
187–183											✶	1	+5	+5	25	+25
182–178										✶		2	+4	+8	32	+36
177–173						✶		✶		✶		9	+3	+27	81	+60
172–168						✶	✶	✶	✶			5	+2	+10	20	+22
167–163						✶		✶	✶			4	+1	+4	4	+6
162–158			✶	✶						✶		8	0	0	0	0
157–153			✶		✶		✶					7	−1	−7	7	0
152–148					✶							1	−2	−2	4	0
147–143					✶	✶		✶				3	−3	−9	27	−3
142–138	✶	✶		✶								3	−4	−12	48	+44
137–133			✶									2	−5	−10	50	+25
f	1	1	3	4	4	6	6	10	4	4	2	45		+14	298	+215
x	−5	−4	−3	−2	−1	0	+1	+2	+3	+4	+5					
$f.x$	−5	−4	−9	−8	−4	0	+6	+20	+12	+16	+10	+34				
$f.x^2$	25	16	27	16	4	0	6	40	36	64	50	284				

Fig. 14.24

CALCULATING THE COEFFICIENT OF CORRELATION

This calculation is in terms of *classes*, not marks.

Mean of x's
$$\frac{\Sigma fx}{N} = +\frac{34}{45} = +0.755.$$

Mean of y's
$$\frac{\Sigma fy}{N} = +\frac{14}{45} = +0.311.$$

Standard deviation of x's $\sigma_x{}^2 = \dfrac{\Sigma fx^2}{N} - \left(\dfrac{\Sigma fx}{N}\right)^2 = \dfrac{284}{45} - (+0.755)^2$

$$= 6.311 - 0.565$$
$$= 5.746$$

$$\therefore \quad \sigma = 2.40.$$

Standard deviation of y's $\sigma_y{}^2 = \dfrac{\Sigma fy^2}{N} - \left(\dfrac{\Sigma fy}{N}\right)^2 = \dfrac{298}{45} - (+0.311)^2$

$$= 6.622 - 0.096$$
$$= 6.526$$

$$\therefore \quad \sigma = 2.56.$$

$\dfrac{\Sigma fxy}{N}$ (corrected) $= \dfrac{\Sigma fxy}{N} - \dfrac{\Sigma fx}{N} \times \dfrac{\Sigma fy}{N} = + \dfrac{215}{45} - 0.755 \times 0.311$

$$= + 4.78 - 0.23$$
$$= + 4.55.$$

Coefficient of correlation $= \dfrac{+4.55}{2.40 \times 2.56} = 0.73 = r_{xy}.$

[*NOTE.* The final column to the right of the scatter-diagram (Fig. 14.24) is used for collecting the xy scores. If we count the stars in the third row, where the total comes to $+60$, which is the row of class $+3$, there are

$$
\begin{array}{llr}
\text{2 in class} & \text{o column, counting o,} & = \quad \text{o} \\
\text{4 in class} & +2 \text{ column, counting } 4 \times (+2) \times (+3) = & +24 \\
\text{3 in class} & +4 \text{ column, counting } 3 \times (+4) \times (+3) = & +36 \\
& \text{Total} & \underline{+60}
\end{array}
$$

It is immaterial whether we add these values for the squares across and then sum the column, or down and then sum the row.]

A coefficient of correlation of 0.73 is a fairly high degree of correlation. From the appearance of the scatter-diagram it is obvious that the two sets of marks are quite closely associated. In general, in the field of examinations and tests, it would be true to say that a correlation as high as 0.73 would mean that the two tests were testing the same set of attributes.

A coefficient of correlation lower than about 0.3 would indicate a very small correlation and would certainly imply that different factors were being tested and that the totals for the scores were made up from tests which explored different fields of ability. An example of this is given in the scatter-diagram relating performance by a group of students in written examinations and their assessment for practical teaching ability (Fig. 14.25). The coefficient of correlation is calculated and is only 0.34, which is quite a low figure. The mark in the written examination tested a student's ability to acquire knowledge by reading and from lectures and to compose well written answers involving the exercising of critical judgment and the orderly presentation of arguments in support of expressed points of view. The mark, therefore, indicated the graduate's ability to use his trained intelligence to learn and to express himself lucidly on paper. The abilities assessed in

Correlation between Assessment of Practical Teaching Ability and Marks in the Written Examination

Marks in the Written Examination

	191–216	217–242	243–268	269–294	295–320	321–346	347–372	373–398	399–424	425–450	f	y	fy	fy²	fxy
A					*		*		*	*	4	+5	+20	100	+35
A−						*					1	+4	+4	16	0
B+					*	*	*	*	*	6	+3	+18	54	+24
B			*	*	*	*	*	*	*	15	+2	+30	60	+16
B−	*		*		*	*	*			16	+1	+16	16	−1
C+	*		*	*	*	*	*			26	0	0	0	0
C	*			*	*	*	*		*	24	−1	−24	24	+8
C−	*	*	*		*	*		*		10	−2	−20	40	+30
D+	*	*			*	*			*	5	−3	−15	45	+18
D			*							1	−4	−4	16	+12
f	6	2	5	5	23	29	14	12	8	4	108		+25	371	+142
x	−5	−4	−3	−2	−1	0	+1	+2	+3	+4					
f.x	−30	−8	−15	−10	−23	0	+14	+24	+24	+16	−8				
f.x²	−150	32	45	20	23	0	14	48	72	64	468				

Practical Teaching Assessment

Fig. 14.25

$\frac{+25}{108} = +0.23$ $\frac{371}{108} = 3.435$ $\sigma_y^2 = 3.435 - 0.053 = 3.382$ $\sigma_y = 1.84$

$\frac{-8}{108} = -0.074$ $\frac{468}{108} = 4.305$ $\sigma_x^2 = 4.305 - 0.006 = 4.299$ $\sigma_x = 2.07$

$\frac{+142}{108} = +1.314$ $1.314 - (+0.23)(-0.07) = 1.300$ $r_{xy} = \dfrac{1.30}{1.84 \times 2.07}$

$= 0.34$

practical teaching included the establishing of personal relations with children in classes, fluency of speech both in presenting prepared work and in questioning and answering, and the vitality of personality needed to stimulate active interest in what was being taught. It is obvious that the written examination and the practical teaching involved different abilities, and the correlation coefficient of 0·34 is about what one might have expected, reflecting the elements of intelligence and basic knowledge common to both.

A good teacher has to be able to acquire mastery of the subject he intends to teach, and to be able to get his knowledge across to his pupils. A satisfactory performance in both written and practical work is required, and the low coefficient of correlation shows these to be largely independent of each other. A poor performance in either is a reason for rejecting a person as a suitable candidate for teaching; those students who are represented either to the left or towards the bottom of the scatter-diagram would not be recommended to be given the status of "qualified teacher" by the Ministry of Education.

The calculation of a coefficient of correlation indicates the extent to which two aspects of ability being tested are independent of each other. This assessment of the amount of correlation is a guide which helps us to decide how best to treat the information we have collected. Generally speaking, results of more or less independent tests should be presented independently, but the results of tests with a high degree of correlation should be averaged and the result presented as a single average, or aggregate, mark. In the example given, the low coefficient of correlation of 0·34 suggests that *separate* passes should be given for theory and practice and distinctions be awarded separately rather than on the aggregate of the two. Had there been a correlation of about 0·7 or over, a pass on the aggregate or a single distinction on an aggregate mark would have been appropriate.

This is a simple example in which statistical analysis helps in the making of a decision about the grounds on which judgments should be made. Personnel managers obviously have similar decisions to make in recruiting employees. For instance, a personnel manager may have to decide whether a deficiency in certain qualities absolutely rules out a candidate for a job, or whether this lack may be compensated by high ability in some other direction. More generally, the employer seeks suitable tests which will enable him to place his staff in the most effective way, and he needs to explore both the reliability and validity of his tests.

Reliability of Intelligence Tests

This is a term used in statistics to indicate the self-consistency of results of tests or operations. The meaning will be illustrated with reference to intelligence tests, but it has a general application.

A question may look, to an examiner, as though it tested exactly what he wanted to test, but its value depends upon the actual responses it evokes from those who are being tested. There may be unexpected ambiguity of wording or its difficulty may have been wrongly assessed. A test item of a deductive type may sometimes be extremely easy if looked at from one point of view and very much more difficult if approached from a somewhat different standpoint, and inconsistent results could be obtained from it. Sometimes such an inconsistency could be removed by a slight re-wording, but sometimes the question may have to be entirely re-cast or even rejected outright. A complete test has to be made up from a number of separate items, and for a test to be acceptable it must produce consistent results. The evidence of the consistency of the test must be obtained from an analysis of the actual results. There are two popular ways of testing for *reliability*, the "split-half" method and the "test re-test" method. The "split-half" method is carried out by summing separately the marks obtained for alternate questions and calculating the coefficient of correlation between the sums of the odd test items and the sums of the even test items. A "split-half" correlation of about 0·9 or over would indicate an acceptable level of *reliability* for a test.

The "test re-test" method simply involves giving the test and then, after some lapse of time, giving it again to the same group of people. Again, a correlation less than 0·9 between the two performances of the same test would indicate that its *reliability* was below the acceptable level, and test modification would be indicated.

Reliability is used to describe self-consistency of a test.

Validity

Tests are used for a wide variety of purposes. There are aptitude tests which might be used for suggesting suitable types of employment for an individual seeking work or for indicating to an employer the suitability of an applicant for a post which is vacant; there are tests for selecting suitable potential officers for Her Majesty's Forces; tests for studying the effects of working conditions on the efficiency of work-people, and tests for selecting candidates for different types of education and training. The *validity* of a test is an estimate of the efficiency with which it does the job for which it was intended. A test for assessing the suitability of a person for employment as a lathe-worker can be validated only by comparing the performance on such a test with the actual lathe-working ability of people who have taken the test. One of the difficulties of testing the validity of tests is that of finding a suitable means of assessing the efficiency of actual performance. In one of the most straightforward of instances, it is very difficult to give an overall rating of a pupil's success at a grammar school and almost impossible to rate how a secondary modern schoolboy would have responded to a grammar school education. Where it is possible to rate ability in the performance or in the occupation for which the test was designed, then the coefficient of correlation between test result and performance rating will indicate the validity of the test. It must suffice here to say that very great pains are taken in assessing validity of tests by correlating them with a variety of assessments and combinations of assessments, and that competent statistical analysis is especially important here.

Significance

If the average mark on a mathematics test given to 5 boys was 68 and the average mark of 5 girls on the same test was 66 then no one would really suggest that there was any significant difference between the mathematical ability of the five boys as a group and the five girls as a group. If the average distance a football was kicked by 100 boys was 50 yards and the average distance it was kicked by 100 girls was 10 yards then we might say that there was a significant difference between the football-kicking abilities of boys and girls. There are usually differences in performance between groups of people; some are trivial, others are very great. Between extremes there is a gradation of differences, and at some stage in between we must begin to regard these differences as indicating the existence of an attribute which is not distributed in the same way or to the same extent in the two groups. The question asked of the statistician is how the importance of these differences can be assessed. There have been many instances where such a question is of great importance. One is the association between cigarette smoking and lung cancer. The proportion of lung cancer victims is greater in the population of cigarette smokers than in non-smokers; we all want to know whether this is a marginal difference or such an inescapably large difference that we may assume beyond a per-adventure that there is a real connexion between the two. A statistic which provides a basis for making such a judgment is a measure of *significance*.

An algebraic deduction of the formulae involved in such a calculation is contained in books such as C. E. Weatherburn's *A First Course in Mathematical Statistics* (Cambridge), and is quite outside the scope of this chapter. It is possible to indicate the way in which such a test could be devised without going into the niceties of a proof. In the paragraph on "Intelligence" (page 242) it was mentioned that 25 per cent of the population have an I.Q. of 110 or more and this was indicated on the normal curve. Put in another way, we may say that if we meet a person at random, the chances are 1 in 4 that he has an I.Q. of 110 or more, or we may say that the probability of his I.Q. being more than 110 is $\frac{1}{4}$. If we select two people quite at random, the probability of both of them having I.Q.s not less than 110 is $\frac{1}{4} \times \frac{1}{4} = \frac{1}{16}$. If six people are chosen quite at random we should expect to find them all having I.Q.s of 110 or more only once in every 4096 (1 in 4^6) groups of half a dozen investigated. This can be expressed in the form: "I have just tested six people I met in the street; they all had I.Q.s greater than 110; the chance that they were a random sample is $\frac{1}{4096}$."

One might expect a conversation such as this to continue: "Where did you meet these people?" "Just outside the University library." "Well, if you go to a place like that to select your group you can hardly describe it as a random sample!"

This last remark can be anticipated from the probability, the appropriate form being "It was obvious that the chances were 1 in over 4000 against this having been a random selection of six people, so it was almost certain that there was something influencing the selection. It is satisfactory to know that the selection was probably from a university and not from an average population."

When we are dealing with the means of groups we have to jump from the more simple case of *all* being over a certain value, to the mean being above this value, and this introduces rather more complicated algebra, but precise formulae can be found in much the same way. From this there is a further step in dealing with the *difference between the means* of two groups.

If A and B are two groups and some attribute is measured for each of the members of each group, then, if N_a and N_b are the numbers of individuals in the two groups and the means of the quantity measured are M_a and M_b and the corresponding standard deviations are σ_a and σ_b respectively, the difference between means will be $(M_a \sim M_b)$ and the estimate of the standard deviation of the difference between means is σ_d, where

$$\sigma_d{}^2 = \frac{\sigma_a{}^2}{N_a} + \frac{\sigma_b{}^2}{N_b}.$$

A quantity t is defined by the equation

$$t = \frac{M_a \sim M_b}{\sigma_d}.$$

Since we know $(M_a \sim M_b)$ and the standard deviation σ_d of its distribution, we can estimate the probability of $(M_a \sim M_b)$ being above a certain value. A table of values of t is given in tables of statistics in terms of the probability and the number of individuals comprising the groups.

$N_a + N_b - 2$	Values of t for probability 5%	Values of t for probability 1%
1000	1·96	2·58
100	1·98	2·63
50	2·01	2·68
40	2·02	2·71
30	2·04	2·75
25	2·06	2·79
20	2·09	2·84
15	2·13	2·95
10	2·23	3·17
9	2·26	3·25
8	2·31	3·36
7	2·36	3·50
6	2·54	3·71
5	2·57	4·03

The mean score of 600 women aged eighteen to nineteen on Vernon's *Graded Arithmetic-Mathematics Test* was 48·1 with a standard deviation of 8 marks. The mean score of 400 men aged eighteen to nineteen on the same test was 49·3 with standard deviation 8·3 marks. Is the difference between these means significant?

$$\sigma_d{}^2 = \frac{8^2}{600} + \frac{(8·3)^2}{400} = 0·107 + 0·172 = 0·279$$

$$\therefore \quad \sigma_d = 0·53$$

$$M_a \sim M_b = 1·2$$

$$t = \frac{1·2}{0·53} = 2·31.$$

For about 1000 individuals, the difference is significant at the 5 per cent level if $t = 1·96$ and at the 1 per cent level if $t = 2·58$. The value $t = 2·3$ is intermediate between these, so we can say that the difference is significant at the 5 per cent level but not at the 1 per cent level. This means that the chances are less than 1 in 100 but more than 5 in 100 (1 in 20) that a difference as great as this could happen by pure chance if the groups were selected at random from a single, normally distributed population. We should not regard as low a level of significance as this as being conclusive, but it does indicate some higher standard among the men. The difference made by the size of sample is illustrated by taking the following example in contrast to the one just calculated.

The mean score of 11 women aged eighteen to nineteen on Vernon's test was 48·1 with a standard deviation of 8 marks. The mean score of 11 men on the same test was 57·5 with a standard deviation of 8·3. Is the difference between these means significant?

$$\sigma_d{}^2 = \frac{64}{11} + \frac{68·89}{11} = 12·08$$

$$\therefore \quad \sigma_d = 3·47$$

$$M_a \sim M_b = 9·4$$

$$t = \frac{9·4}{3·47} = 2·71.$$

For $N_a + N_b - 2 = 20$, the difference is significant at the 5 per cent level if $t = 2·09$ and at the 1 per cent level if $t = 2·84$, so, once again, this difference is not significant at the 1 per cent level but it is at the 5 per cent level. This means that the chances are less than 1 in 100 but greater than 1 in 20 that a difference as great as 9·4 could happen by pure chance if two groups of 11 were chosen at random from a normally distributed population. Again we should not regard this as very strong evidence.

Notice, however, that when we are dealing with groups as large as 400 and 600, a difference of only 1·2 marks is significant at the same level of probability as the difference of 9·4 marks when our groups are as small as 11.

The level of significance to be regarded as critical does depend upon the nature of the problem being investigated. As a first generalization it could be said that a significance below the 5 per cent level would be disregarded, between 5 and 1 per cent would be considered as an indication that there was some bias in the sampling, and a level beyond that of 1 per cent would be regarded as indicating a sampling bias. In any matter of importance a level of significance greater than at 5 per cent would call for further investigation.

It is important to understand that it is dangerous and misleading to jump to conclusions simply on the evidence of means without further analysis.

In this chapter we have discussed distribution, correlation and the reliability and validity of information obtained from a variety of sources, and some reference has been made to the significance of some of the statistics derived from the available information. These are basic statistical ideas that are fundamental to the examination of data relating to a number of different individuals.

The normal distribution described in some detail in this chapter is by far the most important, but there are others which apply to special types of data. Rectangular, binomial and Poisson distributions are dealt with in most elementary text-books on statistics, and form part of any systematic course, but most of the work met with in education, psychology, sociology or biology hinges upon an understanding of normal and approximately normal distributions, as does a very large proportion of industrial investigation. One cannot exaggerate the importance of an understanding of the idea of a normal population, the use of the mean, deviation from the mean, and standard deviation. Anyone with any experience of working with these ideas does, of necessity, think of the particular needs and requirements of an individual in relation to the group of which he is a member. That fantasy, the "average child", is an abstraction which could exist only in the minds of those ignorant of statistics. One has only to look at the provision of chairs and desks in secondary schools, however, to appreciate the extent to which the "average child" is the best customer of firms which supply education authorities.

The idea of correlation has been introduced in this chapter. This enables an extremely important concept to be developed. Some things are associated with one another to a greater or less extent, but they cannot be connected by any precise algebraic formula. There are many problems that can be brought into the realm of controlled experiment only by the use of correlation techniques. The relation between bad housing and delinquency was studied forty years ago by Sir Cyril Burt, using correlation methods, and the association of lung cancer and cigarette smoking is engaging attention at present. In searching for means of reducing backwardness, the evidence of correlation coefficients is important and, at present, it suggests that large classes may not be as potent an influence on backwardness in reading as uncontrolled observation might suggest. The correlation coefficient worked out in this chapter is one of the basic techniques in the exploration of the relationship between sets of numbers or assessments of values and is all that can be included in a single chapter. Readers who are concerned with educational, sociological and biological data should turn to a text-book on statistics and see how other useful information can be obtained by an "analysis of variance". The correlation between examination results and practical teaching ability amounted to only just over $0 \cdot 3$, and it was suggested that intelligence and specific knowledge contributed to both but that there were other factors involved, different for the two tests of ability. The tracking down of such factors can be made the subject of a series of tests and experiments by trying to find other well-defined tests which correlate highly with one but not with the other. "Factor Analysis" is the name given to investigations of this type. It plays an important part in psychology, but the mathematics of the analysis is specialized and could hardly be undertaken without special training. The reader, however, is likely to come across references to these factors and they are discussed in non-technical language in many psychological text-books.

The need to be sure of the reliability, validity and significance of results before acting upon them ought to be obvious, but, unfortunately, a great deal of well-meaning effort is wasted because of neglect of these prudent and necessary safeguards. The public needs to be much more critical in its thinking about large-scale problems and problems of sampling, but statistical modes of thought are hardly touched on in schools. Some 25,000 students take A-level mathematics, yet, in the largest examining body in the country, only about forty students offer statistics as the alternative paper in the A-level examination.

Classical physicists and chemists dealt with millions of millions of molecules as though they were all identical and behaved in the same way at the same instant, or else they explored single, individual entities such as the moon or Mars. Nowadays nuclear physicists have to deal with the probability of events happening within a single atom among millions, and chemists design molecules for particular purposes, as in the making of synthetic fibres. They have joined educationalists, psychologists, sociologists and biologists in thinking statistically, and statistics joins the older branches of mathematics in being more than a tool for finding answers to questions which arise in extraneous contexts. Mathematics is a way of thinking, varied in its methods, rich in its resources, but, above all, calling for imagination and a versatile interest in the world around.

Just as there is a place for academic grammarians so there is an even greater need for academic mathematicians. Nevertheless, an English course consisting only of grammar would be very barren, and command of language is best obtained by using it as a vehicle for disciplining and recording thought and stimulating imaginative thinking. All too often mathematics courses are so restricted to the formal exercises of mathematical grammar, sometimes called "symbol shoving", that the contribution of mathematics to disciplining thought and encouraging imagination is completely ignored. The intention of this book has not been to show what sorts of things can be brought in to illustrate mathematical ideas, but, on the contrary, to show the sort of way in which mathematical thinking can illuminate our understanding of some very ordinary things in the world about us and stimulate a more imaginative interest in them.

FURTHER READING

For students who wish to make use of statistical techniques:

C. E. Weatherburn – *A First Course of Mathematical Statistics* (Cambridge)

H. E. Garrett – *Statistics in Psychology and Education* (Longmans)

D. Huff – *How to Lie with Statistics* (W. W. Norton and Co., Inc.)

(This is an entertaining and poignant discussion of statistics.)

For elementary reading on statistics:

B. C. Brookes and W. F. L. Dick – *Introduction to Statistical Method* (Heinemann)

W. L. Sumner – *Statistics in School* (Blackwell)

M. J. Moroney – *Facts from Figures* (Penguin)

R. Loveday – *A First Course in Statistics* (Cambridge)

(This is an elementary book which should present no difficulties to anyone with little mathematical background, but it does not go very far.)

An introductory treatment of some contemporary mathematical topics:

F. J. Scheid – *Elements of Finite Mathematics* (Addison-Wesley)

An elementary approach to somewhat more advanced ideas and methods:

R. Courant and H. Robbins – *What Is Mathematics?* (Oxford University Press)

A basic textbook for students at the advanced undergraduate level:

K. Kurstowski – *Introduction to Set Theory and Topology* (Pergamon Press)

INDEX

Index